THE
TECHNOLOGICAL
ORDER

THE TECHNOLOGICAL ORDER

Proceedings of the
Encyclopaedia Britannica Conference

Edited by Carl F. Stover
with a foreword by William Benton

Detroit 1963 · Wayne State University Press

These proceedings of the conference, sponsored by The Encyclopaedia Britannica *in cooperation with* The Center *for the* Study *of*
Democratic Institutions and held in Santa Barbara, California, March
1962, were originally published in Technology and Culture, *Volume*
III, No. 4, Fall 1962, by the Wayne State University Press.

Contents

v

Participants

HARRY S. ASHMORE
Editor-in-Chief
Encyclopaedia Britannica

SENATOR WILLIAM BENTON
Publisher
Encyclopaedia Britannica

RITCHIE CALDER
Professor of International Relations
University of Edinburgh

REVEREND W. NORRIS CLARKE, S. J.
Department of Philosophy
Fordham University

ARTHUR GOLDSCHMIDT
Department of Economic and Social
Affairs
The United Nations

WILLIAM GORMAN
The Center for the Study of Democratic Institutions

A. RUPERT HALL
Department of History
Indiana University

WILLY HARTNER
University of Frankfurt

ROBERT M. HUTCHINS
Chairman
Board of Editors
Encyclopaedia Britannica; and
President
Center for the Study of Democratic
Institutions

ALDOUS HUXLEY

MELVIN KRANZBERG
Editor-in-Chief
Technology and Culture
Case Institute of Technology

RICHARD L. MEIER
Department of Conservation
School of Natural Resources
University of Michigan

REVEREND WALTER ONG, S. J.
Center for Advanced Studies
Wesleyan University

GERARD PIEL
Publisher
Scientific American

WARREN E. PREECE
Secretary
Board of Editors
Encyclopaedia Britannica

JAMES REAL
The Center for the Study of Democratic Institutions

JOHN ROBLING
Vice President
Encyclopaedia Britannica

CARL F. STOVER
Assistant to the Chairman
Board of Editors
Encyclopaedia Britannica

VU VAN THAI
The United Nations

ROBERT THEOBALD
Author and Management Consultant

RALPH W. TYLER
Director for Advanced Study in the
Behavioral Sciences

SIR ROBERT WATSON-WATT
Scientist and Author
Consultant to the Center for the Study
of Democratic Institutions

LYNN WHITE, JR.
Department of History
University of California at Los Angeles

JOHN WILKINSON
Department of Philosophy
University of California at Santa Barbara

A. ZVORIKINE
U. S. S. R. Academy of Sciences

vii

Foreword

When " a society of gentlemen " brought forth the first edition of *Encyclopaedia Britannica* in Edinburgh in 1768, the Industrial Revolution was also coming into plain view in Great Britain. The two events were not merely coincidental. The first encyclopaedists recognized clearly that the advent of the power-driven machine had made changes in the order of the day.

For nearly 200 years their successors have worked at maintaining *Britannica* as a cumulative chronicle of the processes constantly reshaping the world in which its readers live.

Today, as in 1768, the editors of *Britannica* must be aware of the past as it has shaped the present, and of the past and present as they are together shaping the future. It was in these terms that the Encyclopaedia Britannica Conference on the Technological Order was called in March, 1962, in Santa Barbara, California.

This volume is a partial record of that Conference, which brought together experts of various backgrounds and divergent views. There was no search for an approved solution to the myriad problems of the technological age, no limiting quest for final agreement. The Conference attempted only to define and illuminate the issues.

The task is vital, and not only to the encyclopaedist. No one can take the measure of this time without taking into account the social, cultural, economic, and political impact of technology. The effects of technological change are already pervasive, and the accelerating rate of that change carries with it promise of reward and threat of danger, each in unprecedented array.

Britannica here makes public the proceedings of its private working Conference, as a contribution to a better understanding of what appear certain to be major critical issues in the second half of the century.

WILLIAM BENTON
Publisher
Encyclopaedia Britannica

Introduction

Three hundred and fifty years ago, Sir Francis Bacon advanced a standard for judging man's scientific achievements. The purpose of understanding, he argued, is to achieve the capacity to act: "The true and lawful goal of science is that human life be endowed with new powers and inventions."

The intervening centuries have seen a gradual refinement of the means for realizing this goal. In our own time, they near perfection. We have drawn science and technology so closely together that often they cannot be distinguished. We have invented the method of invention and developed a technology for producing new technologies. The result is the most powerful technical capacity mankind has ever known —a true fulfillment of the Baconian vision.

A source of great authority over nature, the modern scientific-technology promises to be both the hope of man's future and the instrument of his enslavement or his destruction. If we are to avoid the disasters it lays open to us and take advantage of the opportunities it presents, we must put it in the control of reason. To do so, we must understand what modern technology is, what it means, and what must be done with it if it is to serve man well.

The purpose of the Encyclopaedia Britannica Conference on the Technological Order was to help achieve this understanding. It brought together experienced scholars and thoughtful leaders in public affairs from around the world for a week's discussion of the nature of technology and its significance for human affairs. The aim was not to reach final agreement on the character or solution of the many problems engendered by technology, but to foster the kind of deliberative thought that is essential if we are to identify and comprehend the critical emerging issues inherent in the technological revolution of our time. The fruits of these sessions are to be found principally in the contributions made to the thinking of each participant and to those who share in the proceedings through this written record.

The general pattern of the Conference is reflected in this volume. Sir Robert Watson-Watt opened the discussions with a sprightly and provocative statement on "Technology in the Modern World." The next four days were devoted to four separate probes into the subject:

1. *Ideas of Technology*—an examination of major contemporary schools of thought about technology and its use.

2. *The Technical Act*—a consideration of what can be learned about technology from the history of its development and use: How has it served and been served by man? Under what conditions does it serve man well? What are the causes of technical inno-

vation? What are the social implications of different kinds and rates of technological development?

3. *Nature, Science, and Technology*—an exploration of the relationship between science and technology and their joint relationship to nature. Traditionally, science has been directed to understanding nature; technology to controlling and adapting it to man's ends. Both are now linked in an " attack " upon nature— an effort to make it " give up its secrets " and conform to human ends. What standards should guide and limit this process?

4. *Technology in Focus—The Emerging Nation*—an inquiry into the total impact of modern technology on entire cultures and societies. In technologically advanced countries, it is often difficult to see these relationships clearly. It is relatively less difficult to do so in countries that are now embarking on technological development. What is learned there may contribute significantly to our understanding of technology everywhere.

On the final day, the participants attempted to bring the ideas and issues considered during the week into more unified focus—to achieve " A Perspective on the Technological Order." Ralph W. Tyler closed the Conference with an effective review of the week's deliberations.

The background papers prepared for these sessions and the commentaries on them that opened each day's discussion are presented here in full. The discussions, which ranged widely through the subject, have been skillfully summarized by Warren E. Preece to preserve much of the excitement of the intensive exchange of ideas at the conference table. It is hoped that together they will permit the reader to share closely in the experience of these meetings.

In a cooperative enterprise such as this, there are many people who deserve credit for what was accomplished. I am grateful to the participants in the Conference for their devoted contributions to the realization of its purposes. Appreciation is also due Fritza Bullwinkel, A. Lorraine Hatch, and Betty Rantis Lid for their labors in helping to prepare this publication and Eugene Bailey for preparing the Index. Finally, my special thanks to Lynn White, jr., President of the Society for the History of Technology, and Melvin Kranzberg, Editor-in-Chief of *Technology and Culture*, for their helpfulness in arranging to present this record to a wider audience.

CARL F. STOVER

Technology in the Modern World

SIR ROBERT WATSON-WATT*

The broad field of automation covers, *inter alia*, my first reaction on being awarded the difficult but absorbing task of addressing you on "Technology in the Modern World." I turned automatically and confidently to the *Encyclopaedia Britannica* of 1962 and read avidly every reference indexed under "Technology." Here it is, verbatim: "Moreover, the settled agricultural life needed more tools, at first of stone. Thus a professional technology developed." The rest is silence. I moved my calendar back to 1961, not without gain. For *Encyclopaedia Britannica* 1961 said this: "Moreover, the settled agricultural life needed more tools, at first of stone. Thus a professional technology developed." Both, however, do condescend to the particular in describing "technological education" as "the higher levels at which advanced knowledge of theory is important"—this in contrast to "technical education" directed primarily at the "acquirement of skills in techniques."

Compare these fragments, however, with their counterpart in the great Eleventh of 1910-11, Philip Magnus on "Technical Education" together with the biographic note on Johann Beckmann (1739-1811) who—in 1772—invented the title of "Scientific Technology."

We are, I hope, going to change all this imbalance. As an unrepentant technologist, I hereby dedicate all the effort for which anyone is prepared adequately to pay me, to giving technology its place in the sun. In the sunshine, that is, of an *Encyclopaedia Britannica* which should surpass even the high standards of an epoch when the "E" signified Edinburgh as well as Encyclopaedia.

I do not attempt the difficult task of defining my terms; I can approach them only by indirection.

Science and technology are the *Gemini* of the (not always heavenly) conceptual constellations of the human mind. They are far from identical twins, and endless confusion may be generated by failure to recognize their sharply differentiated identities. They are, however, like Siamese twins; they share a common blood stream, but are divergent in their outlook on their common world. This divergence of outlook denies them the status of heavenly twins—science may pretend to the adjective, but technology is of the earth, earthy.

---

* Sir Robert Watson-Watt is generally known as "the father of radar" and one of the originators of operational research. He is now a consultant to Encyclopaedia Britannica and the Center for the Study of Democratic Institutions. His most recent book is *Man's Means to His End* (New York, 1962).

1

Technology is, by a short head, the elder of the pair—it is in fact just a shade older than the animal whom we so optimistically and rashly describe as *Homo Sapiens.* The *Ur-vater* of technology may well have been the higher ape who, failing to reach, with the longest available stick, his vegetarian breakfast, ingeniously wedged a second stick into a notch on the first, so making, perhaps, the first artifact in pre-history.

Soon, however, as the centuries flew by, science was born, of the careful observation of the lunar pathway through the skies, a varying pathway more readily discriminated, in the lower latitudes favouring the growth of *H. Sapiens,* than was that of the sun. Soon, however, *H. S.* followed the sun and learned its diurnal and seasonal variations of track. From this primitive science of astronomy flowed directly the primitive technologies of agriculture and of land survey, amongst others.

But we need not here dwell on moon-raking and sun-worshipping; part of our task is to examine what are the characters of the still adolescent quasi-twins.

It is comparatively easy to characterize science. Science is the patient and exigent examination of the " technology of nature," with the aim of giving a full description—albeit by analogy only—of every one of the diverse life histories in nature, from that of the blade of grass at our feet to that of the colliding galaxies five billion light-years distant from our tiny spheroid and receding from us at half the speed of light; from that whiff of hydrocarbon vapour which first spelt " life," to that mankind of today which is the proper study of the man of today.

Science is one—the greatest and most exacting—of the representational arts. It paints, patches, and repaints a constantly retouched picture of every naturally occurring phenomenon. This it does in such manner that all serious and informed students can unambiguously recognize the phenomenon which is being characterized. This characterization is achieved in an ensemble of our sensory perceptions, set down as a descriptive portrait of that particular phenomenon and of its relation to other phenomena. The recognition by other scientists is effected by the very close similarity of the sense impressions experienced by two or more educated and qualified, though independent, observers of the same phenomenon.

Technology, on the other hand, is the selective adaptation of one or more of the processes and materials identified and described by science, and their embodiment in devices designed to serve the needs of mankind in its progress from savagery toward advanced social evolution. It includes, but is no longer confined to, the processes defined in June 1828 by the founders of the Institution of Civil Engineers in Great Britain as " the art of directing the great sources of power in nature for the use and convenience of man." That art has had, *inter alia,* to extend itself to genuinely great sources of power undreamt of even in June 1928—well, perhaps not undreamt of, but certainly not then released or directed. I quote from one Winston Spencer Churchill, writing in 1925:

> Then there are Explosives. Have we reached the end? Has Science turned its last page on them? May there not be methods of using explosive energy incomparably more intense than anything heretofore discovered? Might not a bomb no bigger than an orange be found to possess a secret power to destroy a whole block of buildings—nay, to concentrate the force of a thousand tons of cordite and blast a township at a stroke? Could not explosives even of the existing type be guided automatically in flying machines by wireless or other rays, without a human pilot, in ceaseless procession upon a hostile city, arsenal, camp, or dockyard?

Technology is, in short, the mechanism of man's means to his ends. It is, in the mechanic world, based on Part II of the aspiration of the schoolboy James Clerk-Maxwell. He was wont to demand, in relation to any mechanical object or device, that he should know " the go of it, the *real* go of it." But the schoolboy soon grew up into one of the greatest unveilers of Part I of the " go of things "—that science which the English call " Physics " but the wiser Scots call " Natural Philosophy." This close duality of Parts I and II is characteristic of the relations of science and technology.

There is a legitimate but somewhat confusing trend among contemporary philosophers to extend the conception of technology beyond the already explored material universe into the non-material, or only partially material, universe of conceptual thought. Perhaps, the most vocal of these universalists is Jacques Ellul, who is contributing, regrettably *in absentia*, to our forthcoming discussions here. I am far from sure that one treasure-box is better than two, but perhaps we here can worry this out before Saint Patrick's Day. Meanwhile I disclaim any share in the pessimism which Ellul exhibits about the effects of a wide application of technology for the use and convenience of man.

Because I suspect some here of sharing Ellul's pessimism, I am moved to comment very personally—with appropriate apologies—on the imbalance of judgment which is almost inevitable between those who have been brought up mainly on a diet of printed paper, and those nurtured on wood shavings, iron and brass filings, propulsive gases, and other base mechanic offal. It is quite clear to me that pessimism is nurtured by paper, optimism by offal of the kind I have just mentioned.

Let me be personal about myself. I was, as near as makes no matter, born on a pile of sawdust and wood shavings in a carpenter's shop; my toy soldiers were used screwnails which I re-sorted for size, my sculpture was executed in used putty which I was reconditioning for further use. I should add that for a substantial period in my elementary school days I had, from my artisan father, a stipend of one cent per day, applied to the purchase, in fortnightly parts, of an encyclopaedia, *Harmsworth's Enclopaedia* (*Encyclopaedia Britannica* was beyond my dreams but within my reach, thanks to Andrew Carnegie's benefaction, at the local public library). My highest ambition was to become the engineer-in-chief of the electricity generating station in my native city of Brechin—the East Scottish headquarters of the Culdees of the sixth century, its high school with a continuous history from before 1296 A. D. onward. Diverted from Technology towards Natural Philosophy, I yet spent my life as a servant of the British government in the technologies of Meteorology, Radio, Radar, and Operational Research. It is only since my retreat from these technologies that, like Dr. Johnson's visitor, Oliver Edwards, "I have tried too in my time to be a philosopher; but, I don't know how, cheerfulness was always breaking in."

Perhaps then, my failure to share the malaise of my philosophical colleagues, and my confidence in the ability of man to conserve and to serve man's self-determination of man's destiny, are based on the familiarity which does not breed contempt but which discounts both fairies and hobgoblins. All evidence to the contrary evaluated, I stand firmly in the faith that man will, on balance, be both cautious and daring, will use the machine as a tool, but not as an instrument of self-stultification. My disclaimer has, however, a rider which is of the essence. Unless the extension of technological devices for the material use and convenience of man is directed by stringently ethical and profoundly humanitarian policies, the Ellulian pessimism may well be justified.

Moral selectivity is indispensable; all knowledge is good knowledge; not all application is good application. Unless our political servants—who so often believe themselves to be our political masters—avoid the cowardice of a too-limited application of technology, unless they avoid the moral turpitude of mis-application, unless they avoid the immoral squandermania which results from a lack of stringency in scheduling proximate goals, unless they avoid also the immoral deprivation which is inherent in the archaic theory and practice of economics, then, indeed, the advance of technology could be catastrophically disastrous. The *via media* is no longer the *via tutissima*; our fate will depend on our own exercise of the cybernetics of the mind. Only to a wise government does technology promise the horn of plenty instead of the horns of a dilemma.

I take the goal of our world community (and of its regrettable subdivisions) to be that of making the world, as a whole and in its subdivisions, a more satisfying abode for the human race, which is—with all its faults—at once our principal asset and our major liability. Towards this goal we must act on the existing—and, I think, convincing—evidence that the human race is improving, though with a still very unsatisfactory tendency toward that mortal uneconomic sin for which I have coined the name "entropophilia." We must make confession, as best we can, to our fellow citizens, of the probable benefits and the probable harm that may follow from the application of our provisional conclusions on the sciences, the arts, and the technologies.

While constantly seeking to gratify our insatiable curiosity, we must do willful harm to none; we must seek increasing benefit, through a fuller life, to all. As propagandists, we must constantly remember that we speak a language other than that of the market place, and that translators are still traitors—involuntary or voluntary. We certainly need a Hippocratic oath for the technologist, and, I think, also for the scientist.

Constantly, too, must we seek to advance the community consciousness that we are not only our brother's keeper but keeper of our great-great-great-grandchildren, that they may be healthier, genetically better, spiritually wiser, and—again to the nth power—more energetically devoted to the ever-higher goals of social evolution.

To all this, technology in general and automation in particular can make uniquely important contributions—but only if our politicians become statesmen, our administrators philosophers, our economists philanthropists, all of these in the literal sense, and if the electors become well-informed amateur sociologists. This is perhaps the social revolution which can make the world safe for the second Industrial Revolution.

The aim of science is nothing more than to advance in the satisfaction of man's divine gift of inquisitiveness.

The aim of technology is beneficent disemployment, opening the way to more satisfactory employment of a smaller fraction of the individual's total effort, thus releasing a larger fraction of that effort, intellectual and physical, for the fuller enjoyment of life as a whole, all toward living more abundantly.

This aim is to be served by extending the range of man's observation, measurement, classification, control, and active performance, by diminishing the expenditure of human effort, mental and physical, required in the making of such extensions, and in applying them to further modifications and ameliorations of the human condition.

These aims make the range of the subject matter of technology virtually unlimited. Wisdom in technology lies in the selection of fields in which the human beings directly affected by improved technology can achieve a higher ratio of mental to physical effort in the ensemble of their activities, whether occupational or cultural.

These advances from the merely human toward the nearly divine will not be achieved without controversy, opposition, and conflict. My own family history illustrates in a minor way the early resistances to technological advance. My paternal great-grandfather Watson was a smallholder in the parish of Sauchie Burn (in English, "The Willow Stream") and in accord with Scottish custom carried the territorial label " Auld Sauchie."

Auld Sauchie was also a millwright, and in that capacity he installed the first power looms to be introduced in my native county of Angus. Having been burnt at the stake for this sociological heresy, he proceeded to repeat his crime in Dundee, the largest city in the county. Again he was burnt at the stake—but I hasten to add that in both cases the incineration was in effigy only, else I might not be here to plead that Auld Sauchie was on the right road, if perhaps at an excessive speed. I was little more fortunate in this connection, as is shown by a few verses which are not inappropriate to our discussion of technology in the world of today.

Rough Justice

Pity Sir Robert Watson-Watt
Strange target of his radar plot
And thus, with others I could mention
A victim of his own invention.

His magical all-seeing eye
Enabled cloud-bound planes to fly
But now, by some ironic twist
It spots the speeding motorist
And bites, no doubt with legal wit,
The hand that once created it.

O Adam, with your endless crib
Against the product of your rib;
O Guillotine who, it is said
By his devices lost his head
(Example that will have to do
although, by my research, untrue),
O Frankenstein who lost control
Of monster-man created whole,
With fondest sympathy regard
One more hoist with his own petard.

And as for you, courageous boffins
Who may be nailing up your coffins,
Particularly those whose mission
Deals in the realm of nuclear fission
Pause and admire Fate's counter-plot
And learn, with us, what's Watson-Watt.

Through the tinted spectacles with which I view technology in the world of tomorrow, I perceive symptoms of the disease which tied the effigy of Auld Sauchie to the Luddite stake of yesterday. I do not on this occasion dwell on the obvious fact that we shall be wasting our time in discussing technology in the world of today if someone else is allowed to ensure that applied technology destroys the world of tomorrow. I have no faith in the " Delicate Balance of Terror," the " Great Deterrent," or that rump United States which Herman Kahn appears to contemplate with comparative equanimity. I assume a small measure of residual sanity in the world of today.

I have, however, learnt one important lesson—new to me but doubt-less well-known to others. It is that, in one matter at least, Ellul is right. There is little of importance in the world which does not depend in some measure on technology, even in its most restricted sense as man's mechanical means to his ends. I have been deeply im-pressed by the frequency with which some aspect of technology neces-sarily intrudes into the discussion of almost abstract issues—if only by way of the fountain pen, the microphone, tape recorder, the type-writer, and the paper mill, but also in much more formidable shapes.

I keep on straying into the technology of tomorrow—with its auto-matons governing automatons governing automatons—and you are en-titled to doubt whether a rose really is a rose is a rose—but I come back to the man of today because the man of tomorrow will, in the nature of things, be very like the man of today. The dignity of man and the indignities of men are alike the responsibility of the man of today. No one, in my view, has the right to deter any man from think-ing, even from thinking evil, but socially corporate man has some right to dictate the rate of application of the thoughts of the tech-nician. This right is, however, a qualified and limited right, limited by the obligation to exercise as much sociological mind-and-conscience searching as may match the technological mind-searching.

The duty of government is to govern—in the James Watt-Norbert Wiener sense of the word " governor." Government has no more right to slow down technology, through fear born of ignorance, than to accelerate it in the interest of intimidation. The major problems of physical technology in the world of today lie well outside the walls of the study, the laboratory, the drawing office, the model shop, and the production plant. They lie in the lap of the statesman, the politician and the administrator, and—Heaven help us—we haven't taken the trouble to redesign these largely obsolescent cogs in the machinery of government.

Our failure to apply the Ellulian technology of the mind, and of the machinery of government—all of it a fabric of naive means to complex ends—is the Achilles heel of the technological giant. The technologist's robot has power without wisdom; the political philosophers and the statesmen must supply the sociological wisdom. They dare not leave it to the industrialist, the entrepreneur, the corporation, or the think-shop. Yet all these extra-governmental units have clocks that tick much faster than do those on the Hill or in the Executive Building—not by any fault of any individual, but because of the whole political structure, and above all because of what I may call the Einstein-diagnosis. You will remember that when an earnest student of affairs asked Einstein why it was, since we were clever enough to release nuclear energy, we could not solve apparently simpler political problems, Einstein replied, "It's quite simple; it's because politics is vastly more complicated than physics." I imagine he might have translated into a kind of political algebra by saying that the number of independent variables in the simplest political problem greatly transcends that in a very complicated problem in physics—and, additionally, that the number of inter-dependent variables is still greater. Indeed in the social equations there are no major independent variables. The intractability of social science lies in this, that every major variable is one of a tightly linked group of inter-dependent variables of comparable magnitude. Social change is a consequence of technological change, which is a consequence of social change, and so *ad infinitum*—if we be so wise as to prevent its being *ad nauseam*.

The relative freedom accorded to the scientist in all stable societies—and I do not include Nazi Germany among stable societies—is perhaps the nearest approach to an independent variable in the complex of technological development within organized society.

Perhaps I may be allowed to recount once more the minor episode of the admiral, the scientist, and the stockbroker. In the principal home port of the British Navy, Admiral of the Fleet Sir Henry Jackson (a scientist who had run neck and neck with Lodge, Popov, and Marconi in the first stages of wireless telegraphy) was walking with the Director of Scientific Research for the Royal Navy. Their path crossed that of two London stockbrokers, one of whom said to the other, in a powerful stage whisper, "There go the men who make our securities insecure."

In this our complex of variables, who can now say to what extent James Watt was moved and aided by the science of his friend "Latent-Heat Black," by the technology of his near-contemporaries, Newcomen, Savery, *et al.*, by the religious convictions of his great-grandfather, who died in the politico-religious warfare of the Scotland of the sixteen-hundreds, or by his personal observation of the sociologically barren landscape of the mid-seventeen-hundreds. If this is a complex difficult of resolution, how much greater is the difficulty of hearing the still small voice of literal philanthrophy through the clamour of the dark satanic mills, the clash of war, actual and latent, and the clash of politico-social conflict among states whose ethical, economic, scientific, and technological dogmas still fall pathetically short of harmony, of heavenly harmony.

Far from the least of these problems is the worthy utilization of the released time, energy, and attention of the partially-relieved worker.

Technology in general, and automation in particular, must of their very nature relieve the individual work burden; the statesman and the educator are involved in facilitating a worthwhile utilization of the bonus hours of freedom. How different this is from the assertions of the gloomy Ellul: " *La Technique* today takes over the total of the activities of man . . . The machine has created an inhuman milieu . . . Life no longer has any sense." And he achieves a masterpiece of confusion when he asserts that " This is in effect the last word; science has become a means of *la Technique*." This is in fact almost the first word, for all save the very first unsteady steps towards technology have first been steps in science.

There can, in fact, be no more disastrous undermining of the human condition than that of regarding technology as a self-propagated, self-propelled entity not fully controllable by the appropriately designed agencies of the body politic.

Perhaps, after all, there is at least one more preposterous allegation. An egocentric megalomaniac has " defined " technology as broadly including " any and all instruments of man which tend to amplify, project or augment his control over other men. Naturally this includes all communication forms, such as languages, in addition to any social, political, economic or religious structures which are utilized for such control." Surely the exact opposite is nearer the truth; wise technology releases the human from performing tasks which can be effected by machines, and offers him time to deal with more abstract matters of the mind. To be sure, this poses a major problem, that of the worthy utilization of the released time, energy, and attention of the worker.

As for the doubt whether human dignity is not greviously wounded by takeover of " human " tasks by the machine, we need only ask when, in the long series of vehicles: horse-drawn carriage, bicycle, railway train, steamship, automobile, aeroplane, space vehicle . . . , did human dignity suffer continuing harm?

Will the Luddites never learn?

Ideas of Technology

THE TECHNOLOGICAL ORDER

JACQUES ELLUL*

(Translated by John Wilkinson)

I. I refer the reader to my book *La Technique** for an account of my general theses on this subject. I shall confine myself here to recapitulating the points which seem to me to be essential to a sociological study of the problem:

1. Technique[1] has become the new and specific *milieu* in which man is required to exist, one which has supplanted the old *milieu*, viz., that of nature.

2. This new technical *milieu* has the following characteristics:
   a. It is artificial;
   b. It is autonomous with respect to values, ideas, and the state;
   c. It is self-determining in a closed circle. Like nature, it is a closed organization which permits it to be self-determinative independently of all human intervention;
   d. It grows according to a process which is causal but not directed to ends;
   e. It is formed by an accumulation of means which have established primacy over ends;

---

* Jacques Ellul is a Professor in the Faculty of Law at the University of Bordeaux. His books include *La Technique* (Paris, 1954), *Le Fondement théologique du droit* (Geneva, 1946) and *Présence au monde moderne* (Geneva, 1948). John Wilkinson, translator of this article, is Professor of Philosophy at the University of California at Santa Barbara. Wilkinson has also translated Ellul's *La Technique*, which will be published early next year.

[1] In his book *La Technique*, Jacques Ellul states he is " in substantial agreement " with H. D. Lasswell's definition of technique: " the ensemble of practices by which one uses available resources in order to achieve certain valued ends." Commenting on Lasswell's definition, Ellul says: " In the examples which Lasswell gives, one discovers that he conceives the terms of his definition in an extremely wide manner. He gives a list of values and the corresponding techniques. For example, he indicates as values riches, power, well-being, affection, and so on, with the techniques of government, production, medicine, the family. This notion of value may seem somewhat novel. The expression is manifestly improper. But this indicates that Lasswell gives to techniques their full scope. Besides, he makes it quite clear that it is necessary to bring into the account not only the ways in which one influences things, but also the ways one influences persons." " Technique " as it is used by Ellul is most nearly equivalent to what we commonly think of as " the technological order " or " the technological society." (Trans.)

10

f. All its parts are mutually implicated to such a degree that it is impossible to separate them or to settle any technical problem in isolation.

3. The development of the individual techniques is an " ambivalent " phenomenon.†

4. Since Technique has become the new *milieu*, all social phenomena are situated in it. It is incorrect to say that economics, politics, and the sphere of the cultural are influenced or modified *by* Technique; they are rather situated *in* it, a novel situation modifying all traditional social concepts. Politics, for example, is not modified by Technique as one factor among others which operate upon it; the political world is today *defined* through its relation to the technological society. Traditionally, politics formed a part of a larger social whole; at the present the converse is the case.

5. Technique comprises organizational and psycho-sociological techniques. It is useless to hope that the use of techniques of organization will succeed in compensating for the effects of techniques in general; or that the use of psycho-sociological techniques will assure mankind ascendancy over the technical phenomenon. In the former case, we will doubtless succeed in averting certain technically induced crises, disorders, and serious social disequilibrations; but this will but confirm the fact that Technique constitutes a closed circle. In the latter case, we will secure human psychic equilibrium in the technological *milieu* by avoiding the psycho-biologic pathology resulting from the individual techniques taken singly and thereby attain a certain happiness. But these results will come about through the *adaptation of human beings to the technical milieu*. Psycho-sociological techniques result in the *modification* of men in order to render them happily subordinate to their new environment, and by no means imply any kind of human domination over Technique.

6. The ideas, judgments, beliefs, and myths of the man of today have already been essentially modified by his technical *milieu*. It is no longer possible to reflect that on the one hand, there are techniques which may or may not have an effect on the human being; and, on the other, there is the human being himself who is to attempt to invent means to master his techniques and subordinate them to his own ends by *making a choice* among them. Choices and ends are both based on beliefs, sociological presuppositions, and myths which are a function of the technological society. Modern man's state of mind is completely dominated by technical values, and his goals are represented only by such progress and happiness as is to be achieved through techniques.

† This point was touched on only incidentally in my book, and is the subject of a note appended to the present paper.

Modern man in choosing is already incorporated within the technical process and modified in his nature by it. He is no longer in his traditional state of freedom with respect to judgment and choice.

II. To understand the problem posed to us, it is first of all requisite to disembarrass ourselves of certain fake problems.

1. We make too much of the disagreeable features of technical development, for example, urban over-crowding, nervous tension, air pollution, and so forth. I am convinced that all such inconveniences will be done away with by the ongoing evolution of Technique itself, and indeed, that it is only by means of such evolution that this can happen. The inconveniences we emphasize are always dependent on technical solutions, and it is only by means of techniques that they can be solved. This fact leads to the following two considerations:

a. Every solution to some technical inconvenience is able only to reinforce the system of techniques *in their ensemble;*

b. Enmeshed in a process of technical development like our own, the possibilities of human survival are better served by more technique than less, a fact which contributes nothing, however, to the resolution of the basic problem.

2. We hear too often that morals are being threatened by the growth of our techniques. For example, we hear of greater moral decadence in those environments most directly affected technically, say, in working class or urbanized *milieux.* We hear, too, of familial disintegration as a function of techniques. The falseness of this problem consists in contrasting the technological environment with the moral values inculcated by society itself.[2] The presumed opposition between ethical problematics and technological systematics probably at the present is, and certainly in the long run will be, false. The traditional ethical *milieu* and the traditional moral values are admittedly in process of disappearing, and we are witnessing the creation of a *new* technological ethics with its own values. We are witnessing the evolution of a morally consistent system of imperatives and virtues, which tends to replace the traditional system. But man is not necessarily left thereby on a morally inferior level, although a moral relativism is indeed implied—an attitude according to which everything is well, *provided* that the individual obeys some ethic or other. We *could* contest the value of this development *if* we had a clear and adequate concept of what good-in-itself is. But such judgments are impossible on the basis of our general morality. On *that* level, what we are getting is merely a substitution of a new technological morality for a traditional one which Technique has rendered obsolete.

[2] Cf. K. Horney.

3. We dread the "sterilization" of art through technique. We hear of the artist's lack of freedom, calm, and the impossibility of meditation in the technological society. This problem is no more real than the two preceeding. On the contrary, the best artistic production of the present is a result of a close connection between art and Technique. Naturally, new artistic form, expression, and ethic are implied, but this fact does not make art less art than what we traditionally called such. What assuredly is *not* art is a fixation in congealed forms, and a rejection of technical evolution as exemplified, say, in the neo-classicism of the nineteenth century or in present day "socialist realism." The modern cinema furnishes an artistic response comparable to the Greek theater at its best; and modern music, painting, and poetry express, not a canker, but an authentic esthetic expression of mankind plunged into a new technical *milieu*.

4. One last example of a false problem is our fear that the technological society is completely *eliminating* instinctive human values and powers. It is held that systematization, organization, " rationalized " conditions of labor, overly hygienic living conditions, and the like have a tendency to repress the forces of instinct. For some people the phenomenon of " beatniks," " *blousons noirs*," [3] and " hooligans " is explained by youth's violent reaction and the protestation of youth's vital force to a society which is overorganized, overordered, over-regulated, in short, technicized.[4] But here too, even if the facts are established beyond question, it is very likely that a superior conception of the technological society will result in the integration of these instinctive, creative, and vital forces. Compensatory mechanisms are already coming into play; the increasing appreciation of the aesthetic eroticism of authors like Henry Miller and the rehabilitation of the Marquis de Sade are good examples. The same holds for music like the new jazz forms which are " escapist " and exaltative of instinct; *item*, the latest dances. All these things represent a process of " *défoulement* " [5] which is finding its place in the technological society. In the same way, we are beginning to understand that it is impossible indefinitely to repress or expel religious tendencies and to bring the human race to a perfect rationality. Our fears for our instincts *are* justified to the degree that Technique, instead of provoking conflict, tends rather to *absorb* it, and to *integrate* instinctive and religious forces by giving them a place within its structure, whether it be by an adaptation of Christianity [6] or by the creation of new religious expressions like myths and mystiques which are in full compatibility with the techno-

[3] A kind of French beatnik. (Trans.)
[4] The psychoanalyst Jung has much to say along this line.
[5] An untranslatable French play on words. *Défoulement* is an invented word which presumably expresses the opposite of *refoulement*, i. e., repression.
[6] Teilhard de Chardin represents, in his works, the best example of this.

logical society.[7] The Russians have gone farthest in creating a "religion" compatible with Technique by means of their transformation of Communism into a religion.

III.   What, then, is the real problem posed to men by the development of the technological society? It comprises two parts: 1. Is man able to remain master [8] in a world of means? 2. Can a new civilization appear inclusive of Technique?

1.   The answer to the first question, and the one most often encountered, seems obvious: Man, who exploits the ensemble of means, *is* the master of them. Unfortunately, this manner of viewing matters is purely theoretical and superficial. We must remember the autonomous character of Technique. We must likewise not lose sight of the fact that the human individual himself is to an ever greater degree the *object* of certain techniques and their procedures. He is the object of pedagogical techniques, psychotechniques, vocational guidance testing, personality and intelligence testing, industrial and group aptitude testing, and so on. In these cases (and in countless others) most men are treated as a collection of objects. But, it might be objected, these techniques are exploited by other men, and the exploiters at least remain masters. In a certain sense this is true; the exploiters *are* masters of the particular techniques they exploit. But, they, too, are subjected to the action of yet other techniques, as, for example, propaganda. Above all, they are spiritually taken over by the technological society; they believe in what they do; they are the most fervent adepts of that society. They themselves have been profoundly technicized. They never in any way affect to despise Technique, which to them is a thing good in itself. They never pretend to assign values to Technique, which to them is in itself an entity working out its own ends. They never claim to subordinate it to any value because for them Technique *is* value.

It may be objected that these individual techniques have as their end the best adaptation of the individual, the best utilization of his abilities, and, in the long run, his happiness. This, in effect, is the objective and the justification of all techniques. (One ought not, of course, to confound man's "happiness" with capacity for mastery with, say, freedom.) If the first of all values is happiness, it is likely that man, thanks to his techniques, will be in a position to attain to a certain state of this good. But happiness does not contain everything it is thought to contain, and *the absolute disparity between happiness and freedom*

[7] Examples of such myths are: "Happiness," "Progress," "The Golden Age," etc.

[8] French *sujet*. The usual rendering, "subject," would indicate exactly the contrary of what is meant here, viz., the opposite of "object." The present sense of "subject" is that in virtue of which it governs a grammatical object, for example. (Trans.)

remains an ever real theme for our reflections. To say that man should remain *subject* rather than *object* in the technological society means two things, viz., that he be capable of giving direction and orientation to Technique, and that, to this end, he be able to master it.

Up to the present he has been able to do neither. As to the first, he is content passively to participate in technical progress, to accept whatever direction it takes automatically, and to admit its autonomous meaning. In the circumstances he can either proclaim that life is an absurdity without meaning or value; *or*, he can predicate a number of indefinitely sophisticated values. But neither attitude accords with the fact of the technical phenomenon any more than it does with the other. Modern declarations of the absurdity of life are not based on modern technological efflorescence, which none (least of all the existentialists) think an absurdity. And the predication of values is a purely theoretical matter, since these values are not equipped with any means for putting them into practice. It is easy to reach agreement on what they are, but it is quite another matter to make them have any effect whatever on the technological society, or to cause them to be accepted in such a way that techniques must evolve in order to realize them. The values spoken of in the technological society are simply there to justify what is; *or*, they are generalities without consequence; *or* technical progress realizes them automatically as a matter of course. Put otherwise, neither of the above alternatives is to be taken seriously.

The second condition *that man be subject rather than object*, i. e., the imperative that he exercise mastery over technical development, is facilely accepted by everyone. But factually it simply does not hold. Even more embarrassing than the question "How?" is the question "Who?" We must ask ourselves realistically and concretely just who is in a position to choose the values which give Technique its justification and to exert mastery over it. If such a person or persons are to be found, it must be in the Western world (inclusive of Russia). They certainly are not to be discovered in the bulk of the world's population which inhabits Africa and Asia, who are, as yet, scarcely confronted by technical problems, and who, in any case, are even less aware of the questions involved than we are.

Is the arbiter we seek to be found among the *philosophers*, those thinking specialists? We well know the small influence these gentry exert upon our society, and how the technicians of every order distrust them and rightly refuse to take their reveries seriously. Even if the philosopher could make his voice heard, he would still have to contrive means of mass education so as to communicate an effective message to the masses.

Can the *technician* himself assume mastery over Technique? The trouble here is that the technician is *always* a specialist and cannot make the slightest claim to have mastered any technique but his own. Those for whom Technique bears its meaning in itself will scarcely discover the values which lend meaning to what they are doing. They will not even look for them. The only thing they can do is to apply their technical specialty and assist in its refinement. They cannot *in principle* dominate the totality of the technical problem or envisage it in its global dimensions. *Ergo*, they are completely incapable of mastering it.

Can the *scientist* do it? There, if anywhere, is the great hope. Does not the scientist dominate our techniques? Is he not an intellectual inclined and fit to put basic questions? Unfortunately, we are obliged to re-examine our hopes here when we look at things as they are. We see quickly enough that the scientist is as specialized as the technician, as incapable of general ideas, and as much out of commission as the philosopher. Think of the scientists who, on one tack or another, have addressed themselves to the technical phenomenon: Einstein, Oppenheimer, Carrel. It is only too clear that the ideas these gentlemen have advanced in the sphere of the philosophic or the spiritual are vague, superficial, and contradictory *in extremis*. They really ought to stick to warnings and proclamations, for as soon as they assay anything else, the other scientists and the technicians rightly refuse to take them seriously, and they even run the risk of losing their reputations as scientists.

Can the *politician* bring it off? In the democracies the politicians are subject to the wishes of their constituents who are primarily concerned with the happiness and well-being which they think Technique assures them. Moreover, the further we get on, the more a conflict shapes up between the politicians and the technicians. We cannot here go into the matter which is just beginning to be the object of serious study.[9] But it would appear that the power of the politician is being (and will continue to be) outclassed by the power of the technician in modern states. Only dictatorships can impose their will on technical evolution. But, on the one hand, human freedom would gain nothing thereby, and, on the other, a dictatorship thirsty for power has no recourse at all but to push toward an excessive development of various techniques at its disposal.

Any of us? An individual can doubtless seek the soundest attitude to dominate the techniques at his disposal. He can inquire after the values to impose on techniques in his use of them, and search out the way to follow in order to remain a man in the fullest sense of the word within a technological society. All this is extremely difficult, but it is far from being useless, since it is apparently the only solution presently possible. But the individual's efforts are powerless to resolve in any way the technical problem in its universality; to accomplish this would mean that *all* men adopt the same values and the same behavior.

[9] See, for example, the reports of the International Congress for Political Science, October, 1961.

2. The second real problem posed by the technological society is whether or not a new civilization can appear which is inclusive of Technique. The elements of this question are as difficult as those of the first. It would obviously be vain to deny all the things that can contribute something useful to a new civilization: security, ease of living, social solidarity, shortening of the work week, social security, and so forth. But a civilization in the strictest sense of the term is not brought into being by all these things.[10]

A threefold contradiction resides between civilization and Technique of which we must be aware if we are to approach the problem correctly:

a. The technical world is the world of material things; it is put together out of material things and with respect to them. When Technique displays any interest in man, it does so by converting him into a material object. The supreme and final authority in the technological society is fact, at once ground and evidence. And when we think on man as he exists in this society it can only be as a being immersed in a universe of objects, machines, and innumerable material things. Technique indeed guarantees him such material happiness as material objects can. But, the technical society is not, and cannot be, a genuinely humanist society since it puts in first place not man but material things. It can only act on man by lessening him and putting him in the way of the quantitative. The radical contradiction referred to exists between technical perfection and human development because such perfection is only to be achieved through quantitative development and necessarily aims exclusively at what is measurable. Human excellence, on the contrary, is of the domain of the qualitative and aims at what is not measurable. Space is lacking here to argue the point that spiritual values cannot evolve as a function of material improvement. The transition from the technically quantitative to the humanly qualitative is an impossible one. In our times, technical growth monopolizes all human forces, passions, intelligences, and virtues in such a way that it is in practice nigh impossible to seek and find anywhere any distinctively human excellence. And if this search is impossible, there cannot be any civilization in the proper sense of the term.

b. Technical growth leads to a growth of power in the sense of technical means incomparably more effective than anything ever before invented, power which has as its object only power, in the widest sense of the word. The possibility of action becomes limitless and absolute. For example, we are confronted for the first time with the possibility of the annihilation of all life on

[10] See appended note on the theme " Technical Progress is Always Ambiguous."

earth, since we have the means to accomplish it. In *every* sphere of action we are faced with just such absolute possibilities. Again, by way of example, governmental techniques, which amalgamate organizational, psychological, and police techniques, tend to lend to government absolute powers. And here I must emphasize a great law which I believe to be essential to the comprehension of the world in which we live, viz., that when power becomes absolute, values disappear. When man is able to accomplish anything at all, there is no value which can be proposed to him; when the means of action are absolute, no goal of action is imaginable. Power eliminates, in proportion to its growth, the boundary between good and evil, between the just and the unjust. We are familiar enough with this phenomenon in totalitarian societies. The distinction between good and evil disappears beginning with the moment that the ground of action (for example the *raison d'état*, or the instinct of the proletariat) claims to have absolute power and thus to incorporate *ipso facto* all value. Thus it is that the growth of technical means tending to absolutism forbids the appearance of values, and condemns to sterility our search for the ethical and the spiritual. Again, where Technique has place, there is the implication of the impossibility of the evolution of civilization.

c. The third and final contradiction is that Technique can never engender freedom. Of course, Technique frees mankind from a whole collection of ancient constraints. It is evident, for example, that it liberates him from the limits imposed on him by time and space; that man, through its agency, is free (or at least tending to become free) from famine, excessive heat and cold, the rhythms of the seasons, and from the gloom of night; that the race is freed from certain social constraints through its commerce with the universe, and from its intellectual limitations through its accumulation of information. But is this what it means really to be free? Other constraints as oppressive and rigorous as the traditional ones are imposed on the human being in today's technological society through the agency of Technique. New limits and technical oppressions have taken the place of the older, natural constraints, and we certainly cannot aver that much has been gained. The problem is deeper—the operation of Technique is the contrary of freedom, an operation of determinism and necessity. Technique is an ensemble of rational and efficient practices; a collection of orders, schemas, and mechanisms. All of this expresses very well a necessary order and a determinate process, but one into which freedom, unorthodoxy, and the sphere of the gratuitous and spontaneous cannot penetrate. All that these last could possibly introduce is discord and disorder. The more technical actions increase in society, the more human autonomy and initiative diminish. The more the human being comes to exist in a world of ever increasing demands (fortified with technical apparatus possessing its own laws to meet these demands), the more he loses any possibility of free choice and individuality in action. This loss is greatly magnified by Technique's character of self-determination, which makes its appearance among us as a kind of fatality and as a species of perpetually exaggerated necessity. But where freedom is excluded in this way, an authentic civilization has little chance. Confronted in this way by the problem, it is clear to us that no solution can exist, in spite of the writings of all the authors who have concerned themselves with it. They all make an unacceptable premise, viz., rejection of Technique and return to a pre-technical society. One may well regret that some value or other of the past, some social or moral form, has disappeared; but, when one attacks the problem of the technical society, one can scarcely make the serious claim to be able to revive the past, a procedure which, in any case, scarcely seems to have been, globally speaking, much of an improvement over the human situation of today. All we know with certainty is that it was different, that the human being confronted other dangers, errors, difficulties, and temptations. Our duty is to occupy ourselves with the dangers, errors, difficulties, and temptations of modern man in the modern world. All regret for the past is vain; every desire to revert to a former social stage is unreal. There is no possibility of turning back, of annulling, or even of arresting technical progress. What is done is done. It is our duty to find our place in our present situation and in no other. Nostalgia has no survival value in the modern world and can only be considered a flight into dreamland.

We shall insist no further on this point. Beyond it, we can divide into two great categories the authors who search for a solution to the problem posed by Technique: The first class is that of those who hold that the problem will solve itself; the second, of those who hold that the problem demands a great effort or even a great modification of the whole man. We shall indicate a number of examples drawn from each class and beg to be excused for choosing to cite principally French authors.

Politicians, scientists and technicians are to be found in the first class. In general, they consider the problem in a very concrete and practical way. Their general notion seems to be that technical progress resolves all difficulties *pari passu* with their appearance, and that it contains within itself the solution to everything. The sufficient condition for them, therefore, is that technical progress be not arrested; everything which plagues us today will disappear tomorrow.

The primary example of these people is furnished by the Marxists, for whom technical progress is the solution to the plight of the proletariat and all its miseries, and to the problem posed by the exploitation of man by man in the capitalistic world. Technical progress, which is for Marx the motive force of history, *necessarily* increases the forces of production, and simultaneously produces a progressive conflict between forward moving factors and stationary social factors like the state, law, ideology, and morality, a conflict occasioning the periodic disappearance of the outmoded factors. Specifically, in the world of the present, conflict necessitates the disappearance of the structures of capitalism, which are so constituted as to be completely unable to absorb the economic results of technical progress, and are hence obliged to vanish. When they do vanish, they of necessity make room for a socialist structure of society corresponding perfectly to the sound and normal utilization of Technique. The Marxist solution to the technical problems is therefore an automatic one since the transition to socialism is *in itself* the solution. Everything is *ex hypothesi* resolved in the socialist society, and humankind finds therein its maturation. Technique, integrated into the socialist society " changes sign ": from being destructive it becomes constructive; from being a means of human exploitation it becomes humane; the contradiction between the infrastructures and the suprastructures disappears. In other words, all the admittedly difficult problems raised in the modern world belong to the structure of capitalism and not to that of Technique. On the one hand, it *suffices* that social structures become socialist for social problems to disappear; and on the other, society *must necessarily* become socialist by the very movement of Technique. Technique, therefore, carries in itself the response to all the difficulties it raises.

A second example of this kind of solution is given by a certain number of technicians, for example, Frisch. All difficulties, according to Frisch, will inevitably be resolved by the technical growth which will bring the technicians to power. Technique admittedly raises certain conflicts and problems, but their cause is that the human race remains attached to certain political ideologies and moralities and loyal to certain outmoded and antiquated humanists whose sole visible function is to provoke discord of heart and head, thereby preventing men from adapting themselves and from entering resolutely into the path of technical progress. *Ergo*, men are subject to distortions of life and consciousness which have their origin, *not* in Technique, but in the conflict between Technique and the false values to which men remain attached. These fake values, decrepit sentiments, and outmoded notions must inevitably be eliminated by the invincible progress of Technique. In particular, in the political domain, the majority of crises arise from the fact that men are still wedded to certain antique political forms and ideas, for example, democracy. All problems will be resolved if power is delivered into the hands of the technicians who alone are capable of directing Technique in its entirety and making of it a positive instrument for human service. This is all the more true in that, thanks to the so-called " human techniques " (for example, propaganda) they will be in a position to take account of the human factor in the technical context. The technocrats will be able to use the totality of Technique without destroying the human being, but rather by treating him as he should be treated so as to become simultaneously useful and happy. General power accorded to the technicians become technocrats is the only way out for Frisch, since they are the only ones possessing the necessary competence; and, in any case, they are being carried to power by the current of history, the fact which alone offers a quick enough solution to technical problems. It is impossible to rely on the general improvement of the human species, a process which would take too long and would be too chancy. For the generality of men, it is necessary to take into account that Technique establishes an inevitable discipline, which, on the one hand, they must accept, and, on the other, the technocrats will humanize.

The third and last example (it is possible that there are many more) is furnished by the economists, who, in very different ways, affirm the thesis of the automatic solution. Fourastié is a good example of such economists. For him, the first thing to do is to draw up a balance between that which Technique is able to deliver and that which it may destroy. In his eyes there is no real problem: What Technique can bring to man is incomparably superior to that which it threatens. Moreover, if difficulties *do* exist, they are only temporary ones which will be resolved beneficially, as was the case with the similar difficulties of the last century. Nothing decisive is at stake; man is in no mortal danger. The contrary is the case: Technique produces the foundation, infrastructure, and suprastructure which will enable man really to become man. What we have known up to now can only be called the *prehistory* of a human race so overwhelmed by material cares, famine, and danger, that the truly human never had an opportunity to develop into a civilization worthy of the name. Human intellectual, spiritual, and moral life will, according to Fourastié, never mature except when life is able to start from a complete satisfaction of its material needs, complete security, including security from famine and disease. The growth of Technique, therefore, initiates the genuinely human history of the whole man. This new type of human being will clearly be different from what we have hitherto known; but this fact should occasion no complaint or fear. The new type cannot help being superior to the old in every way, *after* all the traditional (and exclusively material) obstacles to his development have vanished. Thus, progress occurs automatically, and the inevitable role of Technique will be that of guaranteeing such material development as allows the intellectual and spiritual maturation of what has been up to now only potentially present in human nature.

The orientation of the other group of doctrines affirms, on the contrary, that man is dangerously imperiled by technical progress; and that human will, personality, and organization must be set again to rights if society is to be able to guard against the imminent danger. Unfortunately, these doctrines share with their opposites the quality of being too optimistic, in that they affirm that their thesis is even feasible and that man is really capable of the rectifications proposed. I will give three very different examples of this, noting that the attitude in question is generally due to philosophers and theologians.

The orientation of Einstein, and the closely related one of Jules Romains, are well known, viz., that the human being must get technical progress back again into his own hands, admitting that the situation is so complicated and the data so overwhelming that only some kind of "superstate" can possibly accomplish the task. A sort of spiritual power integrated into a world government in possession of indisputable moral authority might be able to master the progression of techniques and to direct human evolution. Einstein's suggestion is the convocation of certain philosopher-scientists, whereas Romains' idea is the establishment of a "Supreme Court of Humanity." Both of these bodies would be organs of meditation, of moral quest, before which temporal powers would be forced to bow. (One thinks, in this connection, of the role of the papacy in medieval Christianity *vis-à-vis* the temporal powers.)

A second example of this kind of orientation is given by Bergson, at the end of his work, *The Two Sources of Morality and Religion.* According to Bergson, initiative can only proceed from humanity, since in Technique there is no "*force des choses.*" Technique has conferred disproportionate power on the human being, and a disproportionate extension to his organism. But, "in this disproportionately magnified body, the soul remains what it was, i. e., too small to fill it and too feeble to direct it. Hence the void between the two." Bergson goes on to say that "this enlarged body awaits a supplement of soul, the mechanical demands the mystical," and . . . "that Technique will never render service proportionate to its powers unless humanity, which has bent it earthwards, succeeds by its means in reforming itself and looking heavenwards." This means that humanity has a task to perform, and that man must grow proportionately to his techniques, but that he must *will* it and *force* himself to make the experiment. This experiment is, in Bergson's view, a possibility, and is even favored by that technical growth which allows more material resources to men than ever before. The required "supplement of soul" is therefore of the order of the possible and will suffice for humans to establish mastery over Technique. The same position, it may be added, has in great part been picked up by E. Mounier.

A third example is afforded by a whole group of theologians, most of them Roman Catholic. Man, in his actions in the domain of the technical, is but obeying the vocation assigned him by his Creator. Man, in continuing his work of technical creation, is pursuing the work of his Creator. Thanks to Technique, this man, who was originally created "insufficient," is becoming "adolescent." He is summoned to new responsibilities in this world which do not transcend his powers since they correspond exactly to what God expects of him. Moreover, it is God Himself who through man is the Creator of Technique, which is something not to be taken in itself but in its relation to its Creator. Under such conditions, it is clear that Technique is neither evil nor fraught with evil consequences. On the contrary, it is good and cannot be dangerous to men. It can only become evil to the extent that man turns from God; it is a danger only if its true nature is misapprehended. All the errors and problems visible in today's world result uniquely from the fact that man no longer recognizes his vocation as God's collaborator. If man ceases to adore the "creature" (i. e., Technique) in order to adore the true God; if he turns Technique to God and to His service, the problems must disappear. All of this is considered the more true in that the world transformed by technical activity *must* become the point of departure and the material support of the new creation which is to come at the end of time.

Finally, it is necessary to represent by itself a doctrine which holds at the present a place of some importance in the Western world, i. e., that of Father Teilhard de Chardin, a man who was simultaneously a theologian and a scientist. His doctrine appears as an intermediate between the two tendencies already sketched. For Chardin, evolution in general, since the origin of the universe, has represented a constant progression. First of all, there was a motion toward a diversification of matter and of beings; then, there supervened a motion toward Unity, i. e., a higher Unity. In the biological world, every step forward has been effected when man has passed from a stage of "dispersion" to a stage of "concentration." At the present, technical human progress and the spontaneous movement of life are in agreement and in mutual continuity. They are evolving together toward a higher degree of organization, and this movement manifests the influence of Spirit. Matter, left to itself, is characterized by a necessary and continuous degradation. But on the contrary, we note that progress, advancement, improvement do exist, and, hence, a power contradicting the spontaneous movement of matter, a power of creation and progress exists which is the opposite of matter, i. e., it is Spirit. Spirit has contrived Technique as a means of organizing dispersed matter, in order simultaneously to express progress and to combat the degradation of matter. Technique is producing at the same time a prodigious demographic explosion, i. e., a greater density of human population. By all these means it is bringing forth "communion" among men; and likewise creating from inanimate matter a higher and more organized form of matter which is taking part in the ascension of the cosmos toward God. Granting that it is true that every progression in the physical and biological order is brought about by a condensation of the elements of the preceeding period, what we are witnessing today, according to Chardin, is a condensation, a concentration of the whole human species. Technique, in producing this, possesses a function of unification *inside* humanity, so that humanity becomes able thereby to have access to a sort of unity. Technical progress is therefore synonymous with "socialization," this latter being but the political and economic sign of communion among men, the temporary expression of the "condensation" of the human species into a whole. Technique is the irreversible agent of this condensation; it prepares the new step forward which humanity must make. When men cease to be individual and separate units, and all together form a total and indissoluble communion, then humanity will be a single body. This material concentration is always accompanied by a spiritual, i. e., a maturation of the spirit, the commencement of a new species of life. Thanks to Technique, there is "socialization," the progressive concentration on a planetary scale of disseminated spiritual personalities into a suprapersonal unity. This mutation leads to another Man, spiritual and unique, and means that humanity in its ensemble and in its unity, has attained the supreme goal, i. e., its fusion with that glorious Christ who must appear at the end of time. Thus Chardin holds that in technical progress man is "Christified," and that technical evolution tends inevitably to the "edification" of the cosmic Christ.

It is clear that in Chardin's grandiose perspective, the individual problems, difficulties, and mishaps of Technique are negligible. It is likewise clear how Chardin's doctrine lies midway between the two preceeding ones: On the one hand, it affirms a natural and involuntary ascension of man, a process inclusive of biology, history, and the like, evolving as a kind of will of God in which Technique has its proper place; and, on the other, it affirms that the evolution in question implies consciousness, and an intense *involvement* on the part of man who is proceeding to socialization and thus *committing* himself to this mutation.

We shall not proceed to a critique of these different theories, but content ourselves with noting that all of them appear to repose on a too superficial view of the technical phenomenon; and that they are *practically* inapplicable because they presuppose a certain number of *necessary* conditions which are not given. None of these theories, therefore, can be deemed satisfactory.

IV. It does not seem that at the present we are in a position to give a satisfactory reply to the complex of technical problems. All that appears possible is to inquire into the above-mentioned *necessary* conditions for a possible solution.

In any case, it seems to me that we can set forth the following thesis: The further technical progress advances, the more the social problem of mastering this progress becomes one of an ethical and spiritual kind.

In proportion to the degree that man extricates himself from the domain of the material, dominates it, and multiplies thereby the means of exploiting matter, the problem ceases to be one of human possibilities and limits and becomes one rather of knowing which man (or group of men) will exploit technical means, and what will be the enabling moral and spiritual qualities. (In this point I am not far from that, for example, of Bergson.) It is essential not to consider the problem resolved once this has been said; the current attitude is false according to which, once a matter has been pronounced a matter of morality, it is something simple and also automatically resolvable. On the contrary, the more decision depends on a man or a group of them, the more difficult it appears, *if* we take a realistic view of the matter and refuse to admit *a priori* that man is good, democratic, liberal, reasonable, and so on. The difficulty resides in the following points:

a. It is impossible to trust the spontaneous employment which men will make of the available technical means;

b. Man, as we have already indicated, is *integrated* into the technological process;

c. *If* we desire to preserve man's freedom, dignity, and responsibility, it is precluded to act upon him by technical means, like psychology, and so forth. To transform a man into a reasonable being and a good exploiter of techniques *through* certain psychological procedures is precisely to destroy him as a spiritual and ethical subject.

We are thus caught in a dilemma before the decisive question, the question which may well be the penultimate one.

With this preliminary, what are these necessary conditions? I shall note them as they appear to me at the present, starting from that which is more general and working toward that which is more particular.

1. The first thing needed is a correct diagnosis and an effort to achieve a genuine consciousness of the problem. It is necessary to see the situation clearly and to pose the problem correctly if it be desired to know just what is to be done and if adequate answers are to be forthcoming. Inexact formulation of the problem affords no hope of getting a solution. The diagnostic element, on which I do not insist, must be accompanied by a becoming conscious—by passing from the intellectual to the existential, which means that mankind must accept the fact that his existence is " engaged " and involved in this venture, and that his very freedom is at stake. It is necessary to become conscious of the fact that in every domain, Technique has established stricter and stricter domination over the human being. But this consciousness must not be negative—no scientific determinism or divine fatalism before which man can only bow and confess himself unfree. On the contrary, it must be recognized that man *qua* free is subject

to constraints and determinations which his vocation to be free must make him combat and rise clear of. *But*, to the extent that man clings to the illusion of the present that he *is* free (and uses the vocabulary of freedom) conceiving liberty as inalienable; *or*, to the extent that he holds to the conviction that all will be well though he sees that the Technique actually diminishes the area of freedom, and dreams that possibilities of freedom still exist—in all these cases, his natural inertia is leading him to accept a condition of slavery and to pay for his technological happiness with his freedom. It is only by making men conscious to what degree they have become slaves in becoming " happy," that there is any hope of regaining liberty by asserting themselves, perhaps at the cost of much sacrifice, over the Technique which has come to dominate them. Short of attaining to such consciousness, there is no reason for any human being to lift a finger to secure mastery over his technology.

2. A second essential element consists in ruthlessly destroying the " myth " of Technique, i. e., the whole ideological construction and the tendency to consider technology something possessing sacred character. Intellectuals attempt to insert the technical phenomenon into the framework of their respective intellectual or philosophical systems by attributing to it a quality of supreme excellence; for example, when they demonstrate that Technique is an instrument of freedom, or the means of ascent to historical destiny, or the execution of a divine vocation, and the like. All such constructions have the result of glorifying and sanctifying Technique and of putting the human being at the disposal of some indisputable historical law or other. A further aspect of this element is the *sacred*, i. e., the human tendency spontaneously to attribute sacred value to what so manifestly possesses transcendent power. Technique, in this view, is not solely an ensemble of material elements, but that which gives meaning and value to life, allowing man not only to live but to live well. Technique is intangible and unattackable precisely because *everything* is subject and subordinate to it. Man unconsciously invests with a holy prestige that against which he is unable to prevail. It seems to me that the only means to mastery over Technique is by way of " de-sacralization " and " de-ideologization." This means that all men must be shown that Technique is nothing more than a complex of material objects, procedures, and combinations, which have as their sole result a modicum of comfort, hygiene, and ease; and that it possesses nothing worthy of the trouble of devoting one's whole life to it, or of commanding an excessive respect, or of reposing in it one's success and honor, or of massacring one's fellow men. Men must be convinced that technical progress is not humanity's supreme adventure, but a commonplace fabrication of certain objects which scarcely merit enthusiastic delirium even when they happen to be Sputniks. As long as man worships

Technique, there is as good as no chance at all that he will ever succeed in mastering it.

3. A consequence of this is that, in practice, it is necessary to teach man in his employment of Techniques a certain detachment, an independence with respect to them—and humor. It is naturally very difficult to accomplish this; and above all to get him to give up his illusions, not pretending to be completely free with respect to automobiles, television sets, or jobs, when the plain fact is that he is totally enslaved to them. Man must be capable of questioning at every step his use of his technical goods, able to refuse them and to force them to submit to determining factors other than the technical, say, the spiritual. He must be able to exploit all these goods without becoming unduly attached to them and without becoming convinced that even his most imposing technical conquests are to be taken seriously. Such recommendations must, of course, appear scandalous to contemporary eyes. To affirm that these things have no importance at all in respect to truth and freedom, that it is a matter of no *real* importance whether man succeeds in reaching the moon, or curing disease with antibiotics, or upping steel production, is really a scandal. As long as man does not learn to use technical objects in the right way he must remain their slave. What I am saying refers to Technique itself and *not* to the individual's use of individual techniques. These two problems are situated on different levels. But, *if* the *individual* cannot attain personal liberty with respect to technical objects, there is no chance that he will be able to respond to the general problem of Technique. Let us recall once more that what we are setting forth are certain necessary conditions for finding a solution to this general problem.

4. Everything we have said presupposes an effort at reflection which might be thought of as philosophic. If we admit that the technical adventure is a genuine novelty for the human race, that all that it has excogitated up to now can scarcely be of any use to it at the present; if we admit that it can only be by means of a fundamental and arduous search that we will be able to extricate ourselves from the mess we are in, a *truly* philosophic reflection will be necessary. But modern philosophic systems, like existentialism and phenomenology, have small utility because they limit themselves into desuetude with their assertions that philosophy *in principle* can have no purchase on Technique. How, in the nature of things, can a philosophy which is nothing more than a research into the meaning of words, get any grip on the technical phenomenon? Preoccupation with "semantics" is the reason why modern philosophy immures itself in a refusal to come to grips with Technique. As Ducassé has put it in his *Les Techniques et le philosophe*: "Between the refusal of the philosophers, who claim to open up existence to themselves while evading the technical nature of the existent, and the hypocritical humility of the technicians manifested

by an ambition stronger than their discipline, some very peculiar enterprises get under way, which might be termed "pseudophilosophies" and "pseudotechniques," respectively, and which usurp in man the place of philosophy's absent mediation." Authentic philosophy of real meaning would bring us to precisely that possibility of mediation between man and the technical phenomenon without which any legitimate attitude is inconceivable. But for such a philosophy to exist would mean that philosophy would first have to cease to be a purely academic technique with a hermetically sealed vocabulary, to become again the property of *every* man who thinks while he is engaged in the business of being alive.

5. Finally, it is necessary to point out the importance of the relation between the technicians and those who try to pose the technical problem. None of the preceding is more difficult than this, since the technicians have become an authoritarian and closed world. They are armed with good consciences, but likewise with the conviction of their essential rightness and the persuasion that *all* discourse and reflection of a non-technical nature are verbalisms of no importance. To get them to engage in the dialogue or to question their own creation is an almost superhuman task, the more so that he who will enter this dialogue must be completely aware of what he wants, just what the technician is driving at, and what the technician is able to grasp of the problem. But, as long as such interchange does not take place, nothing will happen, since influencing Technique necessarily means influencing the technicians. It seems to me that this dialogue can only come about by making contact which will represent a *permanent* and *basic* confrontation between technique's pretensions to resolve all human problems and the human will to escape technical determinism.

Such, I think are the five conditions necessary that an opening on the technical problem can even become a possibility.

Note on the Theme:
Technical Progress is Always Ambiguous

It cannot be maintained that technical progress is in itself either good or bad. In the evolution of Technique, contradictory elements are always indissolubly connected. Let us consider these elements under the following four rubrics:

1. All technical progress exacts a price;
2. Technique raises more problems than it solves;
3. Pernicious effects are inseparable from favorable effects; and
4. Every technique implies unforeseeable effects.

1. All Technical Progress Exacts a Price

What is meant here is not that technical progress exacts a price in money or in intellectual effort, but that, when technical progress adds something on the one hand, it inevitably subtracts something on the other. It is always difficult to interpret satisfactorily the bald statement that "technical progress is an established fact," because some people cling to traditional social forms, tending to deny any value at all to such progress, and deeming that nothing can be called progress if it casts doubt on established social values. Other persons, on the contrary, hold that Technique produces extraordinary things of a prodigious novelty, bringing about the consequent disappearance of all sorts of valueless junk.

The fact is that, viewed objectively, technological progress produces values of unimpeachable merit, while simultaneously destroying values no less important. As a consequence, it cannot be maintained that there is absolute progress or absolute regress.

Let me give a few simple examples of this reciprocal action. In the first place, let us consider the fact that modern man, thanks to hygiene in particular and to technical progress in general, enjoys a greater life span than ever before. Life expectancy in France today is approximately 60 years, compared, say, to 35 years in 1890 and 30 years about 1800.* But, even with this indubitable extension of the average life span, all physicians are in agreement that, proportionately to this extension, life has become very much more precarious, i. e., our general state of health has become very much more fragile. Human beings of the present have neither the same resistance as their ancestors to disease or to natural conditions, nor the same endurance; they suffer from a certain nervous "fragility" and a loss of general vitality, sensitiveness of their senses, and so on. In the 60 years during which such studies have been carried out, regression in all these respects has been marked. Thus, though we live longer, we live a reduced life with nothing resembling the vital energy of our ancestors. It is clear that diminution on the one hand has been accompanied by augmentation on the other.

In the sphere of labor, the technical progress of the present has effected a considerable economy of muscular effort; but, at the same time this progress has come to demand a greater and greater nervous effort so that tension and wear and tear on our nerves have inversely increased. Here again, a kind of equilibrium has asserted itself between savings and expense.

To take an instance from the sphere of economics, technical progress allows the creation of new industries. But a just view of the matter would compel us to take into consideration the accompanying destruction of resources. To take a French example, the so-called Lacq case is beginning to be well known. An industrial complex for the exploitation of sulphur and natural gas has been established at Lacq, a simple technical fact. But, from the economic point of view, this is far from being the case, since a serious agricultural problem has arisen because of the excessive destruction of farm products in the region. Up to now, the government has not seen fit to take the matter seriously, although it has been officially estimated in reports to the Chamber that, for 1960, agricultural losses have aggregated two billion francs. Now, the vineyards of Jurançon are being attacked by the sulfurous gases and are disappearing, a not inconsiderable economic loss.

To calculate from the economist's point of view the profits of an industry

---

* I must remark that I am very sceptical of the way in which mean life spans are calculated for periods antedating 1800. When the historian says that life expectancy was 20 years in the thirteenth century, his statement can hardly be looked upon as more than a mere joke. There are no means *in principle* of establishing life expectancies for the past.

of this kind, it would at the minimum be necessary to deduct the value of what has been destroyed, in this case two billion francs. It would likewise be necessary to deduct the very considerable expenses of all the necessary protective devices, hospitals (which, incidentally, have not yet been constructed), schools,—in short, of the whole urban complex which has not yet been brought into being but which is nevertheless indispensable. We must have knowledge of how to calculate the *whole*. The Lacq enterprise, counting all the expenses of which we have been speaking, must be reckoned a " deficit " enterprise.

Our last example has to do with the problem of the intellectual culture of the masses. True, today's technical means permit a mass culture to exist. Television allows people who never visited a theatre in their lives to see performances of the great classics. *Paris-Match*, through its articles, allows masses of people who would be in total ignorance without such articles to attain to a certain literary (and even to a certain aesthetic) culture. But, on the other side of the ledger, it must be recorded that this same technical progress leads to an ever increasing cultural superficiality. Technical progress absolutely forbids certain indispensable conditions of a genuine culture, viz., reflection and opportunity for assimilation. We are indeed witnessing the creation of knowledge, since we are in possession of the means of knowing what we could never have known before; but it is nevertheless a superficial development because it is one which is purely *quantitative*.

The intellectual no longer has any time to meditate on a book and must choose between two alternatives: *Either* he reads through a whole collection of books rapidly, of which a little later but a few fragments survive—scattered bits of vague knowledge; *or*, he takes a year to peruse a few books thoroughly. I should like to know who today has the time to take Pascal or Montaigne seriously. To do them justice would require months and months; but today's Technique forbids any such thing. Exactly the same holds for the problem of the " Musée Imaginaire," which Malraux has put so well. We can be in contact with the whole painting and sculpture of humanity; but this availability has no cultural value comparable to that enjoyed by Poussin, who, in his voyage to Rome, passed several years in studying, statue by statue, the ensemble of artistic works at his disposal. He clearly knew nothing of Polynesian or Chinese art, but what he did know had infinitely more educational value for him because it penetrated his personality slowly.

So, once again, we see that Technique allows us to progress quantitatively to the level of culture spoken of, but at the same time interdicts us from making any progress in depth. In the circumstances, is it really possible to speak of " culture " at all? All technical progress exacts a price. We cannot believe that Technique brings us nothing; but we must not think that what it brings it brings free of charge.

2. *The Problems Posed by Technical Progress*

The second aspect of the ambiguity of technical progress concerns the following point: When Technique evolves, it does so by solving a certain number of problems, and by raising others.

The further we advance into the technological society, the more convinced we become that, in any sphere whatever, there are nothing but technical problems. We conceive all problems in their technical aspect, and think that solutions to them can only appear by means of further perfecting techniques. In a certain sense, we are right; it is true that Technique permits us to solve the majority of the problems we encounter. But we are compelled to note (perhaps not often enough) that each technical evolution raises new problems, and that, as a consequence, there is never *one* technique which solves *one* problem. The technological movement is more complicated; one technique solves one problem, but at the same time creates others.

Let us take some simple examples of this fact. We are well acquainted with the details of the gravest sociological problem faced by the nineteenth century, i. e., that of the proletariat, a problem which we are only now in process of solving (with difficulty). The phenomenon of the proletariat is not to be considered a simple one, and Marx himself did not describe it as " merely " the exploitation of the workers by certain wicked capitalists. His explanation of the " proletarian condition " was very much more profound; he demonstrated that the proletariat was a result of the division and the mechanization of labor. He expressly states that " it is necessary to pass through the stage represented by the proletariat." For Marx, therefore, the problem is not, say, a moral one, with " bad guys exploiting good guys." Marx never puts the problem in this way; he always poses it as lying outside good or bad moral qualities, external to value judgments, and on the level of fact. And the fact is the fact of the division of labor, and of the machine, giving rise to a society in which exploitation is inevitable, i. e., drawing off surplus values. The phenomenon of the proletariat is therefore, even in the Marxian analysis, the result of technical progress. The machine and the division of labor allowed, from the economic point of view, an extraordinary expansion, but, at the same time, and as a result of the same movement, posed the social problem which it has taken a whole century to resolve.

Let us consider in the same way the extension of the above problem as it appears in the questions which will eventually but certainly be posed by the so-called " automation." Again, automation is not just another simple economic fact; indeed, we are gradually coming to realize that it will entail difficulties which, from our present point of view, can only be characterized as insurmountable. *First* of all, automation implies a production of goods in a relatively constant series of types. This means that when production has been automated, it is no longer possible to vary types, so that an unavoidable condition of immobilism with regard to production must ensue. An automated production line, considered in its full context of operation, is so expensive that amortization must occur over terms so long that the exclusive production of certain types of goods without any possibility of modification must be a consequence. *But*, up to the present, no commercial market of the capitalist world is suited to the absorption of the production of an unchanging line of goods. No presently existing Western economic organization, *on the commercial plane*, is prepared to find an answer to automated production.

Another difficulty of automation is the fact that it will result in a massive diminution of the necessary labor force. The simplistic reaction to this problem will clearly be to hold that the solution is easy. It is not necessary to cut down on the number of the workers but only to diminish the number of daily working hours of each. This solution is quite clearly impossible for a very simple reason. Automation cannot be applied to any arbitrarily selected industry or production, and this for reasons which are basic and not due to the temporary exigencies of, say, the money market. Certain kinds of production can and will be automated; certain others cannot and will never be automated. Consequently, it is not possible to cut down working hours over the working class as a whole. There are industrial sectors in which the workers would conceivably work one hour per day, whereas in others the workers would have to continue working a normal day of eight hours. Hence, as a result of automation, there will be extended sectors of the economy emptied of manpower, while other sectors will continue on the normal standard.

Diebold estimates that in the single year 1955-1956, in the United States, automation reduced the total number of working hours by seven per cent. In the automated plants of the Ford Motor Company there was a reduction of personnel by 25 per cent; and in 1957, in industrial branches in which automation gained most (in particular in the manufacture of electric bulbs and in the very highly automated chemical industry), it was possible to dispense with the services of 800,000 workers. In other words, automation does not result in labor saving favorable to the workers, but is expressed through unemployment and employment disequilibration.

It might be alleged that the situation described is true of capitalist countries but cannot be identical in socialist. This statement is not exact; in socialist countries the problem likewise is posed, primarily because of socialist egalitarianism. The problem is the same for the Soviet Union, for example, where automation is commencing, as for the United States. There will be specialized workers in some industries who will be freed from the necessity to work in one way or another, while in other branches of industry the eight-hour day will have to remain in force, a situation clearly unacceptable to the egalitarian theories of socialism.

A *second* problem is bound to arise in connection with the *retraining* of the " liberated " workers for jobs in new industrial sectors in which there is a shortage of manpower. But, such retraining more often than not presents enormous difficulties, since the disemployed worker is generally semi-skilled (or unskilled) and a completely new apprenticeship is implied of such a nature as to steer him toward other branches of industry.

A *third* difficulty occasioned by automation is the problem of *wages*. The wage problem produced by automation has, up till now, not been solved. How is it possible to fix a wage scale for automated industrial plants? It cannot be done on the piecework plan—machines do all the work. It cannot be done on the basis of time put in on the job. If it is desired to reduce unemployment by reducing the work day to, say, two or three hours, a given worker would only be employed for a very short period each day. Should such a worker, then, be paid according to a wage schedule which pays him for two hours of work at the equivalent of a worker who must work eight? The injustice of such a procedure is clear. How, then, should wages be calculated in an automated industry? One is forced to the admission that the relation between wages and productivity, on the one hand, and between wages and job time, on the other, *must* disappear. Wages will be calculated only as a function of the purchasing power given to the worker (with a view to maximum consumption) by dividing the total production value by the total number of workers. Such a method is really the only one feasible. Since 1950, in Russia, it has actually been tried twice. But the results were unsatisfactory, and it very soon became necessary to return to the system of hourly wages, since, in the present state of affairs, the necessary calculations prove unfeasible. But then the difficulties mentioned above (inherent in calculating either according to job-time or according to production) return, and, at the moment, wage calculation in automated industries is completely shrouded in uncertainties.

Still another problem is presented by the fact that modern economic crises most often result from a " distortion " between the different economic sectors, more exactly, from unequal growth of the different sectors. Here, automation must prove to be an economic factor much to be feared: There will not only be disparity of economic growth between the automated and the non-automated industrial sectors, but still more between industry and agriculture. *Either* capitalist countries must look forward to an increase of crises due to automation, *or* they must adopt planning aimed at rectifying the distortions (and planning by authoritarian measures, as in the Soviet Union). At the present time, even the Soviet planners find that their planning is insufficient to meet the problems of automation, since it is not " flexible " enough, on the one hand, and not " extensive " enough to re-equilibrate the out-of-phase sectors, on the other.

Here, then, are a number of problems (and there are a great many others) with which we must expect to be confronted by the fact of automation, all of which furnish us with examples of our thesis that Technique raises, in proportion to its progress, problems of greater and greater difficulty.

Let me indicate one final example of this, i. e., the problem of overpopulation, resulting from the application of medical and prophylactic health techniques, the final result of which is the suppression of infant mortality and the prolongation of human life. The phenomenon of overpopulation, in its turn, produces the tragic phenomenon of underconsumption. A century hence, all of us *without exception* will be menaced by a general underconsumption which will afflict the whole human race, *if* the expansion of the world's population increases. Here we are confronted by a problem clearly provoked by certain techniques, certain *positive techniques*.

The common factor of all these examples is that technical progress raises whole complexes of problems which we are in no position to solve. Examples of such problems are literally innumerable.

3. The Evil Effects of Technique are Inseparable from the Good

An idea frequently to be encountered in superficial inquiries concerning Technique is the following: " At bottom, everything depends on the way Technique is employed; mankind has only to use Technique for the good and avoid using it for the bad." A common example of this notion is the usual recommendation to employ techniques for the beneficent purposes of peace and eschew them for the maleficent purposes of war. All then will go well.

Our thesis is that technical progress contains simultaneously the good *and* the bad. Consider automation, the problem which we have just been discussing. It is indisputable that technological unemployment is the result of mechanical progress. It cannot be otherwise. All mechanical progress necessarily entails a saving of labor and, consequently, a necessary technological unemployment. Here we have an ill-omened effect indissolubly connected with one which is in itself beneficial. The progress of mechanization necessarily entails unemployment. The technological unemployment so produced can be resolved by either of two means, which are the only two means economically or politically possible, viz., spreading it out either in *space* or in *time*.

A capitalist economist holds that the solution to unemployment is " that technological unemployment ultimately dies out of itself." This means that the workers who have been "freed" (the optimistic formula for unemployment) because of technical advances, will ultimately find jobs, either by directing themselves toward industries with manpower shortages or through the fact that new inventions will produce new opportunities of employment and new vocations. The standard example cited in defense of this thesis is that of the vocational opportunities connected with the invention of the automobile. Admittedly, this technological device did suppress a certain number of vocations, but it brought innumerable others into being with the final result that a vast number of persons are now employed by the servicing required by this industry. Hence, the machine in question has actually created employment.

All of this is indeed true. It is nevertheless a terribly heartless view of the situation, because it neglects to mention the *interim* period. It is all very well to say that the worker rendered jobless will, *with the lapse of a certain time*, again find employment . . . and that, after he has been reclassified, unemployment will die out. But, humanly speaking, what is the situation of the unemployed worker in the interim? Here the problem of spreading out unemployment in time is posed.

In the Soviet Union, unemployment of a technological nature (which not only exists but springs from the same sources) is spread out in space. By this I mean that when, in one place new machines are applied and workers "liberated" the affected workers will, without having to wait very long, receive a work-card which tells them in effect: "Two thousand kilometers from here a job has been assigned to you; you are hereby directed to remove yourself to such and such a factory." In one way, such a procedure seems a little less inhuman; but, in another way, it seems just as inhuman as the time procedure of the capitalists, since no account is taken of one's attachments to family, friends, locality, and so on. The human being is only a pawn to be moved about. It is hard to tell, between the capitalist and the socialist ways of handling the problem, which solution presents the worse indecencies.

A further example of the inseparable mingling of good and bad effects is furnished by the noteworthy study of the American sociological historian, J. U. Nef, concerning "industry and war." Nef shows how industrialism, i. e., the development of industry taken as a whole, necessarily prods industrialized societies in the direction of war. His analysis has nothing to do with the inner essence of industrialism; the phenomena described by him lie purely at the level of the human being.

First, industrialism gives an increasing population the means to live. It is a law sociologically irrefutable that, the denser the population, the greater the number of wars. This phenomenon is, of course, well known as a *practical* matter to all sociologists, but only Nef has studied it carefully.

Second, industrialism creates the media of the press, transmission of information, and transport, and finally the means of making war, all of which make it more and more difficult and even almost impossible to distinguish between the aggressor and the aggressed. At the present, no one knows (and perhaps no one can know) which side has commenced hostilities, a fact not solely due to armaments, but also to facility of transport. The extraordinary rapidity of transport allows an aggression to be launched within 24 hours, or even less, without anyone being able to foresee it. Here, the influence of the press is extremely important, since the press function is to confuse and addle the facts so that no one is able to gain any correct intelligence of them.

Finally, Nef indicates that the new means of destruction created by industrialism have greatly reduced the trouble, the difficulties, and the anguish implied in the act of killing people. A bombardier or artillerist has no feeling at all of killing anyone; he is in fact able to reach the conclusion that he has killed someone only with the aid of a syllogism. In hand-to-hand combat all the tiresome difficulties of conscience about the evil of murder keep obtruding themselves. In such ways, then, positive elements of industry result essentially (by very complex expedients) in favoring war and even in provoking it, even if no one has the *intention* of using Technique " badly."

Let us consider, as a final example of the relation between good effects and bad effects, the press and information.

It seems to be a simple matter, for example, to distinguish between information and propaganda. But, closer study of the problem reveals that it is practically impossible to make such a distinction. Considering but a few elements of the situation, the problem of information is today no longer that of the necessity of transmitting *honest* information—everybody agrees on this point. On the moral level it is a commonplace that we ought to transmit true information. I merely inquire, " How do we get it? " To remain on the *moral* level is simply not to understand the situation. The *concrete* situation, to take but a single example, is something like the following: Over the wires and into the offices of the Associated Press pass daily up to 300,000 words of world news, approximately equal to an enormous volume of 1000 pages. From this mass of words, it is necessary for the Associated Press, in competition with all the other world agencies, to choose, cut, and re-expedite as quickly as possible, perhaps a twentieth part of the whole to its subscribers. How is it possible to select from such a flood just what should be retained, what is true, what is possibly false, etc.? The editors have no criteria, they are at the mercy of whatever comes in, and (even when they judge in good faith and knowledge) they must essentially judge subjectively. Then again, even if the editor had only true news, how should he assign it a coefficient of importance? To do so is his business, and here the stereotypes of the editor are true enough: The Catholic editor will deem the news of the latest Vatican Council of great significance, information which has not the slightest importance to the Communist editor. What we have to do with here is not a question of bad faith, but of a difference of perspective on the world. The result is that we never know, even under the most favorable circumstances, if a given piece of information is subjective. And we must always bear in mind that this information, whatever it is, has been worked over by at least four or five different pairs of hands.

My reasons for maintaining that good effects are inseparable from bad are now, I trust, clear. And, as communications improve, the freer will be the flow of the news and the more available to all agencies concerned. These factors will play an ever greater role, making the difficulties of editing proportionately more difficult, and the chance of selecting absurd rather than sound news ever greater.

4. *All Technical Progress Contains Unforeseeable Effects*

The final aspect of the ambiguity of technical progress resides in the following state of affairs: When scientists carry out their researches in one or another discipline and hit upon new technical means, they generally see clearly in what sphere the new technique will be applicable. Certain results are expected and gotten. *But*, there are always secondary effects which had not been anticipated, which in the primary stage of the technical progress in question could not *in principle* have been anticipated. This unpredictability arises from the fact that predictability implies complete possibility of experimenting in *every* sphere, an inconceivable state of affairs.

The most elementary example is furnished by drugs. You have a cold in the head; you take an aspirin. The headache disappears, but aspirin has other actions besides doing away with headaches. In the beginning we were totally oblivious of these side effects; but, I should imagine, by now everyone has read articles warning against the use of aspirin because of its possible dangerous effects, say, on the blood picture. Grave hemorrhages have appeared in people who habitually took two or three aspirins daily. Yet aspirin was thought the perfect remedy a scant ten years ago—on the ground that no side effects were to be feared. Now, such effects begin to appear even in what was, and is, probably the most harmless of all drugs.

Another spectacular example is that of DDT, a chemical which in 1945 was thought to be a prodigiously successful means for the destruction of all kinds of vermin and insects. One of the most admirable things about DDT was that it was said to be completely innocuous toward human beings. DDT was sprinkled over the whole surface of the globe. Then, by accident, it was discovered that in certain areas veal cattle were wasting away and dying. Research revealed that DDT in oily solution causes anemia. Cattle had been dusted with DDT in order to get rid of insects; they had subsequently licked themselves clean and ingested the DDT. The chemical in question passed into their milk and by this route found its way into oily solution, i. e., in the milk fat. Calves suckled by such cows died of anemia, and it is needless to add that the same milk was ingested by human infants. Identical problems are potentially raised by *all* chemicals consumed by animals or men. Recall the recent example of thalidomide.

This is an example of the so-called secondary effects, effects which are essentially unpredictable and only revealed after the technique in question has been applied on a grand scale, i. e., when it is no longer possible to retrace one's steps.

Another interesting example is furnished by the psycho-sociological studies of the particular psychology of big city dwellers, where, once more, we are confronted with the effect of the technical environment on the human being. One of the principal elements of big city life is the feeling of isolation, loneliness, absence of human contacts, etc. One of the leading ideas of Le Corbusier in his *Maison des Hommes* was the admission that " big city dwellers do not know one another." " Let us create," said Le Corbusier, " great blocks of dwellings where people will meet one another as they did in the village, with everything (grocer, baker, butcher) included in the block so that people will get to know one another and a community will come into being . . . ." The result of Le Corbusier's creation was exactly the opposite of what had been planned; problems of loneliness and isolation in such blocks of dwellings proved to be much more tragic than in the normal and traditional city.

Then, it was held (and this is the penultimate word in city planning) that it was necessary to rediscover human groupings *on a human scale*, not on the scale of a block with, say, 5000 separate dwelling units. In the works and writings of sociologists and of city planners of perhaps seven or eight years ago we read: " At bottom, the only ones who understood what a city was were the people of the Middle Ages, who knew how to create a true city corresponding to the demands of a genuine city-planning technique, i. e., a human community centered about a small square surrounded by small houses, toward which converged the (straight) city streets, etc. . . . ." The new city planners in keeping with these theories, applied them to the suburbs of Chicago, and in particular, to the well known "village" of Park Forest. There, it was thought, was to be found the distinctively human formula, one which really allows the human being his full scope. But, the most recent sociological and psychological analyses show this model community to represent nothing less than a new and unexpected difficulty. This time, people are traumatized because they are perpetually under the eyes and under the surveillance of their neighbors. The affected group is indeed much reduced in size; but no one dares to budge, because everybody knows just what everybody else is up to, a frightfully constricting situation, to say the least. It is clear that, even with the best intentions and with the application of hypermodern and profound research in psychology and sociology, we only succeed in coming to results in every case which could not possibly have been anticipated.

I shall give one last example of these unforeseeable effects, this time from agriculture, viz., the massive cultivation of certain plants like corn and cotton. The cultivation of these plants in the "new countries" seems to represent undeniable progress. The deforestation of land too heavily forested is a felicitous operation, profitable from every point of view, and consequently, represents technical progress. But, it could not have been anticipated that corn and cotton are plants which not only impoverish the soil, but even annihilate it by the twofold action of removing certain natural elements and destroying the relation between the humus and the soil particles. Both these last are destroyed by the roots of cotton and corn to the degree that, after 30 or 40 years of cultivation of these agricultural products, the soil is transformed into a veritable dust bowl. A strong wind need only to pass over it to reduce it to bare rock.

The phenomenon is world wide, and is to be encountered in the United States, Brazil, and Russia, among others. It is a bone of contention between Khrushchev and certain Soviet agricultural specialists. Khrushchev essentially emphasizes the cultivation of corn, as is well known; but many Soviet specialists insist that this emphasis is a very dangerous one. It allows a very rapid economic progress for, say, 20 years, only to be followed by a destruction of hitherto fertile lands which may last for centuries.

The inquiries of Castro and Vogt have shown that, at the present, in certain regions 20 per cent of cultivated land is threatened with destruction in this way. If this factor is considered in connection with that of population growth, a very considerable difficulty seems to lurk in the offing. If arable land continues to diminish in extent beyond possibility of recovery, our chances of survival diminish correspondingly. Here we have an example of typical and unpredictable secondary effects, effects which in corn and cotton agriculture do not reveal themselves except after 30 years of experience. It is again impossible, therefore, to say whether technical progress is in essence good or bad.

We are launched into a world of an astonishing degree of complexity; at every step we let loose new problems and raise new difficulties. We succeed progressively in solving these difficulties, but only in such a way that when one has been resolved we are confronted by another. Such is the progress of technology in our society. All I have been able to do is to give a few fragmentary examples. What would be necessary in order to comprehend the problem in its entirety is a systematic and detailed study of all these points.

Ideas of Technology

TECHNOLOGY AND MAN: A CHRISTIAN VISION

W. NORRIS CLARKE, S. J.*

My particular task is to present in brief outline a basic Christian vision of the meaning and place of technology in the total life of man. I say *a* rather than *the* Christian vision, because outside of certain fundamental general principles there is no fixed and obligatory position on technology that all Christians—or even all Catholics—must hold in order to be good Christians. We are dealing here rather with a case of " applied theology," i. e., the creative application of the basic principles of Christian thought to a new concrete problem in the life of man outside of the immediately religious sphere. In such cases there are often several different attitudes it is possible to take toward the same problem, each inspired by some authentic aspect of the total Christian message, hence each with a legitimate claim to be *an* authentic Christian attitude on the point in question. There is far more pluralism of opinion in the Church, especially on matters of applied theology like this, than is generally realized by those outside of it.

In the present question there are two main perspectives among Roman Catholic thinkers. One is predominantly pessimistic, looking on technology primarily as a dehumanizing force, radically if not incurably materialistic and secularist in its roots and fruits, and calculated of its nature, unless severely reined in, to corrupt the humanistic, spiritualist, and religious development of future man. Some have even spoken of it as a " demonic force," which, though not intrinsically evil in itself, is such an apt instrument for the devil's purpose of turning man away from his true spiritual destiny that it is in fact too dangerous a power for sinful man to handle with safety.

Those who hold this view, at least among Catholics, are found principally, it seems, among humanists of a literary and artistic temperament who have never quite accepted modern experimental science as a truly humane enterprise, due mainly to its preoccupation with matter and the quantitative aspects of the world. This group has been slowly dwindling in size, voice, and influence, it seems to me, since the last war,

* Rev. W. Norris Clarke is Professor of Philosophy at Fordham University. He is Editor-in-Chief of the *International Philosophical Quarterly*, and author of numerous articles, including " Cultural Dimensions of the New Leisure," *The Ethical Aftermath of Automation* (Maryland, 1962); " Christian Humanism for Today," *Social Order* (Vol. 3, 1953); and " Christians Confront Technology," *America* (Vol. 102, 1959).

though some of its attitudes still command wide allegiance among sincere religious-minded people.[1]

The second main perspective among Catholic thinkers places a much more positive value on technology as an element in the total development of man as an image of God. A steadily increasing weight of Catholic thought, it seems to me, has been swinging to this position, and it is undeniably in this direction that the teaching of the last three Popes has been tending. It is this view which I intend to present in this paper. Yet even within this general orientation there is a wide spectrum running from strong optimism to deep uncertainty and anxiety as to whether we actually will make use of technology for our fulfillment rather than our destruction, or at least whether we are moving in that direction at present.[2]

I might add one further word in clarification of the term "Christian." I do not restrict myself to the "Catholic" view because, although I am drawing chiefly on Catholic sources, the same general evaluation would seem to me in accord with the spirit of any Christian vision of man that is not professedly anti-humanistic or exclusively eschatological in its outlook. Furthermore, I would like to state very explicitly that most of the fundamental principles in this Christian vision can be subscribed to also by a religious-minded Jew or by anyone, in fact, who believes in a theistic humanism, that is, in the value of the self-development of man in this life as a means of fulfilling his destiny of ultimate union with God in another and immortal life.

Outline of a Christian View of Technology

I. Subordination to the Total Good of Man

I shall now set myself to sketching the broad outlines of the view of technology identified above. The clearest way of doing this would undoubtedly be to move down from above, that is, from God and His plan for man and the universe down to technology as an element in this plan. But in fact I am going to follow the opposite path, that is, to advance in a series of ascending spirals beginning from what is closer to us, from what is more immediately determinable and more widely agreed upon about the relation of technology to man, then rising to the analysis of man as a hierarchy of spirit over matter, next to the theistic vision of the origin and meaning of human life, and finally up to the full Christian vision of man's present and ultimate destiny, a vision accessible only to those who believe in the Christian Revelation given by God to His Church. The purpose of following this ascending path is that, in an audience like this, including as it does persons of all shades of religion or lack of it, I may be able to keep as many of you with me on the ascent for as long a time as your own principles can stand it. Thus our area of agreement can be the largest possible.

The first and very general principle is one which should be fundamental in any serious reflection on man and technology. It is that technology, being a partial activity of man, can be properly evaluated only if it is set in the context of the total reality and good of man and not judged as a self-sufficient whole exclusively in terms of its own inner laws and dynamism. The same is true of any partial human activity, such as, for example, athletics, or recreation, or business, etc. Thus it would be a dangerous distortion of perspective to say that whatever is good for the advance of athletics is good for man, just as it would be to say that whatever is good for General Motors is good for the country. The overall balanced fulfillment of man must always be the center of focus and all particular activities and functions, whether of individuals or of social groups, subordinated to this primary goal.

This principle may seem, perhaps, so elementary that it should be taken for granted. It is, indeed, elementary, and I feel reasonably sure that no one here would be in doubt about it. Yet it would be a great mistake to believe that in proportion as a basic truth is basic and elementary so much the more widely is it realized and practiced. It is the great simple truths that are often the first ones forgotten in the hectic demands of immediate living governed by short range vision. It is thus all too easy for those immediately engaged in the exciting work of technology itself so to narrow their horizons that the mere glimpse of the possibility of some new technical advance can immediately trigger the decision to introduce it into the living organism of human society without any inhibiting second thought about its overall repercussions on the social body as a whole. Hence a first essential principle for the wise use of technology in any culture is the conviction that it cannot (without profoundly disruptive effects) be made an end in itself, allowed to develop and be applied, throttle wide open, with no other guiding principle than the unfolding of its own intrinsic potentialities at the fastest possible tempo. This conviction must be firmly held and acted on by the leaders of our society, from the government down, and impressed by appropriate control from above, if necessary, on the decision-makers within technology itself, if they are not able or willing to see its necessity under their own initiative. As a matter of fact, many of the latter already do see it quite as clearly as anyone else. This vision may not always be equally shared, however, on the lower echelons of technological planning and execution.[3]

II. Subordination of Body to Spirit

This general regulative principle laid down, let us now see how it is to be filled out with more definite content. The first level of analysis establishes a hierarchy or graded order of activities and powers in man. The basic principle of ordering is the superiority of the spiritual dimension in man over the material, and the corresponding prerogative and obligation of the spirit to dominate its corporeal substratum so that the latter becomes the prompt, docile, and efficacious instrument of the higher life of the spirit in man. We might add here in parenthesis that it is still possible to go along with many of the elements in this analysis of the nature of man even if one does not understand or accept the technical philosophical interpretation of the human soul as strictly spiritual or immaterial, i. e., on a level radically different in kind from the material order. The minimum essential is to recognize that the intellectual and moral level of life in man (including freedom, love, art and all their corresponding values) is his highest and most specifically human level of activity, to which all lower psychic as well as biological activities should be subordinated according to a natural hierarchy of values and goals.

According to this analysis of man, the fundamental role of the whole material universe is to serve as a theater and instrument for the gradual evolution of man, both individual and race, to full self-consciousness, self-mastery, self-development, and self-expression of his free, conscious spirit in and through matter. Accordingly, the role of technology is twofold. Its first aim is *liberation* of man from servitude to matter. That is to say, its role is to free man's energies more and more from their primitive state of almost total absorption in sheer brute physical labor as an essential condition for physical survival. By inventing more and more effective techniques for getting nature to work for him instead of against him, man frees himself progressively from absorption in fulfilling his elementary animal needs, in fact from exhausting physical labor in achieving any of his goals, lower or higher. The energy thus liberated can be diverted upwards into his various higher and more characteristically human levels of activity, i. e., more and more penetrated by spirit. The fundamental principle of technology at work here is that in proportion as any activity of man depends more predominantly on sheer physical effort, especially of a routine repetitive kind, so much the more apt is it to be handled by machines, releasing the person himself for other activities requiring skills of a more intellectual and creative order. Thus technology is an indispensable instrument in man's progressive self-realization of his nature and dignity as a man, that is, as superior to all the lower levels of non-rational material beings.[4]

The second function of technology looks in the opposite direction from the first. The first was to liberate or elevate man above servitude to matter. The second looks back again toward matter. It becomes the instrument whereby the liberated spirit of man can turn again toward the material world and dominate it in a new active way, making it a medium for the spirit's creative *self-expression* and *self-realization*.

This involves a distinctively new attitude of man toward nature. The latter now appears no longer as it did to ancient man, as a great

sacrosanct force, moving along its own age-old immutable course in-
violable by man, who merely lives off its natural or cultivated by-
products. It appears rather as a great plastic network of forces open
to its very depths to the creative molding power of the human mind
and will, and inviting by its very malleability the recreative touch
of man.[5]

This profound shift in attitude towards nature opens up a new and
almost limitless perspective in man's relation to the cosmos in which
he lives. Man's relation to material nature now appears as a dynami-
cally evolving dialogue between himself and matter, in the course of
which he first discovers his own self as superior to, and hence destined
to become master of, nature, and then learns to use it more and more
efficaciously as the medium for his own creative self-expression.

One important philosophical as well as psychological by-product of
this new attitude to the world of nature is a new understanding of the
relation between matter and spirit. In the traditional spiritualist vision
of man, at least in the West,[6] the tendency was all too frequently to
look on matter primarily as the negation, the opposite of spirit, weigh-
ing it down, imprisoning it. The most effective remedy was to turn
away from matter towards a world of pure uncontaminated spirit.
Now matter appears rather as a kind of complement or correlative to
spirit, not radically opposed to it and closed to it, but mysteriously
open and apt, if properly handled, to receive the impression of spirit
and to serve as medium for the spirit's own self-expression and self-
development. The Thomistic doctrine of the natural union of soul
and body, not as a punishment but for the good of the soul, and of
the soul as the natural "form" or informing principle of the body,
here takes on a depth and richness of meaning which might have
startled, as it would also have delighted, I am sure, even St. Thomas
Aquinas himself. For now the whole material universe becomes, as it
were, an extension of man's own body, and thus becomes informed by
his soul in an indirect and instrumental way.[7]

The fundamental moral principle relevant here is that man's new-
found power over matter should be used according to the proper order
of values, that is, for the expression and fulfillment of his higher and
more spiritual capacities, and not merely for his greater material and
sensual self-indulgence and catering to the body. It would be a mons-
trous perversion indeed of the whole meaning of man's liberation from
matter by technology if, once liberated, he now freely and deliberately
enslaved himself to it again in a new servitude more debasing than
the original indeliberate subservience forced upon him from without.

III. MAN THE IMAGE OF GOD

Let us now mount one rung higher in our ascending spiral. The
previous level established the order of subordination between matter
and spirit and therefore oriented the aim of technology upwards as

an instrument for the life of spirit. But it left undetermined just what was the deeper significance and ultimate goal of man's self-development through the mighty power of technology which he has now made his servant.

Here the theistic vision of man and the universe opens up new horizons. Man's own origin and destiny now emerge not as a mere accident of landing on top of the heap of the world of matter by some lucky turn of the blind wheel of chance. They are the result rather of God's own creative activity, first bringing into being the material universe as a matrix and instrument for the development of the spirit of man, and then infusing each human soul into this evolving system at its appropriate time and place.

The fundamental perspective here is of man created, as the Book of Genesis puts it, " to the image and likeness of God," with a divinely given destiny to unfold and develop this image to the fullest possible extent in this life, in order to be united in eternal beatific union with Him in the next.

Man's self-development and self-expression through matter, with technology as his instrument, now appear not just as the satisfaction of some egotistic drive for power and self-affirmation, but as the fulfilling of a much higher and more sacred vocation, the God-given vocation to authentic self-realization as the image of God his Creator. The material world which is to be the object of man's technological domination is now seen not as some hostile or indifferent power that man has tamed by his own prowess and can exploit ruthlessly at his own will with no further responsibility save to himself. It is rather both a loving gift and a sacred trust to be used well as its Giver intended, with a sense of responsibility and stewardship to be accounted for.

The notion of a dynamic image of God to be developed lends here a much deeper significance and dignity to man's cultivation both of science and technology. For man to imitate God, his Creator and—in the full Christian perspective—his Father, he must act like his Father, do what He is doing so far as he can. Now God is at once contemplative and active. He has not only thought up the material universe, with all its intricate network of laws, but He has actively brought it into existence and supports and guides its vast pulsating network of forces. God is both a thinker and a worker, so to speak. So too man should imitate God his Father by both thinking and working in the world. By understanding the nature and laws of action of the cosmos and himself in it he is rethinking, rediscovering the creative plan of the universe first thought up by God Himself.[8] But this contemplative outlook alone would not be enough if he wishes to reflect the full image of God. He must also try his hand as a worker, not to create some totally new world out of nothing, which only God can do, but to recreate the world that has been given him, malleable and plastic under his fingers, to be transformed by his own initiative and artistic inventiveness, so that it will express in a new way both the divine image of its Creator and the human image of its recreator.[9]

I think it should be evident enough that this notion of man as dynamic image of God, with the vocation to develop this image by an evolving dialogue with the material cosmos, sets technology in a wider framework which provides strong religious, moral, and humanistic controls on its exploitation. Judaism, together with most theistic thought in the West not dominated by the Platonic tradition, can go along, it seems to me, with most of what I have said so far. As for the East, I understand that even certain recent Hindu currents of thought are departing from their more traditional outlook of complete other-worldliness and renouncement of matter to allow a more positive role in human development to an evolving material cosmos, and hence to man's mastery of it by technology.

IV. THE CHRISTIAN DIMENSION: SIN AND REDEMPTION

Let us advance now to the last and (to a Christian, at least) highest rung of our ascending spiral, the specifically Christian perspective. This adds on, first, the notion of a primordial sinfulness of the human race, or Fall of man, and secondly, redemption from this state of alienation from God by the incarnation, death, and resurrection of the Son of God, the Second Person of the Blessed Trinity, become man.

The first of these two factors is the state of sinfulness of man stemming from a primordial aberration of the race from God, called Original Sin, and compounded further by the individual sinfulness of each human being down the ages. As a result there is a fundamental duality or ambivalence in man's will. Instead of being drawn spontaneously toward God and his authentic good in a properly ordered manner, man tends also spontaneously toward self-centered egotism, sensuality, self-indulgence, lust for power, wealth, pride, and self-aggrandizement. In fact, unless enlightened and strengthened by divine grace, man tends more immediately and spontaneously to satisfy his lower, more material, and more selfish desires than his higher, more spiritual, and more altruistic or self-transcending desires.

Thus technology must now be set in the framework of a radical ambivalence in man toward both good and evil at once, with the resulting very real possibility of grave misuse of this powerful instrument, itself morally neutral and capable of being put to either good or evil use. The danger is especially great in the case of technology, since by its fundamental orientation toward matter it puts in man's hands the power to gratify almost without limit his material and sensual appetites, if he wishes to turn technology primarily toward these ends. There is also the fact that technology has a peculiar power to absorb the attention of those engaged in it, by virtue of its exciting challenge and spectacularly visible results, whereas the fruits of the spiritual activities of man are less immediate, tangible, and easy to assess.[10]

Hence the alert Christian, alive to the full implications of the Christian vision of man, will look on technology with a restrained and carefully qualified optimism, seeing it as at once a great potential good for man by nature and yet in the hands of fallen and selfish human nature an almost equally potent instrument for evil. He will have none of the naïve starry-eyed optimism of those who believe that man if left to himself is really a sweet, innocent, woolly white little creature who will be good as gold except for an occasional rare excursion into naughtiness, or of the *a priori* optimism of those who believe in the religion of automatic constant forward progress, that things are necessarily getting better and better all the time and that any progress in any field at any time is automatically good and for the benefit of man.

The second element in the Christian vision is the redemption through the Son of God made man. This brings along with it several new implications or more strongly highlights implications already present in Hebraic theism. One is the intrinsic goodness and dignity of matter itself, which has been sanctified and elevated by the descent into it of God Himself and His assumption of it into personal union with Himself by means of a human body formed from the basic stuff of the material universe just like any other man's. Here we see the God-man Himself using matter as an efficacious instrument or medium both for expressing His own divinity to man in a privileged, we might say, guaranteed, human image, and also for channeling the salvific effects of His divine grace to men through the seven sacraments, each a synthesis of a visible material sign informed by an efficacious spiritual power. In other words, the Incarnation and Redemption through the God-man gives Christians the perfect archetype and model of the openness of matter to spirit we spoke of earlier and its intrinsic aptness to serve as the medium of the spirit's self-expression and creative power. This is, as it were, a confirmation from above, by God's own example, of what man could already have discovered, at least in theory, by reflection on his own nature and the experience of working with matter, even though historically the lesson had not yet at that time become clear to him. Thus the labor of the young Jesus as a carpenter in Nazareth already lends in principle a divine sanction to the whole technological activity of man through history. And the doctrine of the ultimate resurrection of all human bodies in a new, more " spiritualized " mode of existence, i. e., totally open and docile to the workings of spirit within it, delivers a final *coup de grâce* to the "angelism" of the Platonic and Manichean traditions by presaging the final " deliverance from bondage " and transformation by spirit of the material cosmos itself, mysteriously hinted at by St. Peter when he speaks of " a new heaven and a new earth " to come (II Pet. 3:13; cf. Apoc. 21:1).

There is another and equally important facet, however, to the doctrine of the redemption that acts as a foil to the above highly positive and optimistic perspective. This is the doctrine of redemption through suffering, self-denial, and detachment from this world, symbolized by the death of the Redeemer on the Cross as a sacrifice of atonement to His Father for the sins of men. Thus " No man can be my disciple," in the words of Christ, " unless he deny himself, take up his cross, and follow me." (Mt. 16:24).

Now this central doctrine of life through death, self-fulfillment through self-denial, paradoxical as it may seem, does not by any means cancel out the strongly positive evaluation of technology outlined above, i. e., as an instrument for the self-expression and self-development of man's spirit. For the aim of authentic Christian self-denial, especially of the body, is not simply to repress or crush out the life of the body as something evil in itself or intrinsically alien and hostile to the soul (as the Platonic tradition tended to do). It is rather to discipline and curb its primitive tendencies to rebellion and insubordination against spirit, to blind irrational absorption in immediate satisfaction of its own appetites, either in conflict with, or indifferent to, the higher goals and values of the spirit. In a word, it is precisely to establish in man the proper docility of matter to spirit and, at a deeper level, the dominance of unselfish outgoing love over self-centered egotism.

But as we saw earlier, technology itself, if properly controlled and oriented, should have as its primary objective precisely this same liberation and unfolding of the life of spirit. Hence the spirit of Christian mortification can actually operate as a powerful controlling factor for directing the use of our technological power along the proper lines for the authentic enrichment of man on the highest levels of his human capacities, instead of allowing it to be diverted toward the mere gratification of man's inferior appetites and desires and thus enslave him further to matter rather than liberate and elevate him above it. One might well say, in fact, that only men with something like the Christian virtue of self-denial, whether applied to sensuality or to egotism, would really be safe enough to entrust with the responsibility of deciding in which directions to follow up the almost limitless potentialities made available to us by technology. The wider the range of possibilities open to a man's free choice, as we all know, the greater his need for self-discipline and selectivity, lest he destroy himself.[11]

Nonetheless, there is no doubt that this aspect of Christianity, this spirit of the Cross, cannot help but exercise a powerful moderating effect, not only on the orientation of technology towards serving the life of spirit, but also on too eager and exclusive an absorption of one's energies in the enterprise of technology. If the primary goals of man are held to be spiritual rather than the mastery of matter, then the pursuit of technology will naturally take its place as *one* legitimate and necessary activity of man in an integrated hierarchy of human activities, all subordinated to the total good and ultimate destiny of man.

It seems hardly necessary to point out that, in this perspective of Christ as a divine-human mediator between man and God, the basic theistic notion of man as unfolding image of God on earth receives an immense deepening, elevation, and more efficacious implementation. The goal of natural self-realization as spirit in matter now becomes that of supernatural self-transformation through union with the God-man as adopted sons of God, destined to share ultimately in the infinite richness of the divine life itself.

What I have just sketched are the great lines of the Christian vision of man and how technology fits into it. I have done it in inverse order, from the bottom up, in order to keep as many of you as possible still with me as long as possible as we ascended through progressively higher points of view up to the full Christian idea of man and his destiny. It would have been clearer, perhaps, as I remarked earlier, to have proceeded according to the ontological order of things, from God, the ultimate cause of both man and the universe, down to man and God's plans for man's destiny, as made manifest both by man's nature and by divine revelation. We invite you to follow this descending path for yourselves to complement the ascending path we have just outlined. The notion of man as potential image of God, placed by God in the material universe in order to develop this image by progressive self-realization and self-expression of his spirit through matter, is always the central concept, whether one follows the ascending or descending order.

I have expounded this synoptic vision on a highly theoretical general level, without referring to sources or documents of the Church. One reason was to keep the main lines clear and avoid dispersion of attention. As a result, what I have presented is actually my own synthesis, partly philosophical, partly theological, drawn from many sources, including some elements, as our Soviet colleague has no doubt remarked, from the insights of Hegel and Marx on the dialectic between man and matter. It has always been the professed practice of Christian thinkers to draw truth from whatever sources have either discovered or well expressed it. " All truth, no matter by whom spoken," as the early Fathers of the Church used to say, " is of the Holy Spirit." [12] But the responsibility for the resulting synthesis can be laid only at my door and cannot be attributed to the Church as though all this were some official codified doctrine that could be lifted *en bloc* from some ecclesiastical treasury labeled " Christian Doctrine on Technology and Man " in fortuitous anticipation of our present symposium. Rarely is Christian teaching on contemporary problems available all at once in ready-made capsule form. It evolves slowly in the minds of Christian thinkers as the implications of old doctrines gradually emerge under the pressure of new conditions and problems, and as creative new applications are made never clearly envisaged before.

Grounding in Papal Documents

But I would now like to link up this personal synthesis a little more closely to the present teaching of the Church as reflected in the statements of recent Popes. By way of preface, let me call attention to a few basic landmarks in the Bible inspiring the above synthesis. The most fundamental and all-embracing one is perhaps to be found in the first chapter of Genesis:

> Let us make man to our own image and likeness: and let him have dominion . . . over the whole earth. . . . And God blessed them, saying: Increase and multiply, and fill the earth, and subdue it, and rule over all living creatures that move upon the earth. (Gen. 1:26-31).

This is the fundamental charter of man's dignity in relation to the material universe and the implicit divine sanction for the whole enterprise of technology as a means of carrying out this divinely established vocation. It has been so interpreted not only by the early Fathers of the Church but by the *locus classicus* in our day on the Church's attitude toward technology, the Christmas address of Pope Pius XII on " Modern Technology and Peace." [13]

The second set of texts (in addition to all the other well known general ones) I would like to call attention to is the doctrine of the recapitulation of all things in " Christ and through Him " to God.

> He is the image of the invisible God, the first-born of every creature, because in him were created all creatures in the heavens and on the earth, both visible and invisible. . . . All have been created through him and for him. He exists prior to all creatures, and in him they are all preserved in being. Further, he is the head of his body, the Church, in that he is the beginning, the first to rise from the dead, so that he may have pre-eminence over every creature. For it pleased God the Father that in him all fullness should dwell, and that through him God should reconcile to himself every being, and make peace both on earth and in heaven through the blood shed on the cross. (Col. 1:15-20).

> For all things are yours, whether . . . the world, or life, or death; or things present, or things to come,—all are yours, and you are Christ's and Christ is God's. (I Cor. 3:22-23).

> All creation awaits with eager longing the manifestation of the sons of God. For creation was made subject to vanity not by its own choice but . . . yet with the hope that creation itself would

be delivered from its slavery to corruption, to enjoy the freedom that comes with the glory of the children of God. For we know that all creation groans and travails in pain until now. And not only that, but we ourselves who have the Holy Spirit as first fruits—we ourselves groan within ourselves, waiting for the adoption as sons, the redemption of our body. (Rom. 8:19-23).

The early Greek Fathers of the Church, using these texts and many others, developed a profound doctrine of man as the mediator between the material world and God, with the role of extending the work of redemption by mastering and ruling the material forces of the earth, so as to offer the whole creation back to God in a great "cosmic liturgy." [14] This rich humanistic vision faded somewhat in the Latin West under the influence of St. Augustine's strong emphasis on man's tending to sin and on the division of mankind into two cities, the City of God and the Earthly City.

We have had to wait for our own time to see a strong positive theology of man's relation to the material world and temporal civilization worked out and given official encouragement in the Church. Perhaps the two most important official documents are the following. The first is the stirring Pastoral Letter of Cardinal Suhard of Paris on *Growth or Decline? The Church Today*, February 11, 1947, in which he exhorts Catholics not to withdraw from modern civilization and technological progress but to plunge into it whole-heartedly in order to transform and Christianize it from within, thus bringing out its fullest meaning and capacities for good.[15] This remarkable document was seen and approved by Pope Pius, it is reliably reported, before its publication.

The second document, of considerably greater weight in view of its source, is the Christmas Message of Pope Pius XII, December 24, 1953, on *Modern Technology and Peace*. Here the Holy Father very carefully balances the books for and against modern technology in its relation to the total vocation of man. The predominant tone of moral warning therein should not lead us to diminish in any way the strong positive endorsement of technology as a beneficent instrument for human development that shines forth in this broad-visioned and eminently constructive document.

It begins by stating the need for a proper perspective on the true nature and role of technology in order to counteract the "excessive and exclusive esteem by many of progress in technology" as a kind of "omnipotent dispenser of happiness (which) has finally imposed itself on the minds of men as the final end of man and of life, substituting itself for every kind of religious and spiritual ideal."

Then he launches into an eloquent positive evaluation of technology as of its nature "coming from God and capable of leading us back to God." This highly significant passage is worth quoting in full for the benefit of the members of the Conference who may not easily find available the document itself.

Nevertheless, the aforementioned erroneous consequence does not follow necessarily, nor are our present criticisms to be understood as a condemnation of technological progress in itself. The Church loves and favors human progress. It is undeniable that techno-logical progress comes from God, and so it can and ought to lead to God. In point of fact, while the believer admires the conquests of science and makes use of them to penetrate more deeply into the knowledge of creation and of the forces of nature, that by means of machines he may better master them for the service of mankind and the enrichment of human life, it most often happens that he feels himself drawn to adore the Giver of those good things which he admires and uses, knowing full well that the eternal Son of God is the " first-born of every creature. For in Him were created all things in the heavens and on the earth, things visible and things invisible." (Col. 1:15-16).

Very far, then, from any thought of disavowing the marvels of technology and its lawful use, the believer may find himself more eager to bow his knee before the celestial Babe of the manger, more conscious of his debt of gratitude to Him Who gives all things, and the intelligence to understand them, more disposed to find a place for those same works of technology with the chorus of angels in the hymn of Bethlehem: " Glory to God in the highest " (Luke 2:14). He will even find it natural to place beside the gold, frankincense and myrrh, offered by the Magi to the Infant God, also the modern conquests of technology: machines and numbers, laboratories and inventions, power and resources.

Furthermore, such an offering is like presenting Him with the work which He Himself once commanded and which is now being effected, though it has not yet reached its term. " Fill the earth and subdue it " (Gen. 1:28) said God to man as He handed creation over to him in temporary heritage. What a long and hard road from then to the present day, when men can at last say that they have in some measure fulfilled the divine command!

Technology has, in fact, brought man's domination of the material world to a pitch of perfection never known before. The modern machine allows a mode of production that substitutes for, and multiplies a hundredfold, human energy for work, that is entirely independent of the contribution of organic forces and which en-sures a maximum of extensive and intensive potential and at the same time of precision. As we embrace with a glance the results of this development, nature itself seems to give an assent of satis-faction to what has been done in it, and to incite to further investigation and use of its extraordinary possibilities. Now it is clear that all search for and discovery of the forces of nature, which technology effectuates, is at once a search for and discovery of the greatness, of the wisdom, and of the harmony of God. Looked at in this way, there is nothing to disapprove of or condemn in technology.[16]

The next five pages in my edition are taken up with a detailed warning against the principal religious, moral and humanistic dangers to which misuse of technology has already exposed Western man and threatens to do even more in the future unless appropriate precautions are taken.

The first and most fundamental danger is that men become so intoxicated with the dazzling perspectives of knowledge and power opened up by technology that they elevate its pursuit to the rank of primary value and goal in man's life here below. In other words, it becomes a substitute for religion.[17]

Secondly, it tends to restrict man's horizon to the material universe and material achievements only, thus imprisoning his spirit in a world too narrow for it despite its vastness and diverting his attention from the realm of spiritual values and activities in which alone man can find full outlet for his higher faculties. This blinding effect with respect to spiritual realities affects especially the appreciation of the supernatural truths and mysteries of Christian Revelation, which by their nature are quite alien and incomprehensible to the exclusively technological mind.

This distortion of a mind centered too exclusively on the problems and values of technological mastery of nature is summed up by the Pope as the "technological spirit." He shows how it can infect all the areas of human life with its onesidedness, its superficial penetration into reality, and its tendency to reduce everything, even personal human relations, to quantitative factors which can be approached and solved on the model of engineering problems. Even the term "human engineering" has already become current in certain quarters. In a word, the danger of the technological spirit if it is allowed to take over as the dominant attitude in a culture or in an individual is that its influence is both despiritualizing and depersonalizing, or, in a single word, it is dehumanizing, since spirit and personality are the specific characteristics of man that determine his special dignity.[18] In philosophical terms, the technological spirit is but another thinly disguised form of materialism.

This balanced document of Pius XII, with its blend of basic optimism tempered by realism and a keen sense of the moral weakness of man as he is in the concrete, should strike a responsive chord, it seems to me, in the minds of all who believe that man's true nature cannot be understood save in a theistic and personalist framework. Much of its practical moral wisdom would be acceptable, I believe, even to an atheist and philosophical materialist, as long as he recognizes the peculiar dignity of man and the integrated hierarchy of his powers and values, by whatever name he calls them.

This basic statement of principles on technology and man has pretty much set the tone for other papal documents since then.

The recent major encyclical of John XXIII, *Mater et Magistra*, reaffirms briefly in many places the same guiding ideas. Man's vocation on earth to subdue and rule the material universe as the vicegerent of God is again explicitly stated, appealing to the same text of Genesis as did Pius XII.[19] The orientation of all economic and material progress toward the good of the individual is reiterated in a passage worth quoting:

> National wealth . . . has no other purpose than to secure without interruption those material conditions in which individuals are enabled to lead a full and perfect life. When this is consistently the case, then such a people is to be judged truly rich. . . . From this it follows that the economic prosperity of any people is to be assessed not so much from the sum total of goods and wealth possessed as from the distribution of goods according to the norms of justice, so that everyone in the community can develop and perfect himself. For this, after all, is the end toward which all economic activity of a community is by nature ordered.[20]

Especially interesting, too, is the lapidary formulation of the Church's acceptance of the modern world and its dedication to progress, one of the most explicit commitments of its kind, in fact, that I know of: " The role of the Church in our day is very difficult: to reconcile man's modern respect for progress with the norms of humanity and of the Gospel teaching." [21] No longer can it be said that the Church is really secretly against material progress and only tolerates it because it has to, that it would prefer, if possible, that man devote himself entirely to spiritual activities with a minimum of material subsistence. No, it is committed to the more difficult, because less simplistic and one-sided, task of encouraging the balanced development of *both* levels of man's natural powers, spiritual and material, contemplative and active, interior and exterior.

What seems to me the most significant new note struck in *Mater et Magistra* on the subject that interests us is concerned not so much directly with technology itself as with the complex organization of society that is its by-product. The point is brought up that many today are worried about the steadily growing complexity of organized social relationships, which seem to be closing in on the individual from all sides and progressively inhibiting his freedom, initiative, and opportunity for independent personal development. In other words, is not an ever more organized society, such as technology requires to support it, threatening to depersonalize man, to turn him into a conformist organization man?

Previous papal documents, including those of Pius XII, had tended to emphasize the serious danger of the above consequence and warn against it. The present encyclical takes a considerably more optimistic view of the outlook:

> One of the principal characteristics of our time is the multiplication of social relationships, that is, a daily more complex interdependence of citizens, introducing into their lives many and varied forms of association, recognized for the most part in private and even in public law. . . . As a consequence, opportunity for free action by individuals is restricted within narrower limits. . . . Will men, perhaps, then become automatons, and cease to be personally responsible, as these social relationships multiply more and more? It is a question which must be answered negatively. . . . Rather we can hope that this will enable man not only to develop and perfect his natural talents, but will also lead to an appropriate structuring of the human community.[22]

He then goes on to discuss the general principles of order necessary to achieve such a positive result in an increasingly interdependent society. It is again a question of balance, hierarchical ordering, and integration of multiple forces for the common good. The task is a difficult one, admittedly, but the specter of the organization man or of George Orwell's *1984* no longer seems to loom as large on the horizon, at least for technological civilization as such, as it did for the previous Pope. Recent developments in the Soviet Union seem to point in the same direction, though the opposite is still the trend in The Republic of China.

We might now sum up as follows the general message of the contemporary teaching of the Church on technology, as reflected especially in recent papal documents.

1) It expresses a firm approval in principle of the technological enterprise of modern man. It evaluates it as an activity rooted in the very nature of man as a spirit-matter composite and as a necessary instrument for the adequate fulfillment of his vocation of self-development and self-expression in and through the material universe.

2) It affirms equally, however, that technology by its nature is ordered to be an instrument towards a higher end of full personal and spiritual development, not a self-justifying end in itself. Hence its execution in practice should be clearly kept subordinate to its higher aim. It should be treated as an instrument, not as an end in itself, as a servant, not an idol.

3) Because of the moral weakness of man and his strong propensity toward indulging his lower nature and self-centered egotism at the expense of his higher goals and faculties, the cultivation of technology

for its own immediate rewards as ends in themselves presents a strong temptation for modern man, perhaps the central temptation for human society in the present and coming chapters of human history. Clear-cut realization of the hierarchy of human values and firm moral self-discipline, both on the part of individuals and of social groups at all levels, are therefore essential if man is to handle safely the powerful but ambiguous instrument of technology. To train the young properly for wielding this responsibility should be one of the primary aims of moral, religious, and humanistic education today, and should be explicitly recognized as such by the teaching community itself. It is not clear, we might add, that this awareness is at all sufficiently recognized and widespread as yet.

4) Even when the development of technology is carried out in the proper spirit and intention, it tends, like all human activities, to produce its own dangerous side-effects. These fall principally under the head of depersonalizing and dehumanizing effects on the individuals engaged in the enterprise or those affected by it, such as the families of workers, etc. They arise from various tendencies, such as subordination of human life excessively to the rhythms and needs of a machine economy, suppression of human freedom and initiative by social regimentation or submergence in the organization for its own sake, etc. Hence constant vigilance over the system in practice must be exercised by responsible business, political, moral, religious, and educational leaders. In other words, to use the language of cybernation, there must be built into the system what we might call humanistic and moral self-regulating devices or feedback controls. Perhaps one peculiarly apt organ for such a function would be foundations specially oriented in this direction. The brochure on *Cybernation* by Donald Michael recently put out by the Center for the Study of Democratic Institutions is itself a significant contribution along these lines.

In the light of the latter, plus my own reflections and those of many others, I think it is worth adding to the previous sketch of the dangers accompanying technological progress the following. In accordance with the general principles we have laid down, technological progress will be in order and beneficent only if it develops always in subordination to, and at the service of, the general common good of the nation or culture using it. But one of the most vexing problems of our civilization as it is evolving today is that we are far more skillful at technological advance than at solving the social, economic, and human problems it raises. Thus our ability to control and order material nature races ahead, whereas our ability to order and control social, economic, and cultural and moral forces, i. e., human nature, is fumbling, uncertain, and lagging far behind. Hence there is grave danger that if the tempo of technological change is allowed to go on accelerating as fast as its own internal rhythm will permit, it can create an atmosphere of constant rapid flux that can be seriously disruptive of the psychological and social stability of a culture. Where external cultural landmarks disappear too rapidly, the effect can be demoralizing and disorienting to all save strongly principled and "inner-directed" people.[23]

How to handle this gap between the different rhythms of technological as compared with cultural development is a difficult challenge to meet. It will need the concerted theoretical and practical wisdom of many thinkers and specialists. I have no easy solutions to offer, myself, only the urgent call to awareness and reflection. One thing, however, is clear to me. In a world of ever more rapidly changing external environment, where deliberately stimulated change is part of the very "biological rhythm" of modern industrial society, it is essential to educate the young more consciously than ever before in the basic human skill of how to remain psychologically and morally stable in a world of external flux. Otherwise a restless, shallow, rootless, and anxious people will be incapable of making any truly fruitful use of the ever increasing cornucopia of means poured out by our technological genius. Like the overspecialized dinosaurs of prehistory, we may suddenly find ourselves ripe for extinction. Or like so many civilizations in history, we may decay from within, like rotten fruit, and be swept into the dustbin of history.

The essential principle of education involved here, it seems to me, is a shift of emphasis from means to ends, from teaching customs or *ways* of doing things—so quickly obsolete or irrelevant today—to teaching basic values or *goals* to be aimed at steadily through the flux of changing ways and means. For it is the unique property of ends or goals, as any good philosopher can tell you, to unify and confer intelligibility on action and motion. A single stable goal can give fixed sense and meaning to a vast interweaving flux of otherwise chaotic actions. The stability of goal-oriented action derives from its single direction and point of arrival, not from its particular *path* of getting there. It is the stability of the compass for the ship, rather than that of the railroad track for the train, that must be the ideal of education for the future.

In conclusion, the phenomenon of modern technology, of man's sudden coming into his natural inheritance as master of material nature, poses a staggering challenge to our whole race as we scan the horizons ahead. The stakes are higher than they have ever been in human history before. And the risks are proportionately great. But the passage to maturity is always a risk, a striking out into the unknown, whether for an individual, a society, or the race as a whole. In the light of the Christian vision of man there should be no hesitation either that we should be willing to rise with courage and hope to the challenge, rather than turn back in fear, or that we can meet it successfully, with the humbly implored aid of the Master of History. For it is God Himself, our Father, who is calling us on, through the pull of our own unfolding powers, to assume the full stature of our vocation to become sons of God and images of the Creator in this world, and hence to become wise masters of the material universe that God has given us in stewardship as the theater and instrument of our own self-discovery and self-development.

But the condition of any durable long-range success—possibly even of short-range survival—is that man recognize at least the general lines of his authentic nature and destiny. We can bear the responsibility, with God's help, of trying to be sons of God and stewards under Him of the cosmos that He planned and made for us. We cannot bear the burden of trying to be lonely gods of a purposeless universe we did not make, with no other place to go, and no strength or wisdom but our own to rely upon.[24]

REFERENCES

[1] Cf., for example, E. Mounier's exposition of this attitude among French Catholics especially and his vigorous answer: "The Case against the Machine," in *Be Not Afraid* (London: Rockcliff, 1951); also G. Bernanos, *La France contre les robots*, (Paris, 1938); N. Berdiaeff, "L'homme dans la civilisation technique," in *Progrès technique et progrès moral*, Recontres internationales de Genève (Neuchatel: La Baconnière, 1947), esp. p. 84: "La technique est créée par l'homme et pour l'homme, mais elle est anti-humaniste; c'est une force déshumanisante." Gabriel Marcel has also frequently linked technology with depersonalization. See also D. von Hildebrand in *Technology and Christian Culture*, ed. R. Mohan (Cath. Univ. of America Press, 1960). For the whole problem of the place of science in a Christian humanism, my own article might help, "Christian Humanism for Today," Special Symposium on Christian Humanism in *Social Order*, 3 (1963), 269-88, and my debate with Fred. Wilhelmsen "End of the Modern World?" *America* 99 (April 19 and June 7, 1958), 108, 310; and "Christians Confront Technology," *America*, 101 (Sept. 26, 1959), 761.

[2] In addition to references in note 1, see J. Mouroux, *Meaning of Man* (New York: Sheed and Ward, 1948), and G. Thils, *Théologie des réalités terrestres* and *Théologie de l'histoire* (Bruges: Desclée de Brouwer, 1949) for general expositions of this point of view. The whole debate on the meaning and value of history, i. e., the theology of history, between incarnationalists and eschatologists, underlies this question. One of the best overall philosophical (only to a limited extent theological) discussions by a Christian is A. J. van Melsen's *Science and Technology* (Pittsburgh: Duquesne Univ. Press, 1961).

[3] Cf. Guido de Ruggiero, "La fin et les moyens," in *Progrès technique et progrès moral*, cited in n. 1; and Van Melsen, *Science and Technology*, Ch. 13, sect. 31: "The Technological Order as a Culture of Means." See also the very strong remarks of George Kennan at the *Colloques de Rheinfelden*, last section on "La société industrielle et la bonne vie," on the need of strict control by governments of new exploitations of technology.

[4] See the strong and unequivocal statement of this principle by Eric Voegelin in the *Colloques de Rheinfelden* on technology and man (Paris: Collman-Levy, 1960), p. 60: "Le noyau essentiel d'une bonne société, sans lequel elle ne vaut rien, quelles que puissent être ses réalisations dans d'autres domaines, est la vie de la raison."

⁵ Cf. Van Melsen, *Science and Technology*, Ch. 9: "Changes in the Conception of Nature and World View."

⁶ I understand that in certain of the traditional Indian views of man matter is also looked upon as profoundly open and receptive to spirit, rather than as opposed to it, though the notion of self-realization or self-expression *through* matter still does not seem to me to have been given the strong value I am giving it here.

⁷ Van Melsen, *Science and Technology*, p. 257: "Just as in the human body matter is organized in such a way that it becomes the embodiment of the spirit, so also the body as permeated with the spirit acts upon nature outside the body to organize this nature in such a way that it begins to function as an extension of the body so as to make possible in a limited fashion the realization of man's spiritual desires which go beyond the power of the body alone." Also the essay of Claude Soucy, "Technique et philosophie," in *La technique et l'homme: Recherches et débats du Centre Catholique des Intellectuels Français*, Cahier 31, 1960, p. 117: "Il reste vrai globalement que, jusqu'à la Renaissance, la pensée occidentale voit surtout dans le corps la prison de l'âme, et dans le travail 'servile' l'obstacle ou à la rigueur le moyen extrinsèque de la contemplation, seule valeur authentique. Toute autre est l'orientation des Temps Modernes. D'obstacle ou de prison, le corps va devenir instrument de l'âme." And in the same volume, M. D. Chenu, "Vers une théologie de la technique," p. 163: "Qui si, au contraire, dans la consubstantialité de l'esprit et de la matière, l'homme, comme être corporel, est solidaire du cosmos, il apparaît que sa perfection ne consiste pas à surmonter une existence-dans-le-monde, comme une conjoncture accidentelle assez pesante, mais à réaliser dans ce monde le plein équilibre ontologique et moral de son être. L'homme n'est pas un étranger descendu d'un autre monde; il ne se comprend lui-même que dans la mesure où, récapitulant le cosmos, il s'en empare en quelque sorte en le pénétrant lentement et laborieusement de son esprit, en le rationalisant, comme il rationalise vertueusement son propre corps . . . La vérité humaine, la vérité divine sur l'homme, c'est que l'esprit pénètre profondément le domaine du corps, de son propre corps, mais aussi de tout le corps du monde, en lui accompli; il en est le démiurge, responsable devant le Créateur, à l'oeuvre duquel il participe ainsi, selon les lois d'une providence, obscurément et lumineusement à la fois inscrite dans la nature. Il s'accomplit lui-même en accomplissant la nature."

⁸ One might recall the words of the astronomer Kepler as he began to understand the workings of the planets: "I am thinking God's thoughts after him."

⁹ Cf. J.-L. Kahn, "La valeur culturelle de la technique," in *La Technique et l'homme*, p. 85 ff.: "Nous croyons que la place de l'ingénieur se situe dans la perspective de la création." In addition to the references in note 10, esp. the last one, see Mouroux, *Meaning of Man*, p. 28: "God has confided it [the earth] to his care that he may put his stamp upon it, give it a human face and figure, integrate it with his own life and so fulfill it." Also see the fine book of a Protestant scientist, C. R. Coulson, *Science, Technology and the Christian* (New York: Abingdon, 1960), Ch. 3, 5.

¹⁰ Cf. Coulson, *op. cit.* (n. 9), p. 60: "This is probably the gravest danger in all our considerations of technology and the machine—that we get so busy with it that we forget the spiritual background without which all our expertise will become positively harmful."

¹¹ In addition to most of the above references, see E. Mascall, *The Importance of Being Human* (New York: Columbia Univ. Press, 1958), p. 101: "It is only in so far as man's natural powers are taken up into the supernatural order that the venom which has infected them can be drawn from them and that they can become fully instrumental to the true welfare of the human race."

¹² Cf. the saying of Justin Martyr, *Apology*, II, 13: "Whatever has been well said anywhere or by anyone belongs to us Christians."

[13] Given Dec. 24, 1953 (National Cath. Welfare Conference edition, Washington, 1954), p. 3. Just before the printing of this paper there has appeared a useful collection of documents, *Pius XII and Technology*, ed. L. J. Haigerty (Milwaukee: Bruce, 1962).

[14] These considerations were given rich expression by St. Gregory of Nyssa (quotations in E. Mersch, *Le Corps Mystique du Christ*, Brussels, 1936, Vol. I) and by Maximus the Confessor.

[15] Eng. trans. published by Fides, South Bend, Ind., 1948.

[16] Nos. 6-9 (NCWC ed., note 13).

[17] Cf. the important essay of A. Dondeyne, "Technique et religion," in *La Technique et l'homme*, pp. 127-35.

[18] Cf. Karl Stern, "Christian Humanism in an Age of Technocracy," *Critic* 17 (April-May, 1959), p. 86: "It is only where *communication* threatens to destroy *communion*, where the *mechanical* imperceptibly encroaches on the *human*, that we have to watch out."

[19] Trans. W. Gibbons (New York: Paulist Press, 1961), n. 196. We might add here the remarks of Pius XII to the VII Astronautical Congress (an apt occasion certainly: "The Lord God who has put into the heart of man an insatiable desire to know did not intend to set a limit to his efforts to conquer when he said, 'Subdue the earth.' It is the whole of creation that He has entrusted to him and that He offers to the human mind so that he may ponder it and thus be able to understand more deeply the infinite goodness of his Creator" (quoted from *Commonweal*, July 25, 1958, p. 422).

[20] No. 74.

[21] No. 256.

[22] Nos. 59, 62, 67.

[23] Cf. Coulson, *Science, Technology and the Christian*, last chapter, and Thomas O'Dea, "Technology and Social Change: East and West," *Western Humanities Rev.*, 13 (1959), pp. 151-62.

[24] "We do not want a spiritual life in a dreamworld, nor an eternity which is not prepared for us by time. But neither do we want a closed humanism, an 'inhuman humanism.' 'Nothing but the earth' is the cruellest of illusions." H. de Lubac, S. J., *The Discovery of God* (New York: Kenedy, 1960), p. 179.

Ideas of Technology

TECHNOLOGY AND THE LAWS OF ITS DEVELOPMENT

A. ZVORIKINE*

As is known, the word "technology" is derived from the Greek word "*techne*" meaning "art" or "skill"; the word "*technikos*" means one who possesses a certain art. With the development of handicraft production the concept's basic sense shifted from the sphere of individual art to that of techniques, methods, and formulas handed down from generation to generation.

Some scholars define technology as the aggregate of techniques directed towards the attainment of some purpose; specifically, the aggregate of techniques directed against the forces of nature and towards the modification of materials. Others define technology as the aggregate of skills, abilities, techniques, and knowledge enabling man to utilize, for desired goals, the huge resources of raw material and energy existing in nature. In the five-volume British *History of Technology* edited by Charles Singer, technology is defined as "activities directed to the satisfaction of human needs which produce alterations in the material world."[1]

On reading these definitions one is immediately struck by their inadequacy. They do not reckon with the material aspect of technology, the system of tools and machines, which actually determines its content. On the other hand, they also fail to disclose the social aspect of technology.

What, then, is technology? *Technology may be defined as the means of work, the means of human activity developing within a system of social production and social life.* The means of work become technology only within a system of social production.**

---

* Professor A. Zvorikine is on the staff of the U. S. S. R. Academy of Sciences Institute of Philosophy; he heads research in the history of culture at the Academy's Institute of History and is the author of more than one hundred books, pamphlets, and articles on the history, philosophy, and sociology of science and technology, with particular emphasis on mining. From 1949 to 1960 he was Assistant Editor-in-Chief of the *Great Soviet Encyclopedia*.

** There persists the former concept of technology as techniques applied in one or another sphere of human activity—the techniques of playing the violin, dancing, etc. Accordingly, the English language distinguishes between "technology" and "techniques." Some researchers extend the concept of technology to mean all purposeful physical and mental activity; such an extension, by virtue of its very scope, deprives the concept of technology of its characteristic content.

Work is a process occurring between man and nature, a process in which man by his own activities becomes the means, the regulator and the controller. The elements in the process of work are the following: purposeful activity or actual work, the object of work, and the means of work. It would appear that technology is first and foremost the *means of work.*

As Marx pointed out, the means of work is the thing or set of things which man places between himself and the object of work and which serves as the conductor of his influence upon that object. Man uses the mechanical, physical, and chemical properties of things in order to compel them to act as the instruments of his power, in accordance with his purpose. If, however, one turns to a concrete analysis of technology, it becomes clear that technology includes a large number of objects which man makes not for direct impact upon the object of work, but for the creation of conditions for the normal production process.

This may be observed in mining. In addition to the whole system of tools and machinery, there still remain a number of mechanical contrivances in the pit designed to ensure normal production, such as the whole ventilation and lighting system and the complex system of drainage. The most superficial acquaintance with these shows the impossibility of regarding them as means of work in the limited sense defined above. Therefore, the means of work in a broader sense, and consequently technology, must include *all the material conditions necessary to enable the production process to take place at all.*

The Natural-Scientific and Social Bases of Technology

The whole history of technology discloses the dialectical interaction of technology and natural science. By solving this or that technological problem on the basis of natural laws already known, man at the same time discovers new properties of things and in this way advances natural science.

Speaking about this, V. I. Lenin wrote that " the laws of the outer world, of nature . . . are the foundation of the *purposeful* activities of man. In his practical activities man is faced with the objective world, he depends upon it, it determines his activity. . . . *Mechanical and chemical technology* serves the aims of man for the very reason that its character (essence) consists in the determination of it by outer conditions (the laws of nature)." [2]

The possibilities of technology depend upon the level of man's knowledge of the laws of nature. Modern technology is the material embodiment of the knowledge garnered by man in the struggle to subdue the forces of nature, the struggle to dominate them. " In both industry and agriculture," said Lenin, " man can use the working of natural forces only if he is cognizant of their action, and can *facilitate* this use by means of machines, tools, etc." [3]

But utilization of the achievements of natural science is only one side of technology. The means of work are created by man in the process of social production. They enter as an inalienable element into the system of productive forces. Natural science merely shows the possible variants for solving technical questions, but it does not in itself determine the direction, scale, or speed of their solution.

The unity of the material content of production and the social form of its implementation was scientifically expressed in the Marxist-Leninist teaching about productive forces and the relations of production. Technology, an element of productive forces, enters organically into the mode of production, which also includes the relations of production. Technology does not develop outside the mode of production. For this reason technical progress cannot be understood if abstracted from the laws determining the development of the given mode of production, or if withdrawn from the relations of production of a concrete socio-economic formation. Only the economic laws of the given social system which are determined by the mode of production can provide an answer to the question of sources and speeds of technical development and its direction.

It is impossible to explain the contradictions in technical development under the conditions of modern capitalism without first understanding capitalist relations of production. In the same way, only by understanding the production relations of socialism can one explain technological development under socialism. The Program of the Communist Party of the Soviet Union, which puts forward the aim of building the foundations of a communist society within the coming twenty years, envisages unprecedented scientific and technical progress. Communism can be victorious only on the basis of a powerful growth and improvement of productive forces. This calls for the most up-to-date technical means and their constant improvement.

The utilization of inventions, too, depends upon economic conditions. The history of technology contains instances where inventions were not exploited owing to the social and economic conditions prevailing at the time. For example, in the mid-eighteenth century the Russian inventor Ivan Polzunov presented the brilliant idea of replacing the water wheel, the main motive power at the time, by a steam engine. But this epochal invention was never utilized in Russia because the production relations of the feudal system offered no scope for the development of productive forces. In Britain, however, where bourgeois relations had already emerged at this period, the universal steam engine produced by that great English inventor James Watt became one of the links in a major industrial revolution.

One may define at least three features of the development of technology. Although its development is subordinated to the economic laws of a given social formation, its development does not cease with a change from one social system to another. Moreover, technology enters into contradiction with the existing relations of production when these cease to be a form of development of productive forces and instead become their fetters. When the old production relations are broken up in the process of social revolution, technology remains and, subordinating itself to the economic laws of the new social system, attains further and quicker development.

The second feature of technology is that its profound revolutionary transformations do not take the form of an explosive change, but change rather by the gradual accumulation of elements of the new quality and the withering away of elements of the old; and this applies both to the whole aggregate of technology and to its individual branches. An example of this was the transfer from handicraft production to production by machinery. Although a real revolution, it occurred throughout a whole historical period—from the concluding third of the eighteenth century up to the 1870's.

The third feature of technology is that its development is immediately connected with the laws of natural science, whereas economic phenomena are connected with the laws of natural science through technology. Technology actually develops only to the degree to which it conforms with these laws, irrespective of whether they are used in technology unconsciously, as in the first stages of its development, or consciously, as is the case today.

Opponents of Marxism-Leninism often dispute the Marxist concept of the laws of technical development, asserting that Marxism is unable to coordinate recognition of the objective laws of technical development with the fact that technology is developed by people and in accordance with the aims they set themselves. In reality, Marxist-Leninist science does explain the interconnection between the laws of technical development and the aims of the people developing it.

The people developing technology are guided by two kinds of aims: first, those aims which arise from the nature of production as such—from the natural and scientific foundation of technology; and secondly, the aims which cause man to improve technology and production.

The first group of aims is determined by the technical requirements of production, by the level of science and technology, and is, in the final analysis, limited by natural laws. The second group of aims is determined by social life—economic, esthetic, psychological, political, and other purposes. Such purposes seem to lack all regularity. One man will strive for technical development because of a naturally inventive turn of mind, another is moved by ambition, still others try to find easier ways of doing their job, to improve their material conditions, or to dominate and exploit other people, and so forth. In addition to this, it is a matter not only of subjective aims, but of objective conditions, which operate differently upon different people. In capitalist society the man who possesses capital and wants to advance technology has different opportunities compared to the man without means. Moreover, a man is often not free to reject technical development. In capitalist countries the owner of an enterprise is compelled to use modern technology, otherwise he will be ruined by his competitors.

Is it possible to find a certain regularity to guide one in this sea of human desires, bearing in mind all the while that the aims which guide men in improving technology may themselves change? Marxism-Leninism considers that such a tendency revealing the main line of technical progress can be found. At this point it is again necessary to revert to work—regarded in a social, instead of a scientific-technical, context. People do not work in isolation, but together. It is the relations of production, and, primarily, the property relations which characterize the given society, that constitute the other aspect of work. We shall obviously fail to understand the history of technical progress in the United States without paying attention to the desire for enrichment under conditions of private property in the means of production, to competition and many other factors arising from the nature of capitalist production. The whole scale of other objective and subjective elements in technical development, however important, is subordinate to the major laws of social development.

An analysis of technical progress in the Soviet Union will likewise yield a multitude of objective and subjective factors. But, if one ignores the laws arising from the character of socialist relations, it will be impossible to understand how a formerly backward country could, in the lifetime of one generation, make such enormous strides in its development. Only an analysis of the new economic and social relations created in Russia after the Great October Socialist Revolution will enable one to understand both the basic social aspirations of the people and the thoroughgoing technical changes in the Soviet Union in these years.

Soviet scholars, while examining technical progress in connection with objectively existing laws of the progress of nature and society, which operate independently of the human will, do not belittle the subjective factors, the role of the scientist, the inventor, and the designer. The significance of leading scientists, inventors, and engineers lies in the fact that they realize the technical requirements of production, note the contradictions arising in production earlier than others, and, on the basis of contemporary science and technology, open up prospects for the further development of science and technology.

Apart from the important creative work of prominent individual engineers, inventors and scientists, a tremendous part in technical progress is played by the working masses. Socialism has brought about a notable rise in this. The working people, who are directly engaged in the production of material values, are the makers of technology. By their everyday work they promote regular changes in technology, preparing a leap forward in its development. The working people constantly advance from their ranks inventors, scientists, and engineers who work far-reaching changes in the development of technology.

The actual history of the development of world technology shows that it is created by all peoples. Every nation, large or small, possesses its own qualitative features, its specific character which is all its own and which is manifested in the national culture. These specific national features are to be found in technology, too.

Every people, according to its concrete historical traditions, makes its contribution to the development of world technology. How can one speak of the development of heat engineering without mentioning the contribution made by the Russian inventor Ivan Polzunov, the English inventor James Watt, the French scientist Sadi Carnot? The history of aviation would be incomplete if one forgets such names as Lilienthal, Mozhaisky, and the Wright brothers.

The Role of Technology in Present-Day Society

There is a school in present-day bourgeois writing which presents the crisis of modern capitalist society, with its military and economic upheavals and unemployment, as a crisis of all mankind, asserting that modern civilization, culture, and humanity itself are heading for inevitable ruin. Many representatives of this school try to lay the blame for human suffering upon technology. They speak of the collapse of culture. Modern technology, as they see it, means destitution for the millions huddled in huge, soulless cities. Technology, they write, means an asphalt culture, monotony and standardization, unemployment and insecurity.

A number of foreign scholars approach the role of technology in modern society more soberly. G. Eichelberg of Switzerland, in his work *Man and Technology* [4] shows the contradictory nature of technical progress in modern society but does not regard technology as the cause of these contradictions. Reducing the whole issue to a question of ethics, he says that contradictions should be overcome by the subordination of the mercantile principle to the common weal.

One of the greatest American scientists, N. Wiener, in his book *Cybernetics*,[5] writes that modern technology possesses unlimited possibilities for both good and ill. Wiener stresses in his work the impossibility of utilizing the new technology for the benefit of man in a capitalist society, admitting in essence that the new technology has outgrown capitalist relations.

Marxist-Leninist science gives the only correct answer to the question of the significance of technology for society. It draws a clear line between technology and the conditions of its utilization. Marx said that the machine possesses the wonderful power of lightening labor, but in capitalist conditions its brings hunger and exhaustion. Lenin in a number of works subjected the contradictions in technical development under imperialism to a detailed examination and showed that imperialism turns technical achievements against mankind and that only socialism uses technology for the well-being of the people. The launching of the artificial earth satellites, the building of the first atomic power station, the construction of an atomic icebreaker, the flight of cosmic ships, and finally the historic flights into space of Yuri Gagarin and Gherman Titov clearly testify to the possibilities for scientific and technical progress in a socialist society.

Dialectical Materialism and Technology

The methodological foundation for an analysis of technical progress is dialectical and historical materialism. In recent years Soviet scholars have investigated at length the special features of the basic laws of dialectic in natural and social development. Less attention has been paid in this regard to the dialectic of technical progress, although among all spheres of human activity technical activity in our day assumes a really gigantic scope. By investigating the special features of the basic laws of dialectic in the sphere of technology, not only do we advance a broader application of Marxist method to the laws of technical development, but are also able to see the prospects of this development.

Man is concerned with two types of material phenomena: those of nature and those of social life. The phenomena of both nature and social life manifest the laws of dialectical development.

What, then, are technological phenomena? It may be said that these form a peculiar third sphere with which man is in contact, alongside nature and social life. Nature, society, and technology—this is the world which surrounds man. According to its character, according to the laws of its development, technology may be defined as an independent sphere of phenomena.

Some scholars assert that technological phenomena in no way differ from natural phenomena. Indeed, both minor and major technological solutions possess significance only to the extent to which natural laws are realized in them. But the laws of natural science treat only of the potentialities of technology, whereas its development is determined by social laws. Thus technology may be regarded as a sphere developing at the juncture of natural science and social life. It is only in this light that one can examine the manifestation of dialectical laws in technical progress. Let us take as an example the law of the unity and struggle of opposites in the sphere of technology. Technology has two types of opposites: those of technology and social conditions, and the opposites inherent in technology itself. At certain states of social development, technology, as an element of productive forces, enters into contradiction with the social conditions of its development, which leads to changes in the relations of production and to changes within technology itself.

A more complex unity of opposites and their struggle appears within the framework of technical processes and designs of separate machines. If one compares any kind of machinery according to the basic operating characteristics (say, power or productivity) and follows the modification of other characteristics (load capacity, speed, force, strength, etc.), one can find indices which will change in the opposite direction. For instance, with an increase of power in a machine, its useful load capacity diminishes. At a certain stage this rules out development of the machine in the given direction. If one compares these data with the economic effect of the machine, one can see that the increase in opposites between various characteristics will lessen the productivity of the machine. The economic effect in this case gives a summarized illustration of the working of the law of the unity and struggle of opposites.

The law of the unity and struggle of opposites is connected with such categories as quantity, quality, the transition from quantity to quality, leaps, etc. At the same time, the task is not to introduce the dialectical concept into technology but to reveal the actual dialectical process of technical progress. Take, for instance, the problem of leaps. To recognize leaps is not sufficient. Lenin, in analyzing this or that phenomenon, demanded that concrete forms of leaps be established. Investigation of the actual dialectical development of technology, investigation of the law of unity and struggle of opposites is both of theoretical and practical interest.

The study of a number of machines designed for one purpose, as for instance transport (the steam locomotive, diesel locomotive, and turbo-locomotive) shows that at first the efficiency of these machines rises quickly, but then the curve showing the efficiency changes alters according to the law of asymptote. The approach of the curve to the straight line is an indication, as it were, that the potentialities of certain machines are exhausted, an indication of an approaching leap. It is interesting to trace the dialectic of development of metal-working tools. The internal contradictions of these machines lead to the stage where, as the development of metal-working tools lowers the productivity of metal cutting (machining by single point contact), the transfer takes place to a new type of tool where machining is effected by broaching and rolling (machining by line contact). The further development of the machine through its internal contradictions raises the question of transfer to machining by surface contact (forming), and opens the prospects of machining the entire part (utilizing the process of internal crystallization). All this shows the leaps in the development of the design of a group of machines, leaps connected with the radical modification of equipment, technology, and the nature of production processes.

The problem of content and form is of great importance in the development of the design of machines and the production processes. The content determines the technical form and promotes the utilization of scientific laws which are the foundation of this or that type of production process. But form in technology is frequently conservative and often persists until the form is made by designers to accord with the new content.

In addition to the dialectical laws of technical development analyzed above, other problems of great methodological importance are the relations between man and nature, between man and society, and between man and technology. In general, the most important aspect here is the correlation between the objective laws and the subjective role of human beings, which concerns the problem of freedom and necessity.

Despite a common foundation, solutions to the problem of human freedom in relation to nature, in relation to social phenomena, and in relation to technology proceed in different ways. The general form for all is the thesis that freedom is the recognition of necessity. In other words, man, in recognizing the law on which this or that phenomenon is based, uses it in his own interests. At first glance it might appear that in technology the freedom of man is limited by the laws of nature. But an endless number of laws of nature are utilized in the most varied combinations. On these grounds it may be said that within the framework of the most varied laws of nature known to man, man possesses a vast number of possibilities. One may take the following example. Man feels his way through a forest unknown to him. How many paths does he know? Evidently, only the one which he is following. It is quite a different matter with a man going through a forest with which he is familiar. He may take various directions and still reach his destination.

Science as a Direct Productive Force

The problem of productive forces is one of the most important in the Marxist theory of social development. V. I. Lenin regarded the growth of productive forces as the main criterion of social progress. Unfortunately, the study of the productive forces has not been developed sufficiently in the Soviet Union, and that became especially evident when the CPSU Program revealed that there were new aspects to the problem.

It has been said that science is one of the forms of social consciousness and not an element of the productive forces. What is more, it has been stressed that science can contribute to the development of the productive forces, but that its inclusion in the productive forces will lead to a confusion of two kinds of phenomena—spiritual, linked with consciousness, on the one hand, and material, linked with production, on the other. That these arguments are groundless may be seen from the fact that, apart from their material content, production and the productive forces also include a spiritual potency, of which Karl Marx spoke.

Marx pointed out in his time that the productive force of labor was determined by numerous circumstances, including " the state of science and the degree of its practical application." [6] The development of basic capital was an indication of " how much social knowledge generally—science—has turned into a direct productive force." [7]

If we approach the role science plays in the development of productive forces historically, we shall see that it is possible to single out certain characteristic periods: 1) the pre-scientific application of the laws of nature to technology and the productive forces; 2) the first phase of conscious, large-scale application of science, as such, to the productive forces; 3) the conversion of science into a direct productive force.

Science really became an element of the productive forces with the appearance of machinery. " The implements of labor, in the form of machinery, necessitate the substitution of natural forces for human force," Marx wrote, " and the conscious application of science, instead of rule of thumb." [8] Science is applied not so much in the development of the productive process as in the creation of machines and other implements of labor. What is more, it is chiefly the laws of mechanics and, to a lesser degree, the other laws of physics and chemistry that are applied.

The conversion of science into a direct productive force will mean an enormous leap in the development of production in communist society. The path to it has been laid by the earlier development of the productive forces, and it is linked: 1) with widespread development of science; 2) with the change of the nature of production under the influence of science; and 3) mainly with the change in man's place and role in production.

The primary prerequisite for the conversion of science into a direct productive force is large-scale development of theoretical natural science. The intense development of mathematical science is linked with broader application of mathematics in the most diverse branches of science, technology, and economics, with the increasingly profound interpenetration of ideas, arising in branches of mathematics that seem very remote from one another at first sight.

In modern science knowledge of the laws of the microcosm and the formerly unknown properties of space and time have brought about a revolution in physics and in science as a whole. The achievements of physics have vastly influenced the development of modern chemistry. The links between these sciences grow constantly stronger. The achievements in the spheres of chemistry and physics and the accumulation of vast descriptive biological material have predetermined the intense growth of biology. Electronic amplifiers, electronic microscopes, isotopes, tracer atoms, etc., make it possible to elucidate thoroughly the structure of biological elements and the nature of physiological processes. Such is the new quality in the development of biology in the present phase.

The second prerequisite for the conversion of science into a direct productive force is linked, as pointed out above, with the changing nature of production. Science, which formerly played a supporting role, is growing increasingly into the decisive factor in the expansion of production forces. Scientific institutions are turning into large enterprises and, what is extremely characteristic, science itself is actually demanding the establishment of such enterprises and huge outlays of material resources.

It is difficult to characterize even briefly the scientific problems that arise and to assess their relative significance in the next twenty years. The prospects here depend on: 1) the discovery of principles and laws capable of being used in production and other spheres of human endeavor; 2) the elaboration of technically feasible decisions ensuring the implementation of these laws; 3) the economic potential of these decisions, for the most alluring prospects remain merely an object of theoretical research so long as they are economically unfeasible. However, the economic factor recedes into the background when it is a question of saving lives, or people's welfare, or of any other tasks of importance to our society.

It is quite significant that the tasks mentioned in the CPSU Program are headed by electrification, the task of ensuring electric power for society.

There have been many estimates regarding the amount of electric power resources available to mankind—restorable (water power resources, etc.) and unrestorable (gas, oil, coal, etc.). It is clear that it is already necessary to discover new power resources and find ways of using them, for the present fuel resources will one day be exhausted. The potentialities in this sphere are theoretically unlimited. The potential reserves of atomic, solar, and geothermal (heat of the earth) power, the power of sea tides, and other types of inorganic power are practically inexhaustible.

Let us dwell on the importance of atomic energy. We are now completing the construction of the first sections of atomic power stations near Voronezh and Beloyarsk. But atomic power engineering is still in its infancy, and the economic coefficient of the ordinary atomic reactor working on slow neutrons is low. There are now prospects of employing new-type reactors working on fast neutrons, which will not only produce energy but make it possible to solve the problem of usefully utilizing all the uranium extracted and will thus satisfy man's needs in electric power for a long time. The prospects of utilizing thermonuclear reactions are better still, although the solution of this problem will require no little effort.

The Influence of Science on the Nature of Production

Modern technology makes rigid demands on the objects of labor. These demands can be fully satisfied by metallurgy jointly with the chemistry of organic synthesis. The relative capacities of metallurgy and chemistry are now being discussed in modern scientific literature. It is believed, for instance, that the high temperatures and velocities applied in modern technology require broad utilization of metals, their carbides, and ceramic materials. The new, rapidly developing branch of physics—the physics of solids—shows that metals can be strengthened substantially by certain methods of treatment. Specialists in metallurgy believe that in the next 25 years it will be possible to enhance the strength of most metals by about 100 per cent even by the methods available today.

Others assert that the new demands made upon the objects of labor can be satisfied by chemistry through the improvement of plastics. Methods discovered in recent years make it possible to obtain the so-called graft polymers, which appropriately combine the qualities of different polymers. By applying new methods of polymerization, we receive polymers of strictly regular structure (stereoregular polymers) and possessing a number of valuable qualities. In the field of fluoric plastics, atoms of fluorine are substituted for atoms of hydrogen, and we obtain polymers of a new class. Of increasing importance for science is the development of the so-called element-organic compounds, their distinguishing feature being the introduction of inorganic elements—silicon, oxygen, boron, phosphorus, aluminium, titanium, tin, etc.— into the main polymer chain.

There are vast potentialities for science to improve the existing methods of mineral exploration. Drilling of super-deep holes and combined geological, geographical, and geochemical research into the earth's riches make it possible to establish the new laws governing the formation of minerals and discover new vast mineral resources. Hence, our mining establishments, now narrowly specialized and exploring for just one element, will turn into complex combines producing not only the basic concentrates and metals, but also a whole series of additional products.

Soviet science has done more than just open wide the door of nature's treasure house. It is transforming nature. One vivid example is the plan to transfer water from the northern rivers to the Volga basin and to raise the level of the drying Caspian Sea. What is more, apart from artifically regulating the level of the Caspian Sea, it will make it possible to irrigate between 12 and 15 million hectares of arid land and increase grain harvests by approximately 1.5 to 2 million poods a year.

In his celebrated classification of sciences, Engels spoke of mechanics, physics, chemistry, and biology as sciences that study the increasingly complex forms of the motion of matter. If we approach things from this point of view, we see that at the beginning the decisive part in production was played by mechanics, then by heat and electricity. In the present stage of production an increasingly big role is played by the branches of physics dealing with the more complex forms of the motion of matter. One vivid example is modern radio-electronics and quantum radio-electronics. The remarkable properties of radio-electronic and electronic devices and systems are being used more and more —because of their extremely slight inertia and exceptionally high stability and accuracy, the possibility of utilizing a huge number of primary elements connected with one another by extremely complex structural affinities, and the potential possibility of reducing the size of primary elements to that of the molecular.

Science not only helps to perfect the implements of labor but also to alter them fundamentally. A decisive role in this is played by automation. Automation of production is a new phase ushered in by the joint development of science and technology, primarily by the switch-over of production to an electric power basis and to the employment of electronics and other improved technical means. Automation will lead to the creation of a new production apparatus in communist society. As communist construction progresses, the automatic system of machines will grow more and more into the general form of production, changing man's role in production, since it constitutes the material basis for overcoming the substantial difference existing between physical and mental labor. Automation opens up wide possibilities for enhancing the productive forces of communism.

Yet there are many tasks that still await a scientific, theoretical solution. For instance, the task of ensuring the reliability of automatic lines and enhancing the reliability of automatic machines. Automation sharply reduces the number of workers needed to operate machines, but for the time being in quite a few cases it increases proportionally more the number of people required to repair automatic equipment. All that is only part of the questions science faces today.

A special role in the improvement of the implements of labor will be played by the elaboration of the theoretical foundations and the technological improvement of computing, control, and information machines—these wonderful scientific creations of the past decades. Intense work is now being done in investigating the capacities of storage systems. Theoretically, it is possible to work out storage systems of several billion units of information and a velocity of obtaining each unit in 1/100,000,000th part of a second.

Machinery still plays a decisive role in the development of productive forces. But it is not the only type of labor implements. Science is now working on the creation of such implements of labor which will mean transition to production without machinery. One example is machineless generation of electric power (magnetic-gas-dynamic transformers). Intensive work is now being done all over the world to design sufficiently powerful machineless generators based on this principle.

In the classification of sciences made by Engels, biology ranks even higher than chemistry. Today biology is on the threshold of vast discoveries linked with the cognition of the laws governing the formation of live substance. What is more, direct influence of science on production will probably not manifest itself more vividly than where biological processes form the basis of production. In mechanical, electric power, and even chemical production processes, we see that special devices are necessary for regulating and automating the process; in the biological production process regulating is automatic with the aid of "devices" created by nature. Soviet scientists hold that it is necessary to investigate the processes of live tissue; if we learn to reproduce them in production, in technology, it will enable us to raise the level of productive forces to a point higher than any that can be reached by productive forces based on the utilization of machines.

The Change of Man's Place and Role in Production

While now and in the next few decades man is and will be a direct participant in the production process, in the future production efficiency will be determined directly by the general level of science and the degree of its technological application. Man's role in production, however, will become still more important, not because he will take a direct part in production, but because he will take part in the development of science.

Marx discovered these new traits of production when he said that " as large-scale industry develops, the creation of real wealth becomes less dependent on the working time and the amount of labor expended than on the power of the agents set in motion all through the working time, agents whose mighty productivity itself does not accord with the direct working time their production costs, but depends on the general state of science and on the degree of technological development or the application of this science in production." [9]

In the early phase man will only supervise and control the production process. Later on, the function of supervising, controlling, and even regulating will pass over to the new technical means created by man. Receiving information about the nature of the raw materials going into production and the progress of the production process, these devices will by themselves prevent all inadmissible deviations from the given operating conditions and will eventually set the optimal operating conditions for the given production.

It is only in our time that prerequisites have been created to switch over production to a fundamentally new basis. In designing automatic lines, automated shops, and automated enterprises, we are merely making the first steps towards the time " when huge, natural forces can be pressed into the service of production . . . and the transformation can be effected of the process of production into a technological application of science." [10] Man will be freed not only of direct participation in the production process but even of directly controlling it; the functions remaining for man are those of designing, building, and improving automatic systems in both chemical and mechanical technology.

The task of communism is to alter all concepts of production engendered by capitalist society—the shortcomings of its material and technical basis and all concepts about the source of wealth. Its task is to show that labor, once it is no longer onerous, acquires a new content, organically combining physical and mental functions, forming increasingly closer links with scientific activity, which will determine the new content of production. In the words of Marx, " The plunder of another's working time, on which wealth now depends, is a miserable basis compared to the newly developed basis created by the biggest industry. Inasmuch as labor in direct form ceases to be the main source of wealth, working time ceases to be its yardstick and, consequently, the exchange value ceases to be a yardstick for the commodity value. Likewise, the surplus labor of the masses ceases to be a prerequisite for the development of common wealth, just as the idleness of a few people ceases to be a prerequisite for the development of all the forces of the human mind." [11]

It is the widespread opinion of foreign scientists working in various branches of cybernetics that the improvement of computing, control, and information electronic machines and their employment in production and science will render man's labor valueless. That is not right. In the new conditions man will indeed be excluded more and more from the direct production process. " He takes his place alongside the process of production instead of being its main agent," Marx wrote. " In this transformation it is neither the direct work done by man himself nor the time he works, but the realization of his own, general productive force, his understanding and mastery of nature thanks to his existence as a social body, in short, the development of a social individual that manifests itself as the main basis of production and wealth." [12]

Here we come to the change of man's position outside production, to the problem of leisure. The working hours are growing shorter in the capitalist countries too. But the conditions in an exploiter society are such that the reduction of the working hours entails reduction of wages. This forces the worker to use his potential leisure for side jobs. Under socialism, transformation of production on a scientific basis and development of the social productive force will be accompanied by a steady increase in leisure, which will not only be the time for rest and play, but also "the time for loftier activity." [13] Free time in these conditions is the time " for the fuller development of the individual who, being the greatest productive force, will in his turn exert influence on the productive force of labor." [14]

These theses of Marx form the basis of the program of communist construction in the U.S.S.R., which envisages reducing the working day to five and less hours as labor productivity rises and accordingly increase the amount of time for social and scientific activity and cultural and physical development, that is, for molding a completely developed individual.

Does that mean that man will be relieved of labor? No. The development of technology and science will put him into a new position in production, and the success of his labor will be determined by his all-round development outside production. Marx stressed that free time, including leisure and the time for loftier activity, turns "the one who disposes of it into a different being and that it is as a different being that he takes part in the direct process of production."

Production continues to be:

1) for a man just entering life, a "school of discipline from the viewpoint of its [production's] influence on the maturing man"; and

2) for a man whose mind has already absorbed the knowledge accumulated by society, "an arena of practical utilization of forces, experimental science, materially creative, and objectively embodied science." [15]

The process of the qualitative transformation of production on a scientific basis takes a long time and requires, first and foremost, the creation of a material and technical basis, which will help to convert science into a direct productive force on a large scale. This process will in the future be linked with scientific development in directions outlined by the CPSU Program. Lastly, this process will be linked with overcoming the antithesis between mental and physical labor, with the rise of the people's cultural, technological, and scientific level, with the ever-growing role played in society by communist labor.

REFERENCES

[1] Oxford University Press, 1954-58.
[2] Collected Works, Russ. ed., Vol. 38, pp. 178-180.
[3] Collected Works, Russ. ed., Vol. 5, p. 103.
[4] 1953.
[5] John Wiley & Sons, New York, 1948.
[6] *Capital*, Russ. ed., Vol. 1, 1955, p. 46.
[7] From an unpublished manuscript *Bolshevik*, Nos. 11-12, 1939, p. 63.
[8] *Capital*, Russ. ed., Vol. 1, p. 322.
[9] From unpublished manuscripts.
[10] *Capital*, Russ. ed., Vol. 1, 1955, pp. 629-630.
[11] From unpublished manuscripts.
[12] *Ibid.*
[13] *Ibid.*
[14] *Ibid.*
[15] *Ibid.*

Ideas of Technology
COMMENTARY

WALTER J. ONG, S.J.*

My remarks bear chiefly on the paper of M. Ellul. In many ways I find it extremely profound. I like its humility. It faces the fact that we do not understand technology in any depth and that we have trouble assessing its full significance. I find myself in agreement with much of it, at some crucial points in enthusiastic agreement. But M. Ellul now and then misses the mark.

There are several queries I would like to pose for discussion. Ellul defines "Technique" as "the translation into action of man's concern to master things by means of reason; to render accountable everything which is subconscious, and to quantize everything which is qualitative." He says that the new technological *milieu* has the following characteristic: "It is self-determining in a closed circle." This concept needs considerable examination. I frankly suspect that it is not true, that technology has its roots in man, that it is conducted by man, and that it is better conceived of as open and opening onto horizons we still cannot really see.

Secondly, Ellul maintains that the technical *milieu* is formed by "an accumulation of means which have established primacy over ends." Everyone recognizes that there is some drift in this direction. For instance, when a corporation discovers through research that it can manufacture something or other, it sets out to establish a need for the product. Thus the means dominates the end. But to what extent? How far was the "created" need really in some fashion always there? Can it be said that the technical *milieu* is entirely formed by this process?

Ellul treats the "fake problems" of technology extremely well. He says, first: "We make too much of the disagreeable features of technological development, for example, urban overcrowding, nervous tension, air pollution, and so forth. I am convinced that all such inconveniences will be done away with by the ongoing evolution of Technique itself." I agree, and am persuaded that many critiques of contemporary conditions are based on a romantic symbolic transformation of the past. Those who dwell on these obvious faults of present technological society pretend there weren't worse inconveniences before.

Secondly, Ellul points out: "We hear too often that morals are being threatened by the growth of our techniques. For example, we hear of moral decadence in those environments most directly affected technically, say, in the working class or urbanized *milieux*." People moderately familiar with the moral habits of the working class in the Middle Ages would perhaps not be so disturbed by this "decadence." The present situation may not be good, but it's no worse than it used to be. A moral threat can hardly be attributed especially to technology.

---

* Rev. Walter J. Ong is a Fellow at the Center for Advanced Studies, Wesleyan University, and Professor of English at St. Louis University. His books include *Frontiers in American Catholicism* (New York, 1957) and *Ramus, Method and the Decay of Dialogue* (Cambridge, 1958).

Thirdly, Ellul states: "We dread the 'sterilization' of art through Technique" then responds to the implication by saying, "On the contrary, the best artistic production of the present is the result of the close alliance between art and Technique."

In his last example of the spurious problems of technology Ellul says: "[We] fear that the technological society is completely eliminating instinctive human values and powers. It is held that systematization, organization, 'rationalized' conditions of labor, overly-hygienic living conditions and the like have a tendency to repress the forces of instinct." Perhaps this fear has basis. But we know the tendency exists, and can and do take deliberate steps not to suppress the "forces of instinct." Society has an astonishing resilience due to the fact that intellect is a reflective power.

Certainly these are not the real problems of technology. Furthermore, I think the opposition commonly assumed between technology and humanism is false. It is a conflict impossible to imagine without an uninformed, even dishonest romantic transformation of the human element in earlier societies. The first assembly line was the printing press. When man began mass production he didn't make shoes, or clothes, or knives but dealt with his own thoughts. The early humanists were simultaneously printing craftsmen and humanistic scholars. Today, certainly, humanistic studies of any kind—that is, studies which, as Alphonse de Waelhens has put it, help man situate himself in his present in terms of his past and future—are impossible without technology.

The real problems technology generates raise other questions. Ellul has the honesty and vision to point out these difficulties, but at the same time he makes technology a Frankenstein's monster. He has what might be called a tragic bias. Ellul points out that "the individual's efforts are powerless to resolve in any way the technical problem in its universality." This is true. But is this inadequacy of the individual peculiar to technology? What problems that affected man universally have an individual's efforts been able to solve in the past? I know of none. Technology has made this powerlessness apparent by both extending and tightening our network of communication and providing us with an extremely circumstantial and detailed knowledge of the past. We see ourselves situated in the universe with a clarity of detail hitherto inaccessible. We can consider the technological pattern in ways man could not use to consider earlier phenomena. Seeing the magnitude of the technological problem we realize the impossibility of one individual's handling it. But an individual could not cope with man's problems in their universality before. For instance, getting the members of the entire human race into contact with one another has been a universal problem throughout human history. Not only could one man do nothing effective about this in the past; he didn't know it was his problem. The American Indians didn't know there were other people in the world until Columbus pulled into view. Neither did Columbus. Technology has made us more fully aware of our collective dilemmas, including the difficulties of technology itself. It has not made us less able individually to resolve them.

Ellul argues that "spiritual values cannot evolve as a function of material improvement." If this means that material improvement does not produce spiritual values, I agree. But I completely disagree if it means that material improvement cannot implement the realization of spiritual values. Technology actually has a curious spiritualizing effect. Material improvement has put the human race in contact with itself. This is a tremendous spiritual value. It has made possible the greater penetration of the intellect into the material world. This is a spiritual value. Technology appears to me as a Christian, as a Catholic, to be a central development in the greater and greater spiritualization of the universe which is part of God's plan for His creation destined to be dominated more and more by man—although by man tainted with sin. Technology underlies the very criticism of itself. Ellul's paper depends on technology, not only because it has been mechanically reproduced, but also because the codification of information it involves would have been impossible without technology.

Specifying conditions for the control of Technique, Ellul says: " It seems to me that the only means to mastery over Technique is by ' de-sacralization ' and ' de-ideologization.' This means that *all* men must be shown that Technique is nothing more than a complex of material objects, procedures, and combinations which have as their sole result a modicum of comfort, hygiene and ease." This statement denies the fact that technology results in other things besides " a modicum of comfort, hygiene and ease." Technology serves knowledge. There is no mistaking this. Man must learn a certain detachment and independence in his employment of techniques, and use humor in his approach. But he has learned a great deal already. There is a whole literature of relevant humor, like the recent cartoon showing a technician pulling a tape out of UNIVAC and saying, " Well, I'll be damned! It says ' *Cogito ergo sum*'! " Humor is a release of hostility, and the fact that we make jokes about the technological world is a pretty good sign that we are equipped with an adequate hostility toward it. We shouldn't be taken in by technology, and I don't think we always are.

One important problem is emphasized in Ellul's conclusion. He says: " It seems to me that this dialogue can only come about by making contact which will represent *permanent* and *basic* confrontation between Technique's pretensions to resolve all human problems and the human will to escape technical determinism." We are confronted here with a kind of impasse. Technology is something we have to have, something which everything in our being makes us want to develop. Yet it has, as all human developments have, built-in problems. One of the most serious is its deterministic bent. But Ellul is too pessimistic. He doesn't recognize the passage between the technological and the spiritual in man. It is a passage which is narrow, dark and tortuous—but real. Not only, as he says, does technology raise more questions than it answers, but despite this fact and perhaps because of it it leaves man better off than he was before. We should recognize flat-footedly that we are better off in society today, even as men, than paleolithic man was. To have brought technology this far is a tremendous human achievement. Technology represents an irruption of the spiritual into the material world, which the spiritual transcends but in which it is nonetheless present. Controlling technology's momentum is not necessarily beyond its creator.

Technology is mysterious, as Ellul says, but some of its mystery is heartening. One of the strangest things about it is that it is kind of a game. The game metaphor has come more and more into our parlance recently. Huizinga, in *Homo Ludens*, has shown that there is a strong play element in almost all serious human activity—social, military, liturgical, and so on. It is strange that no one has gone into this element in technological culture. Certainly the space race between the United States and the U. S. S. R. is a game if anything ever was. There is nothing sensible about it, but this does not mean it is not serious. There is nothing sensible about a golf match or a crack drill team, yet these activities grip us as human beings. What is not sensible may be very serious.

Play is one of the most striking features of technology. Ask a man in basic research what he is doing and he is likely to say that he is " playing around."

This has a profound meaning. Men "tinker" with machines—with machines typically, in a way in which they do not tinker, or play, with nature. And now they play even with the design of machines. In earlier societies the design of tools was fixed. Paleontologists can identify a civilization by a particular hand axe which did not vary for as long as ten thousand years. Now no design is proof against the tinkerers, the engineers hired at substantial salaries to "play around" with ideas and mechanisms.

The game element in technology is liberating because it hints at something very human inside technology which our thinking on the subject still commonly neglects, something Ellul does not touch on. Technology does not have only one face; it is a Janus figure. One of its faces is in the shade and wears what might well be a smile. Technology does, under one of its aspects, alienate man from himself. Paradoxically it does this under its objective, bright, rationalistic aspect. But it is a human product grown out of man's inner consciousness. There is a peculiar human excitement attendant not only on a psychological discovery, but also on the successful organization of a technological operation such as orbiting a man around the world. Technology has to do with the exterior world, but it is a creation of the mysterious interior which is man himself.

Ideas of Technology
COMMENTARY

GERARD PIEL*

The paper by Jacques Ellul, which particularly interested me, is in many respects more surprising than that of the Jesuit contributor, Father Clarke, and the Marxist contributor, Academician Zvorikine. The latter two discussions both settle for the conventional dichotomy that places value outside of the concerns of technology. They both hold technology neutral, though each recognizes the interplay between value and technology—the Marxist via the dialectic, the Jesuit via the command in Genesis which instructed man to seek mastery of the earth in expression of his creation in the image of God. With technology thus neutralized, it may be discussed much as it appears in various editions of the *Britannica*—as nuts and bolts, or thermodynamics. But we are talking about technology at this Conference because we suspect—as Ellul argues—that there is more to it than isolated objects and techniques.

The attainment of a free and just society in a world transformed by technology has been a concern of the humanists since the end of the first third of the last century. For a moment, moralists like Jeremy Bentham were able to envision the solution to all ethical and social problems in the improvement of man's material state. British poets shared this vision. But the vision took shape as disaster and catastrophe—child labor, the Enclosures Act that drove the yeomen into city slums, and the crime against man represented by the dark, satanic mills. Out of Black England came the dichotomy of two cultures that C. P. Snow speaks of. The humanists, technologically and scientifically ignorant, despair at the ascending role of technology in the life of our culture. The technologists remain blissfully convinced that all will be well because man will somehow manage technology rationally, for the good of humanity.

Ellul attaches ethical questions directly to technological activity, although he dismisses them as "false questions" and specifies that they are minor considerations. I would like to get at what he is trying to convey at a deeper level.

He is, he assures us, not embracing simple-minded, technological determinism. He is saying that man, morals, politics and aesthetics all exist today in a technological *milieu*. Man himself, working and living in this environment, becomes conditioned by it and imprisoned by it because technology comes to embrace all social phenomena. Curing the ills of "Technique" requires more technique. Choice is subsumed by technology; the choices are made between techniques. Ellul sums this up in an aphorism: ". . . when the means of action are absolute, no goal of action is imaginable." The technological process becomes "self-determining in a closed circle," because technology has transformed men's attitudes and values.

* Gerard Piel is publisher of SCIENTIFIC AMERICAN. His latest book is *Science in the Cause of Man* (New York, 1961).

Ellul asks next whether a free society can survive this transformation. He replies: The operations of Technique are contrary to freedom, for the inexorably compelling logic of efficiency becomes the determinant of choice and action.

This transformation of man and his values is the more tragic because, Ellul declares, it need not happen—it is not determined. Ellul offers us a crack in the wall of the technological prison by identifying five " necessary pre-conditions for escape." But he looks at these conditions pessimistically and says that it is too late to create them.

In our own country we see evidence that sustains his view. The Atomic Energy Commission's Operation Ploughshare affords an extreme example. Ploughshare is directed at demonstrating the peaceful uses of atomic explosions. One of its enterprises is Project Chariot, which calls for the digging of a harbor on a remote coast of Alaska by the detonation of three small atomic bombs. Apparently nothing is going to deflect the Atomic Energy Commission from its commitment to this reckless and foolish course. In response to the protest of informed scientists the A. E. C. has created a department for the study of ecology, which will produce the most ingenious ecological rationalizations of the validity and utility of this enterprise. Obviously, I do not share the values that underlie the justification of this project. One may say, therefore, that at least one member of our community has not been captured by the closed circle of self-determining technique. But in this major agency of government, staffed by men of high training and education and presumably of sound judgment, the mere possibility of pulling the thing off has so entranced them that they are bound to do it. Perhaps this relates to the play aspect of technology Father Ong spoke of. There is a kind of supertechnological logic that makes this enterprise compelling and, in the Ellulian sense, inevitable.*

Something of the same determinism was, of course, represented by the first demonstration of atomic weapons in warfare. A reasonable analysis of the circumstances at the end of World War II suggests that there was no decisive military reason for the use of atomic bombs. I suspect that what settled the argument was something akin to Ellul's self-determining technological closed circle. I'm not attaching special moral opprobrium to the action: people are just as dead killed by high explosives as they are by atomic weapons. But I think this was a case in which action and policy were dictated by mere technological feasibility.

Ellul makes a good case for his despairing view when he shows how often the conveniences of technology have been employed to make life not more convenient, but less. The history of our cities in the past 30 or 40 years demonstrates our failure to resist the dictates of technology. No human values were advanced to protect urban life against the immediate and convenient utility of the automobile. The building of superhighways has only generated more automobile traffic, and the cities, cut off from their surroundings, are becoming rotting ghettoes and slums.

One may, therefore, argue for Ellul's premise that technology is not morally neutral in the sense of the classical dichotomy. Technology does set goals and impose values. In what was called the " age of steam and cant " the classical formulations of value were advanced for as well as against technology. But, considering ethics from an anthropological rather than the classical philosophical point of

---

* In support of my essential premise that technology may be brought under rational and purposive direction, it is pleasant to record, three months later, that Chariot has been ditched.

view (defining ethics as the summary description of conduct rather than as rules for conduct), it is apparent that morality has evolved with technology.

Slavery provides a large-scale example of what I mean here. The institution of slavery is not found among primitive peoples. It entered human history with the invention of agriculture. For the first time the social division of labor was possible. With the increase in yield per acre of cultivated land the labor of four-fifths of the population could support one-fifth of the population in the first cities that began the history of urban civilization. Slavery was the technological underpinning of high civilization and of history until very recent times. Slavery was abolished only when the biological energy of man was displaced by mechanical energy in the industrial revolution.

What about the role of ethics in this story of man's inhumanity to man? Slavery is condemned in the Old Testament only when the chroniclers are concerned with the Egyptian captivity. There is no condemnation of slavery in the centers of Jewish culture in Palestine; there is no suggestion of the immorality of this peculiar institution. In the New Testament, Christ assures us that the poor will be always with us. In Plato's view, some men were natural slaves. His opinion was echoed by no less a figure in our own history than Thomas Jefferson. Slavery became immoral when it became technologically obsolete.

Automation affords newer examples of the interaction of technology with value. Automatic production is now in the process of transforming the underlying virtues on which our economy has been predicated. Abundance has made thrift, for example, an archaic, foolish, and economically inimical practice. The entire lower middle class of our affluent society—people with incomes under, say, $10,000 a year—live in perpetual hock. Their net worth is negative. In the same sense, automatic production has made the virtue of "hard work" questionable. The idea of hard work as the way to moral perfection becomes foolish when machines can do that hard work better. It becomes necessary to define the good life in new and more generous ways and to open up other routes to moral perfection for all members of our society.

Against Ellul's monistic Technique I would argue that technology is, as Father Clarke says, a "partial activity," one that does not embrace all human actions, nor contain the answer to all human questions. But we must recognize the profound and undiscovered connections that tie technology to value and to all the activities of man. It is not only that technology requires ethical direction. Morals and ethics evolve under technological pressure. Ellul sees the pervasive nature of technology, and he fears for man. If we mean to deal with technology rationally and use it for humane ends, we cannot look at it in isolation. Technology must be comprehended in its relationship to the life of our society as a whole.

Ideas of Technology
A REPORT OF THE DISCUSSION

WARREN E. PREECE*

Morning Session

Mr. Hutchins presided. In opening the discussion, he pointed out, by way of a summary, that Fr. Ong had agreed with Ellul concerning the "fake problems," had wanted further discussion of the notion of the self-determination of technology within a closed circle and of the "Ellulian statement" of the primacy of means over ends in technology; believed that technology results in something more than mere comfort and doubted that man has "been taken in" by his technology; while Mr. Piel did not believe technology is morally neutral; saw the existence of a technological milieu in which man and society are imprisoned; believed that the state of American society confirms his analysis; and argued that the values and goals by which we rule our action are established for us by the factor of technological feasibility.

In an effort to clarify his own position about the alleged neutrality of technology, Fr. Clarke pointed out that the perspective required to assess morality demands that we make judgments on the basis of the whole man. He said that while this does not mean that technology is "value neutral," since it obviously is not, it does mean that we should judge technology only within the context of our judgments about the whole of which the thing judged is only a part and that, therefore, as an only "partial activity" of man technology itself must logically "be morally neutral."

Pointing out that the central issue might appear to be whether or not technology is really self-determining within a closed circle, an argument which Fr. Ong had rejected and Mr. Piel had accepted with reservations, Mr. Ashmore asked Mr. Piel specifically how far he would go in following Ellul. Mr. Piel replied that he would certainly agree that, in America at least, whether or not the self-determination "is in being," it quite obviously is "in process" of emerging. We can escape from it, he said, only by formulating a social policy for dealing with it, and he warned that he does not now see any sociological process at work which is likely to lead to such policies.

Mr. Huxley commented that technological development tends always to obey the laws of its own logic, but pointed out that the same thing is also true of, for example, art. This means, he said, that the question to be asked is whether the laws required by technology's own logic are the same as those required by human logic and he suggested that when looked at in this way there does indeed seem to be a good deal to be said for the theory of the closed circle.

* Warren E. Preece is Secretary of the Board of Editors of *Encyclopaedia Britannica* and Assistant to the Editor-in-Chief. Formerly on the faculty of the University of Chicago, he has also been a literary critic for the *New York Times* and the *Chicago Tribune.*

Pointing out that most people usually answer the question with the statement that the process of self-determination is going on "to a certain extent," Fr. Ong argued that the reservation itself keeps the circle from being entirely closed. Further, he said, he is certain that we do not know what the "laws of technology's own logic" are and, except in retrospect, never can know. Finally, he said, he would not agree that technology "makes every goal feasible" which would be a logical prerequisite to a "fully closed circle." Although Ellul has created a "nice structure" which is suggested by the state of affairs, he said, the fact is that the structure simply cannot be made to cover as much of human life as Ellul wants it to. He suggested, further, that this historically has been the fatal flaw in almost every "total system."

Mr. Theobald said he did not believe that Ellul looks on his notion of technology as being either a model or a closed circle but does look on technology as a process in being, a process which has become powerful and is likely to become more powerful since it would appear that man is not likely to be able to overcome it. In this sense, he suggested, the optimism of Sir Robert's address was really a mirror-image of Ellul. He proposed that the Conference should concentrate on the power of technology as portrayed by Ellul and should realize, and be always aware, that "great wisdom" will be required to control it.

In regard to the control of technology, Mr. Theobald rejected Ellul's argument that man's freedom and dignity require that we not act on him by technological means. He insisted that the fact is that man has always used technological means "in bringing up man," that, indeed, the primitive innocence required to sustain a situation in which man would not be subjected to technological means has never existed. What we need now, Mr. Theobald argued, are institutional frameworks to allow for the rapid introduction of technology in the short run, on the one hand, and knowledge which will make technology marginal to the goals of life so that man can benefit from what is beneficial in it without letting it dominate him, on the other. He warned that the problem of technology will weigh even more heavily on us in the future; that, for instance, technological factors will relate to the necessity of limiting population to that point at which birth rates and death rates meet, and are importantly involved (1) in the possibility of controlling the sex of unborn children and of artificial insemination, (2) in the problems created by the fact of senility and the possibility of keeping people alive for many years beyond that which was earlier possible, and (3) in the whole area of "miracle drugs" and the questions raised by the feasibility of transplanting human organs from one body to another.

We can, Mr. Theobald concluded, provide a better society by planning for and with technology, but to do so the planning will have to be aimed at a truly rational world, which will raise the question of whether man can remain human in a rational world; or "is tragedy necessary to humanity?"

Mr. White commented that although Ellul despairs of the situation which he portrays, he does so "with an evangelical intention," and in this respect is like one who has "discovered sin but has not yet found grace." It is appropriate, he submitted, that Ellul talks in poetic, rather than intellectual, terms. In general, he said that, whereas Ellul and Mr. Piel see some novelty in the present technological situation, he himself does not believe that the newness is real. The most primitive tribes of which we know, he pointed out, are as enmeshed in the technological problem as we are. By way of example, he told of one such tribe which had constructed its entire civilization on the basis of the rarity of the

" axe stone " only to see that civilization disintegrate under the impact of the importation of metal axes. This, he suggested, is a tragedy and may even suggest that the human condition has always been tragic by nature. Mr. Theobald replied that he could agree that there is nothing novel about the present situation; that the real novelty lies largely in the fact that people are talking about it.

Mr. Wilkinson noted that Ellul's use of the phrase " self-determining within a closed circle " is " almost an exact replica " of phraseology from Hegel, " perhaps through Marx," and recalled that when he had used it, Hegel had been speaking of a future that is in part in the " here and now," at least in the sense that the present is always pregnant with the future. He suggested that this is the context within which we must understand Ellul, who, he said, argues that although there are solutions to the problem, technologically-oriented man will never accept them.

Mr. Kranzberg asked if it is not possible that the so-called " inner logic of technology " is really only a human view of technology and of its uses. Technology, he argued, is not artificial, as Ellul believes, but is " profoundly human."

Fr. Ong pointed out that the term " technology " goes back to ancient Greece, where it meant originally an ordering of subject matter in a logical fashion so that it might be taught. It therefore pertained, he argued, to the ordering of the possessions of the human mind.

In comment on Mr. Kranzberg's point, Mr. White said that technology is " not uniquely human." He suggested, for instance, that even the beaver may be encapsulated by its technology. Mr. Kranzberg replied that even this is a " life activity " and, therefore, not foreign to humanity.

Mr. Piel suggested that in so far as anthropological diggings tend to sustain the theory that the very first toolmakers were really subhuman primates whose activities played a major role in shaping the development of man, man may be less a toolmaking animal than a " tool-made animal." He noted, further, that anthropologists have been unable to find any " intermediate man "; that, for instance, the primitive tribes of today have fully developed, rather than intermediate or developing, languages, and have intricate technologies in so far as they have any technologies at all.

Mr. Calder warned that, although we must exercise human judgment in dealing with technology, the fact is that we have only a very weak basis for making such judgments. He said that the pace of invention is, because of this lack of a basis for making judgments, " carrying us along with it " so that we find we are turning our problems over to " pseudo-technologists," such as the Atomic Energy Commission, who have vested interests in the technology they should be helping us to control. He said he is not afraid of technology as much as he is of the fast pace at which man is being dragged along by it. It is alarming, he suggested, that in the case of " Operation Chariot," the harbor to be built by atomic explosions, we find men reaching decisions in ignorance of their possible consequences.

Mr. Hutchins asked, then, how man might attempt to exercise control in such a situation. Mr. Calder replied that he might best start by attacking the reality of the " two cultures," each of which exists in ignorance of the other. Mr. Hutchins said that he could not be hopeful about such an approach, because it would make education the key, and the fact is that it takes " at least 25 years " to change education. Despite this, Mr. Calder replied, education is " entirely and profoundly " central to the solution we seek and is, indeed, " our only hope." He pointed out that this belief was implicit in Sir Robert's keynote call for " politicians who are wise men." Senator Benton commented that " this is indeed a most important point," and recalled that although the late Senator Brian McMahon had been wise enough in his day to foresee the need of getting the atomic bomb out of the hands of the generals, he did not foresee—and at the time no one could have foreseen—the equal necessity of keeping it out of the hands of the technicians.

Mr. Meier said that he was optimistic about the hope for the future; that he thought, for instance, that it is significant and encouraging that there are right now " at least 500 people of Ph. D. level " in government bureaucracies who see their mission as being that of halting the misuse of science and technology. It is because of such groups, he said, that only a very small percentage of really bad ideas ever reach the level of the Atomic Energy Commission's atomic harbor-building project. There is, he said, a " throttling process going on " constantly.

In agreement with Mr. Meier, Mr. Kranzberg said he was certain that there are a number of professional government people interested in the social impli-cations of technology, that even the Pentagon finds itself " retaining a Rand Corporation " to make studies for it. These people, he insisted, are thinking in terms of controlling technology for mankind.

Pointing out that moving from an environment dominated by nature to the United States and its environment dominated by technology had made it possible for him to be able to enjoy the luxury of thinking for the first time in his life, Mr. Vu Van Thai suggested that it would be helpful to think of the evolu-tion of technology as a part of man's continuing struggle against his environment and, as such, a cumulative process. When we control one part of a total environ-ment, he said, we inevitably create new problems and thus become involved in a cycle of continuous action and reaction. He suggested, for example, that the invention of the axe to meet one environmental problem had immediately created the new problem of building capital, and that the solution to this problem had in turn created the necessity of finding ways for man to live together. By the same token, he continued, capitalism in the West would not be what it is today if it had not had to react at one stage of its development to Marxism, which in earlier turn had itself been a reaction to capitalism. All of this is best visualized, he suggested, as a spiraling process.

Mr. Thai said that it is apparent that the rate at which action and reaction go on has dramatically accelerated, and the spiral has thus " became flatter," perhaps flat enough to create the illusion of Ellul's closed circle. Since a part of Ellul's malaise may well stem from the massive development of society in terms of numbers and complexity and the consequent feeling that man has lost command of his own destiny, the problem, he said, becomes that of achieving an adequate psychological adaptation to an accelerating pace of evolution.

Pointing out that he had said earlier that he is optimistic about technology, Fr. Ong said he would have to concede that his optimism might well stem from the fact that he does "not expect too much to begin with." In brief reply to Mr. Theobald's earlier remarks, he said it may indeed be true that life is, at least in part, "tragic," and the basic value of Ellul's work is its insistence on a full confrontation of technology and the problems which it creates. It is, he said, obvious that technology alone cannot free man; technology has two sides and that only through a full confrontation can we be aware of both.

Continuing, Fr. Ong suggested that many hopeful developments in our own society have had their origins in technology but have then gone beyond the mere machine aspect of technology. Modern anthropology, depth psychology, semantics, the development of personalist philosophy, the development of discussion groups (representing a personalizing of abstract problems), the development of better methods of joint research, and the emergence of a "present focused historicism," he submitted, are all typical concomitants of the twentieth century which could not have existed without technology. A serious question for further examination, Fr. Ong said, would have to do with the sorts of groups which should be planning for a technological society, if we believe that planning is necessary, and with the types of training these groups should be required to have.

Mr. Piel said that the question raises still another dimension of the total problem—the fact that much planning now goes on in our own system but does so without any relation to "the whole of life." This, he said, would seem to have some bearing on Ellul's notion of the self-determining aspects of technology. Further, he warned, the planning problem is most complex because our highly developed technology presents us with such a wide variety of alternatives that the selection from among them cannot always be made on the basis of purely technological or purely non-technological considerations, so that, e. g., many diverse considerations are clearly evident in such things as the design of the American automobile. Noting that the Russians have a simple answer to the planning dilemma, one which presumably involves some sacrifice of freedom and justice, he suggested that solving our problem may well require us to vest more responsibility for planning in units larger than the private corporation. He said he hopes that we will be able to invent ways of motivating such planning democratically, and that if this can be done a great variety of actions will be opened to us. He explained in this connection that one of the hopeful aspects of technology is that it makes possible greater flexibility in planning in so far as (1) the basic production unit becomes something very flexibly designable and (2) it becomes less necessary to consider the location of power or raw material sources in the creation of new social entities.

Mr. Theobald said the answer to Friong's question of who would sit on the planning board would obviously be "the person who can do the planning." He noted, too, that the process will inevitably be extremely complex. Complaining that Mr. Theobald's answer was "certainly circular," Mr. Gorman suggested that Ellul would argue that planning itself, by its very nature, involves technique and might, therefore, be an "even worse rationalistic monster" than technique alone.

Mr. Kranzberg said he believes that at least four hopeful trends now appearing may ameliorate the problem: (1) the development of operations research; (2) the development of systems engineering; (3) the new insistence on the humanities in the training of engineers; and (4) a new awareness of the importance of education in the history and philosophy of science for those being educated in the humanities. The first of these is particularly hopeful, he suggested, because operations research is oriented toward optimization rather than maximization.

Mr. Hutchins asked what optimization would mean in the context of Ellul's thesis. Mr. Kranzberg replied that optimization, unlike maximization, involves the consideration of "all of the factors" in reaching decisions rather than, for example, merely the improvement of profits or production. Mr. Piel said he personally could not feel optimistic about, for example, the literature emanating from the Rand Corporation, which, he submitted, "is a fine example" of the systems engineer operating under a system of self-determination within a closed circle.

Mr. Meier said that since education will obviously be important in meeting the problems of technology, it is a hopeful sign that already there has been a notable increase in the amount of interdisciplinary education and research going on, with the result that graduate schools are getting a "quite different flow" of entering students from that they experienced ten years ago. The nature of the manpower available for handling the problems is changing advantageously, he suggested.

Fr. Clarke said he was encouraged that the discussion had changed its emphasis from "can we control" technology to "how do we control" technology. He said he could not believe that it is impossible for man to reflect on an important problem and then solve it. Further, and in relation to the fears which had been expressed about the ability to plan in a democracy, he said that he could not accept the implied proposition that freedom must be merely and simply "freedom from constraint" or the proposition that any process "once started must run its natural course." It is quite possible, he argued, for man to bind himself to technology in one sense in order to free himself for the pursuit of higher ends in another.

Mr. Hartner said that he wanted to associate himself with Fr. Clarke's remarks about freedom; that he is certain that unlimited personal freedom is little more than total chaos. In more general comments, Mr. Hartner said he recognized the beneficent possibilities inherent in a technology used in the right way, but was equally aware that technology cannot be allowed to become an end in itself. Man, he said, should not permit his technology to be combined with the purely financial interests of his community. As an example of the dangers of such a development, he suggested that, while in themselves radio and television can be good things, to concede this point is not to argue that radio and television manufacturers should be permitted to wage great campaigns to get a set into every house in the country, nor that having been permitted to do that, they should then be allowed by their programing methods to destroy "our very ability to think" and carry on conversations. It is even more dangerous, he continued, that the average "UNESCO thinker" wants to export all of the tools of technology to the least developed and the most developed nation alike. In wrestling with the problem of technology, Mr. Hartner concluded, we should be guided by the notion that the final aim of man must, after all, be to become humane.

Mr. Calder said that he objected to the implied criticism of UNESCO; that it is his understanding that "UNESCO philosophy" is that there is enlightenment in all of the cultures of the world. It is a serious fact, he warned in this connection, that the Copper Eskimo, under the impact of the radio and its "mechanized cowboy singers" is losing everything that was valuable in his culture. Low standards of taste are achieving a dangerous universality, he said.

Afternoon Session

Mr. Hutchins suggested at the outset that it would appear from the morning meeting that, with due recognition of the importance of technology in history, the conference was in agreement that technology is today "revolutionizing the world" at a rate faster than ever before, and that in order to deal successfully with the problems thus created man will require more wisdom than he now seems able to demonstrate. Further, he pointed out, it had been suggested that three "approaches to solutions" might be hopeful: (1) educational improvements which may already be in process, but about which, he said, he is dubious; (2) the recruitment of scientists into government to work on the problem from within government; and (3) "planning," which would, however, raise the related problems of who would do the planning and how planning could be carried out without in itself resorting to the use of further technology.

Despite a general agreement with the proposition about the rate of acceleration, Mr. White pointed out that there have been earlier historical periods in which the technological situation has changed with extraordinary rapidity. The almost unbelievable impact of the invention of the windmill as a source of power, he suggested, might at least reassure us that ages other than our own have faced the problem of change and survived.

Mr. Kranzberg said that one of the biggest questions raised in the morning, and left unanswered, had been whether or not technology is even " capable of being controlled." Mr. Calder said he would be willing to accept the notion that technology can, at least, be regulated, and Fr. Ong agreed that it might be " guided." Mr. Ashmore insisted, however, that there had been implicit in much of the earlier discussion the notion that specific instrumental controls might have to be imposed. Mr. Calder said he thought that this would be unnecessary if ways could be found to control " the cults of technology." The important question, he said, is what kind of wisdom is necessary to the task at hand. Mr. Meier said it is his impression that most " so-called cults " are really self-regulating in that they usually undergo an explosive development, quickly reach a saturation level, and then undergo " an inevitable leveling off " until such time as society is able to mobilize the resources necessary for the next burst. Mr. Kranzberg pointed out that Mr. Meier's description raised questions about the rate at which society might use up its supply of " theoretical capital " (he said he thought we will be able to replenish ours at a suitable rate) and the accelerating rate at which new theoretical knowledge is now given application.

Pointing out that it had been suggested earlier that the introduction of more education in the humanities into engineering curricula offered some hope, Mr. Ashmore asked if such a move is even possible in view of the increasing length of schooling said to be necessary if the technologist is to master all of the technical education he requires. Mr. Kranzberg said it is possible because the new trend among engineering schools is to de-emphasize " training the student for his first job," which does indeed require masses of specific knowledge, and instead to emphasize sound education in basic principles. Mr. Ashmore asked if this would mean that the new emphasis in engineering training will be in the graduate school, and it was agreed that this is already taking place.

Mr. Thai suggested that the real problem in controlling technology relates to factors of economic motivation; that in so far as it is the desire to maximize profits which leads to a speed-up technology, the very idea of profit itself might have to be revised in such a way as to emphasize a notion of social optimization. Mr. Hutchins asked Mr. Thai if he believed that such a revision will take place of its own accord or that we should be making an effort to achieve it. Mr. Thai replied that although he did not think such a change could happen self-deterministically, he felt that there might be several factors at work which could help bring it about.

Mr. Piel emphasized again the earlier point that the newly developing countries now just entering their own technological ages will have to face up to the necessity of building their values. This, he said, is now seen most clearly in the United States, where (because the economy invests only ten to fifteen per cent of its labor force in meeting subsistence needs, tolerates a chronically unemployed segment running from four to seven per cent, involves twelve per cent in preparations for war, and uses, in fact, at best only thirty per cent of the labor force in production of any kind) the economy must now "face up to the fact" of the displacement of labor from the economically least useful functions by machines.

Mr. Piel suggested that the important implication of all of this is that Americans already express their major concern about full employment in terms of its efficiency as a device for keeping people in the market as consumers rather than as producers. Since the profit sector of the economy cannot even now meet the necessity of maintaining full employment under the impact of technology, he said, the time is rapidly approaching when both the economy and society must recognize new values in many "social jobs" from which a profit cannot be made. This, he pointed out, will require a rapid revision of our economic, sociological, and political notions.

Mr. Hutchins asked if technology has been the prime cause of this development, and Mr. Piel said that it had. Mr. Calder suggested that Walter Reuther had summed up the situation when, in discussing automation, he had asked if machines will buy automobiles.

Senator Benton said he was interested in predictions that white collar automation will be more rapid than has sometimes been anticipated. He pointed out in this connection that *Encyclopaedia Britannica* already handles four times the volume of business it had ten years ago with the same sized staff.

Pointing out that government is already concerned about the effects of economic policy on full employment, Mr. Theobald suggested that both labor and management may themselves be sitting on the edge of a precipice, that management may have to recognize that it must slow down its speed toward automation and, at the same time, labor may have to recognize that it must stop pushing wages up, if only so that one of the pressures toward automation may be lessened. Senator Benton said he thought that the logic of the situation might be effective in persuading labor but doubted that it would convince management.

Fr. Ong asked if it is not possible that the economy can work out a *de facto* equilibrium between labor and automation. Mr. Theobald said he did not believe so. We will have to develop new basic notions about how an economy can best distribute its values among its people, he said.

Mr. Meier contested this prediction and said he believes that since automation is a piecemeal process, an equilibrium is in fact established as each individual segment acts and reacts to the actions of the other; that, e.g., when Detroit Electric automated its billing procedures, it found that it had personnel available to solicit information which it needed for its decision-making processes which could best be secured by people rather than machines, so that a relative balance was maintained. Mr. Hutchins asked if this was to suggest that more jobs are created because management discovers more things that it wants to know. Mr. Meier said "yes" in part, and in part because better controls make the new enterprise feasible. He noted in this connection that it is now anticipated that by 1970 most girls with secretarial training will still be able to find work, but that fifty per cent of the boys who graduate from high school will be out of work.

Senator Benton asked if the ability to maintain job equilibrium will last indefinitely, and Mr. Meier said that extrapolations indicate that it will. Mr. Theobald said he did not believe it is wise to extrapolate about such a situation. Senator Benton agreed, and pointed out, for instance, that management actually makes its investment in automation in the expectation of being able ultimately to cut down on its labor force rather than to expand it. Mr. Meier replied, however, that the important fact is that, so far, only linear operations can be automated economically; that non-linear operations, under any methods now known, are "performed more economically by people." Mr. Hutchins asked again, then, if it was Mr. Meier's argument that the automation of linear operations inevitably opens up increasing opportunities for personnel to be employed in new non-linear occupations. Mr. Meier said that it was.

Mr. Theobald said he would violently disagree with implications that the situation is a good one. Even if the Meier prediction is true, he said, it will be "a pretty poor equilibrium if 50 per cent of the male population is unemployed."

Mr. Goldschmidt pointed out that our current concern about automation recalls the position in which the country found itself twenty years ago when it was similarly concerned about agriculture. The fact is, he said, that we still haven't "caught up with what really happened" to agriculture in the period around World War II; that even today most people, including those in agriculture, do not think of the farm problem as technological. Recalling that only recently Walter Lippmann wrote that 40 per cent of the production workers in the United States are really obsolete, he said it is significantly hopeful that, whereas in 1947 people were not willing to look at the farm problem in terms of technology, there now seems to be a willingness to examine the labor problem in this more fundamental way.

Mr. Kranzberg urged that the Conference be "quite pragmatic" in considering such questions as who will control technology, when the control will be applied, and how it will be applied. The pragmatic approach, he said, is necessary lest we miss the even more basic problem of how one can change, control, and guide all of the related and dependent individual units involved in a technological revolution. Mr. White warned, too, that the problems of technology are not limited to organization and intellectual factors; emotional aspects are also involved. Despite the many stages through which civilization has moved, he pointed out, American values are still expressed in terms of a deep nostalgia for the vanishing, if not vanished, agrarian culture.

Fr. Ong agreed that nostalgia is a prevalent feature of most of the dialogue concerning society, and said that "it is something we have to fight against." Mr. Goldschmidt also agreed, and suggested that nostalgia is revealed by the fact that the problem of the underdeveloped nations is almost always attacked in terms of agriculture despite the "reality of a world trend" toward urbanization. Mr. Calder commented that this trend is what he would like to halt, and Mr. Goldschmidt replied that it is probable that Mr. Calder's reasons for opposing urbanization would themselves be based on nostalgia. Mr. Thai and Mr. Huxley suggested that urbanization is increasing now because "tending for the land" simply cannot employ all of the peoples of the world; there is simply nothing left for most people to do on the farm.

Mr. Goldschmidt said that such an argument misses the point that in parts of Asia, for example, life on the farm is "simply not worth living."

Pointing out that even if it should prove possible "to guide" technology, it is likely that it could be done only in a thoroughly planned society, Fr. Clarke asked if planning necessarily involves authoritarianism or even totalitarianism. Mr. Meier said that, to the contrary, a totalitarian society could not "handle the problems involved," since planning for technology requires kinds of abilities different from those associated with totalitarianism.

Mr. Thai asked if it is not likely that planning succeeds best only when it is used to reinforce the basic motivations of the people subject to it. If the objective of the planning and the motives of the people are divorced from each other, he said, planning must certainly fail. He pointed out that this related to his earlier remarks that it might be necessary to change the basic notions and attitudes of the people and he said, further, that this step should be accomplished before planning is even attempted.

In going back to his last point, Mr. Meier explained that he had wanted to indicate that factors other than either an abundance of natural resources or the existence of an authoritarian planning power might be importantly involved in a nation's capacity for dealing with its technological and developmental problems. He pointed out, for instance, that nations able to invest from three to ten per cent of their capital in education have done "remarkably well" in this area despite their lack of natural resources. This, he submitted, would seem to indicate that a milieu of flexible attitudes, which education can provide, is more important than authoritarian planning. Further, he pointed out that the most truly effective planning in Puerto Rico does not even look like planning to the average person.

Mr. Goldschmidt said that "planning" is a "loaded" word, and, therefore, a bad one to use. We should decide first what it is that we are really talking about when we use it, he said, and he suggested that all of those present could at least agree that the world is going to have to apply great intelligence in meeting its problems, that it is going to require a standardized statistical language that all can agree on, and that there is going to have to be some consensus as to the goals to be achieved. If we have these things, he said, we can probably succeed and, further, if these are the only prerequisites, then "planning" need not be totalitarian. Mr. Ashmore argued, however, that the problem is more difficult than that; that in addition to the requirements listed by Mr. Goldschmidt, it is probable that we will also require methods of allocating resources, and these will involve the problem of adjusting the notion of centralized allocation to our preconceptions of freedom and liberty. Mr. Theobald asked for further discussion of "what planning is" and what the difference between "totalitarian and non-totalitarian planning" would be. Fr. Clarke explained that he had meant only to ask how a thoroughly planned country would comport with our notions of democracy.

Charging that Mr. Meier's view of the kind of planning required is "too simplified," Mr. Real said that a better understanding might come from the implications of the problems of the United States government in dealing with its "major systems purchases." At the present time, he explained, California gets approximately ten per cent of the contracts for all such purchases, and studies indicate that the percentage is likely to go to 40 per cent. Politicians from other states, he said, seem unable to face up to such a situation, even though it is based almost entirely on the logical fact that 25 per cent of the nation's research and development work is now done in California and that it "does not make sense" to separate production too far from research and development. The problem, he said, is that instead of facing such a problem on a long-term planned basis, most political leaders hope simply for some "amorphous intervention" to occur which will either change the situation or make it tolerable.

Mr. Hutchins asked for further discussion as to what planning is, how it works, and how it can be applied to the technological problem.

Mr. Meier replied that, essentially, planning involves the "application of intelligence to a problem" in such a way that all available information concerning the problem is brought into play in reaching a solution. This requires, he said, the invention of methods for getting great quantities of information to the point at which specific issues can be seen and specific questions raised. In planning, he said, we try to see deficiencies and problems in advance so that we can plan services to meet them when they occur. Thus, he continued, one example of planning could involve inventing means of attracting boys to study shorthand now in order to meet what is likely to be a shortage of women able to take shorthand in the future. Another kind of planning, he said, might involve the allocation of major national resources within the economy, and would obviously require assurances that the allocation would be handled with due regard to all of the costs of all of the alternatives.

Senator Benton asked Mr. Meier if he would say more about such allocations in respect to such things as comparative national investments in education and the returns expected from them. He suggested that the Russians would seem to be investing more than the United States in this field.

Mr. Meier said that recent studies indicate that investments in education yield a return of "better than ten per cent before taxes." Senator Benton said he was "skeptical" of the figure, but Mr. Meier said he was certain it would be an understatement if all of the benefits from education were to be considered. In relation to the matter of Russian *vs.* United States planning, he suggested that the problem might be that the more educated a person is, the more antipathetic he is to orders. Senator Benton argued, however, that there has been no major trend away from authoritarianism in Russia despite their "very great investment in education." Mr. Meier argued to the contrary, however, that the fact is that the Russians have decentralized their planning apparatus and in fact that the whole decision-making process in Russia is today quite different from what it was twenty years ago—all "largely as a result of education."

Mr. Wilkinson said he believes that the main fact about planning is that it is really essentially the same whether in allegedly authoritarian Russia or in the United States; that more planning goes on in a democratic nation than we usually recognize but that in a democracy most people have to be "dragged into the future" with bad grace, while in Russia most people accept planning with better grace. Mr. Meier said he believes that there is "more planning going on in the United States" today than in any other part of the world.

Mr. Theobald suggested that the basic problem then is to determine what will be necessary if planning is satisfactorily to control technology. He argued that planning based on national income figures, for example, won't work; that the types of planning mentioned earlier by Mr. Meier which involved one city or industry and in which the basic problem is identifiable and thus manageable won't be sufficient. What we will need, he said, is planning on a national and international scale, and this will involve answering such questions as: should water supplies be diverted in order to meet the needs of an expanding population, or should they be left as they are in order to choke off rapid population growth? Although the individual citizen and notions about him are irrelevant to this kind of question, he said, such planning can be made compatible with democracy, although not necessarily with the way we normally think about democracy. We must, he urged, recognize that the economic and the technological orders are not really vital factors to all citizens and that people can therefore be freed to lead good lives by making it unnecessary for them to concern themselves with these aspects of life.

Mr. Hutchins asked Mr. Theobald if this was to say that the control and regulation of technology will require "government by elites," and Mr. Theobald said that it will; that if we accept the necessity of planning we must also accept the fact that it will have to be by elites. Mr. Hutchins pointed out again, however, that this will inevitably also involve control of the government by elites and, again, Mr. Theobald agreed, but said he thought that freedom would still be possible. Mr. Hutchins suggested that such a pattern might be said to pertain in France today. Mr. Theobald agreed and said that it could also exist anywhere else that the government first decided it would provide the necessities of life without cost to its citizens.

Mr. Hutchins asked if "this authoritarian view" was generally accepted. Mr. Piel agreed that both the planning function and the economic production function will, in the future, undoubtedly "involve only small minorities of the people." Mr. Goldschmidt said he would agree, but did not see why these minorities should be called elites.

Mr. Theobald said he would argue that, in theory at least, the government he had suggested could be organized "right now," and Mr. Calder agreed that, in a sense, it is already going on; that already we find great "hunks of planning" going on, usually by "faceless men standing at the elbows of the uninformed." Fr. Ong said, however, that he was still concerned about the apparent cleavage between the people and those doing the planning; he said that the cleavage is not necessary and planning need not be restricted to very small groups since it is demonstrable that fairly esoteric knowledge such as that which would be required in planning "has a way of getting itself pretty well spread" among the people. Mr. Theobald agreed that knowledge of the techniques of planning is susceptible to dissemination among the people, but warned that the planning process itself will require access to so much specialized information that, for example, a democratic vote on issues would simply be implausible. Fr. Ong said he was still not certain of this. Mr. Hall pointed out that what Mr. Theobald was really saying was that the answers to the questions to be faced in national planning will be so clear, once all of the facts are known, that there will be no room for argument about them and, thus, no "democratic vote" will be necessary.

Mr. Theobald said that the major attraction of the planning for which he was arguing is that it would take the individual out of the planning-economic process so that he would have greater freedom and would no longer need to be a tool of the system. Mr. Huxley asked, then, how products would be "justly distributed" in such a situation; how, for example, we would distinguish between the man who worked only one hour a day and the barber who would still have to work eight hours a day. Mr. Theobald conceded that the distribution of national income would be a serious problem and suggested, further, that it is really the most pressing problem of our day.

Mr. Thai asked what factors would determine the actions of the planners called for by Mr. Theobald. Mr. Theobald replied that the planners would be motivated by the twin necessities of achieving sufficient production so that everyone could "take anything he wants from the economy," and of maintaining individual liberty. He said again that the basic aim would be to take technology and economics out of life so that man may "become human." Pointing out that such a view implied that technology is subhuman and something which "should be got rid of," Fr. Ong argued that the tendency to quantify, which is inherent in technology, is a human tendency. Mr. Theobald argued that it is a Western, but not a human, tendency and said his argument is that having first put man in slavery with the invention of agriculture and the development of a system within which he has to earn his living, we can now free him by taking him out of that system. Fr. Ong asked whether, if we take the notion of "earning" out of life, what is left will be satisfactory. Mr. Theobald said he did not believe that the question was "real," since we are already in a situation in which "earning a living" is no longer the factor that it once was and that, indeed, we are making an artificially great effort simply to find ways of keeping people busy. The real illusion of our time, he said, is the belief that the employed are really "earning" a living. In the new system, he argued, many, many people will be able to spend their time making "beautiful things." Mr. Hall pointed out that this would be to "go back to the beginning" but "with the essentials supplied." That it might be liberating, he said, is suggested by the fact that though frozen fish are now available many men prefer to go out and catch fresh fish.

Mr. Ashmore argued that the notion of the control and regulation of technology by a detached elite ignores the danger that the elite itself would be "either controlled or regulated." How, he asked, can this be squared with the demands of justice and freedom in a democracy? Mr. Theobald said that all that he wanted to do at this time was to establish that the production of goods and the achievement of technology are not in themselves "man's highest goals." He conceded that he sees no method by which technology can be controlled by traditional democratic methods, and would agree that the elimination of work would create problems of social control, prestige, etc.

Mr. Piel said that there would be no lack of opportunity for the exercise of freedom in a planned society; that all that the planning outlined by Mr. Theobald would do would be to eliminate the problem of earning a living.

Senator Benton suggested that "the fact is that we are already governed by elites." If this is true, he said, then the weakness of the model projected by Mr. Theobald would be that it would, in fact, destroy the method by which the best of all possible elites is selected. He argued, for example, that the United States Senate "constitutes a very excellent elite," and, moreover, that its excellence cannot be separated from the methods by which it is chosen. Mr. Theobald argued that merely taking economic and technological factors out of the life of the ordinary citizen will not make the problem any more difficult. He said further that he would not feel that the method by which we now pick political leaders "is entirely adequate, either." Senator Benton conceded that the method could be improved; that we need, for instance, a new constitutional convention. He insisted, however, that the present method of selecting the elite which guides our country is a good one in principle and that he would want further reassurance on his point that Mr. Theobald had so far been able to provide.

Mr. Meier suggested that the identity of the elite is already changing; that, for example, technology, in the person of the planner as a professional man, is even today joining the elite and that others from the "so-called leisure type professions" are moving in and out of government with the result that the elite is getting larger and government is no longer necessarily a lifetime career so much as it is a group of people willing to accept responsibilities for a relatively fixed number of years. Mr. Piel suggested, further, that it is significant that many of our basic decisions are not even now made "by government," so much as they are by private, undemocratic, self-perpetuating elites within the corporation. He said he believes the basic motivation for the planners of tomorrow will arise from within a population which "has become human" and that this can happen more easily and more efficiently when the population is not tied to "degrading employment in fraudulent research, advertising," etc.

Mr. Hartner warned, however, that elites may improve with time on the one hand, or deteriorate on the other; that the alternatives which we might have to face are that an elite can indeed become totalitarian or ineffective because of its inability to force compliance with its plans when brakes are applied by the population. He said we should concentrate on improving the moral qualities of the populace by education; that education in this sense will involve much more than merely stuffing the student with knowledge. We may, he said, have to elevate the people to a point at which they are willing to sacrifice what they now call freedom in order to pursue common ends and goals, and he warned that if this is not done democracy may, and almost certainly will, deteriorate.

Mr. Hutchins noted in conclusion that it would be fair to say that the method by which "technology may be controlled, guided or regulated has not yet appeared to us." He pointed out (1) that the Conference was not agreed that education can meet the need because it was not agreed on what it meant by education; (2) that the Conference had been told that planning will "have to be done" on a world scale by elites which will come to power by methods not yet defined, and will operate by means not yet clear, but that it had been suggested that these operations will be limited to relatively small areas of the totality of human life, but (3) that an important question had been unanswered: that is, that although the difficulties which will result for the human race if technology is not controlled had been shown quite clearly, participants had not yet succeeded in seeing the outlines of a program for control which would not be subject to the charge that it might be worse for the human race than unchecked technology might be.

Senator Benton suggested hopefully that the climate is changing so that planning is not "the bad word" it was 25 years ago, and in America, at least, is readily accepted "for other countries." He suggested further that American political leaders, particularly those in Congress, now seem to be more willing to recognize the need for planning and to consider new and different methods of distributing national income. We are, he argued, getting a better interplay "between our intellectual leaders on the one hand and our political leaders on the other."

Second Afternoon Session *

Mr. Tyler presided. In opening the afternoon session, Professor Zvorikine said that in considering technique and its effects on society he would want first to underline much of what already had been said at the Conference; that, in respect to Ellul and others who agree with him, he would insist that he "understands the problem" better than Ellul does and accepts more willingly the arts of technique; that as an atheist he could not accept the views of Fathers Ong and Clarke, though he would agree with them that the evil to be dealt with is not in technique but in the people who use it and would therefore support the idea that military competition between capitalism and socialism should be replaced by competition for "a better condition for all human beings."

Professor Zvorikine said that he did not agree with Ellul concerning the influence of politics and felt, further, that Ellul incorrectly stresses "an inadequate

---

* Because Professor Zvorikine was unable to be present on the first day of the Conference when his paper was first discussed, the afternoon session on the third day of the Conference was devoted to it.

understanding " of technique, which he reduces to " a mere matter of machines." The two things are not, and cannot be thought of as being, identical, he insisted, since technique is only one of many means of work in which man applies the machine to achieve pre-determined needs. Our times, he pointed out, have been marked by a colossal transformation in the means of work.

Continuing, he said that although he does not believe that " technology " can be thought of only as a matter of production, he would still argue that Ellul's " limits " are far too wide. It is necessary, he suggested, to strike a balance between the general and the specific, and many " ways of thinking " which had been apparent in much of the work of the Conference really belonged to a class of phenomena other than science. The growth of man's ability to transform his world and the nature about him, Mr. Zvorikine continued, shows the true character of knowledge and its dependence on the laws of the development of nature and of society. He said that since " the correlative " between man and technique is the social importance of the subject, we cannot comprehend the effects of technique without also considering the social context within which its impact is manifested, that is, the impact of the means of work on man in both socialist and capitalist countries.

The speaker complained that Ellul has pictured the society emerging from technique as sterile, one, for example, wherein man will artificially reproduce and even human feelings will be controlled by the administration of " special preparations." Though he conceded that such a society could evolve if the technocrats and the leaders of the people were left free to do with society whatever they want to do, he insisted that such will not happen since the people do not want that kind of a society and the people " are not guinea pigs." He submitted that one of the unique values of socialist life is that the whole of society must decide how to take the best of technique for the good of all people, and said that he would, therefore, agree with Ellul that we must find ways to develop science and technique in the good society.

It is important, Mr. Zvorikine said, to demonstrate the relationships which exist between our understanding of social life, the state of our knowledge, and the ways in which social knowledge is formed. To this end, he suggested that there is " practically no one " today who refuses to agree that social knowledge is formed materialistically. He noted that Marx has pointed out that in socialist society, people will " fall into life " by means of " their own creation " and will thus be able to develop their own creative powers. This means, he continued, that socialist knowledge is formed at " political and juridical levels " under the influence of the inherent memory of a spiritual past, that is, of traditions, national origins, and other ideological factors. Great meaning, he said, attaches to the analysis of mechanisms in the notion of social knowledge, and, believing that human norms of kindness, evil, justice, etc., are formed so early in culture that they seem to have existed from the very beginning, Russia is trying to establish " a society representative of humanity," in part through the utilization of a scientific outlook and in part " through the use of labor training " as an influential agent of " moral bringing up." To the socialist, he said, common norms of justice and morality, which are parts of the " unshakable forces of life " between people, " should become so between nations."

Continuing, Mr. Zvorikine said that level which socialist countries try to attain in " bringing up " their people relates to the value of " honest labor for the good of society," the concern of all people for human betterment, the acquisition of " high knowledge " as a common duty, the desire to " break up social classes," the acceptance of collectivism and of "one for all and all for one," and a "high regard of people for people." To a socialist, he submitted, a human being "is a friend and a brother to others," and socialists place high value on honesty, decency, regard and respect for each other within the family, and reject injustice, dishonesty, and miserliness. He said he "would like to ask" if anyone could seriously believe that such a program of "social knowledge" can possibly lead to the degradation of personality proclaimed by Ellul.

Factors of material and spiritual condition best providing for the development of human beings, the speaker said, include: (1) the greatest possible betterment of the material conditions of all so that the citizen may be freed from material concerns; (2) education; and (3) the creation of leisure. These conditions, which, he said, technology enhances, will create a "beneficial situation for personal development" in the acquisition of greater knowledge, in the development of personal art and in the enhancement of culture.

In conclusion, Professor Zvorikine said that humanity is awaiting the "future which this kind of humanity will create." He suggested that social progress is tied to the development of science and technique and to such other developments as bring about the goodness of people under the name of humanism. These, he said, are the directions being followed in the U.S.S.R. and are something "of an answer to Ellul's question as to how humanity will reach its golden age."

Mr. Kranzberg pointed out that it is easy to agree with "practically everything" substantive which the Soviet scholar had said; that we could all agree that technology is important and pervasive in modern life and could also agree with much of his analysis. Noting that Mr. Zvorikine called technique a link or bridge betwen the natural sciences and social life, he suggested that this might mean that technology is actually more humanistic than science, for while science tries to take the human element out of work, technology is "up to its neck in social acculturation" and is for human use. Despite the wide area of agreement, however, Mr. Kranzberg said he "bridles when the Marxist-Leninist dialectic is applied to the problem," for this "is not the only solution." He pointed out that Zvorikine himself seems, at the end of his paper, to agree that "there are many ways through the forest." He conceded, however, that as an "important social thinker," Marx has much light to shed on our problems.

Mr. Wilkinson suggested that Professor Zvorikine had misread Ellul, for Ellul would insist that, since he is recording only facts, ideology is irrelevant and doctrine "means nothing." Mr. White said he would want to "dispute that point," and would argue that there is, in truth, "nothing but doctrine" in Ellul.

In regard to the matter of doctrine and dialectic, Zvorikine said that he "considers that everything of value in life" develops in accordance with the laws of dialectic and that it is, therefore, necessary in every case to "look for the internal contradictions in order to discover the law." He said that laws of technique are discovered in two ways, that is scientifically and/or socially, and he pointed out that in analyzing the development of technique we "are met face to face by its internal contradictions" as manifest primarily in "the social forms of technique." New techniques, he argued, demand new social treatment. In this connection, he recalled the notion that the "basic content of revolution" is always the result of the contradictions which necessitated the revolution, and pointed out that technique, too, develops in terms of the discovery of contradictions and the correction of them. The social contradictions manifest in technique, he continued, are the first and perhaps the most dramatic contradictions we face, but there are other forms of contradictions also existing within the technique itself. He reported, for example, that some 25 years ago, he had undertaken a complete analysis of " the machine "—mainly the steam engine, but running " from the level of hydraulic wheels to the reciprocating piston and the steam turbine "— and that he had been able to establish that at each stage of development " there had appeared an internal contradiction " in that as the overall size of the machine increased, there was a decline in its curve of efficiency. This meant, he said, that with each " quantitative jump in design " the machine became " very powerful " for a while, but that the relative power then declined. Mr. Kranzberg said he could not believe that the mere fact that increasing one factor in an equation served to cause a decrease in another constitutes a true internal contra- diction, and Mr. Wilkinson agreed, noting that Professor Zvorikine was really only " backing Engels " on the law of diminishing returns.

Mr. Theobald said that he was primarily interested in discussing Mr. Zvorikine's papers in the terms developed earlier at the Conference and in learning what he could add about the exrcise of " human " control over a machine civilization. He asked, for instance, " how the control of the computer " is handled in Russia. Mr. Tyler said it was his understanding that " this kind of control " is effected by raising prices to limit consumption, but Mr. Theobald said he had meant something at a " more complex level than that—that is, how do you control *humanly?* "

Mr. Thai said he would like to hear from Mr. Zvorikine how research is con- trolled in Russia; who sets the objectives, why particular objectives are set, how much of research is dictated by social pressures and how much by the interplay between inventions and, finally, who decides when to apply scientific knowledge?

Mr. Goldschmidt said he would like to discuss the problems involved in trans- ferring technology from developed to less developed sectors. He pointed out that the Russians seem to have done a " remarkable job " in this field within one generation.

In response to Mr. Theobald and Mr. Thai, Professor Zvorikine said that technological decision-making in Russia represents an accommodation to the same problems that exist in the United States and that one factor largely involved is the matter of economic effectiveness. We try, he explained, to determine what the economic results of a given decision will be, that is, how quickly we can expect a return on any proposed investment in a new technique. He said that the government normally assumes that it must have a return on its investment within one or two years, " so that the money may be reinvested in new tech- niques," but he noted that if it is determined that " we have unwanted jobs " in certain industries, automation is speeded without regard to the rapidity with which returns can be realized. Russia, like America, he said, makes continuous studies of the possibilities of technique, and, among other things, these studies have shown that automation applied to an industry characterized by developing, and, therefore, " incomplete " technique will produce undesirable effects.

In regard to the matter of the application of electronic computers, Mr. Zvori- kine said these are used more and more widely in the metallurgic and chemical industries and that, unlike the United States, Russia has set up regional computer stations to which every factory in the area reports data required for economic analysis.

Turning to Mr. Thai's question about the direction of research in Russia, the speaker pointed out that, in the first place, research is going on over " a wide front," some directions of which are always more promising than others, and that these " most promising directions " are centralized for research. The demands of the whole country are considered in order that impetus can be given to those lines which are felt to be most important, he said, and he pointed out that this criterion requires that the government have " good information " about the " state of technique and science " and that this information be studied by special committees, including factory and institutional representation but centered in the government and coordinated by Soviet ministers. The specific institute involved in any given line of research, he said, coordinates the actual conduct of research relating to its specialty. He pointed out that the information require- ment creates a major problem in setting up research programs; that the basic principles are all stated in the " party program," but that before they were finally formulated they were " subjected to tremendous research " within the Institutes and that, despite this preparation and although they have been " carefully de- veloped and minutely researched," it is still " necessary to say " that the develop- ment of science is going so fast that conditions frequently require modifications in the program.

Pointing out that the concern of the Conference seemed to have turned on the question of whether technology and science may be tending in directions inimical to human welfare, and that this highlights the importance of considering the problem of, and possibilities for, controlling science and technology, Mr. Ashmore asked Professor Zvorikine if he was satisfied with the control methods employed in Russia or believed that they would have to be revised.

Dr. Zvorikine replied that Russia does " not at all understand why the development of technique " should not be beneficial to humanity. He pointed out, for instance, that although the development of automation is said to create unemployment, the fact is that if the United States were to attempt to apply present Russian growth rates to its existing productive capacity it would immedi- ately have a shortage of workers because all of the gains in productivity " would be used up in expansion," while if Russia were to slow its development to the rate at which the United States is now growing, she would have unemployment. This means, he suggested, that we cannot make flat generalizations about the effects of automation. Rapid development of an industrial base, he said, requires a faster growth of industry and a shorter working day, but with proper organiza- tion the conflicts between automation and employment can be removed.

Continuing, he pointed out that it is frequently said that " automation deper- sonalizes labor " because it requires an involvement of fewer of the worker's personal qualities. This, too, he charged, is not true " as American labor shows." " How," he asked, " can technique be harmful to man? "

Mr. Tyler suggested that the problem of technology in America has in great part been a matter of the dislocation of the worker so that, for instance, most farmers' children now grow up to become engineers, and while coal miners as a group are not industrially retrained for other work, their children simply do not become miners. He pointed out that Mr. Zvorikine had suggested that Russian practice is to train those workers likely to be put out of work by automation before automation occurs.

Suggesting that a second concern manifest at the Conference related to the bases on which judgments can be made as to when to use technology, Mr. Tyler pointed out that this question is now usually settled on the basis of " how many people may be presumed to buy a product " but that many who have studied the problem distrust the ability of the " common people " to make this decision for themselves. Still a third concern, he concluded, had to do with the influence of the military and the waste which military activities involve in the development of technology.

Mr. Thai said that he personally was also concerned about the implications of such things as, for example, a decision to " apply to social life the latest findings in genetics." Mr. Tyler noted parenthetically that " forced mating is unlikely," but Mr. Theobald replied that it is not difficult to imagine a situation in which artificial insemination might be dictated.

Pointing out that the Soviet scholar had said that there is a dialectic at work within the machine, Mr. Theobald said his fear is that in trying to correct the internal contradictions in the machine itself, man might be too likely to follow the laws of the machine rather than the laws of the human race. Mr. Zvorikine replied that his paper dealt with this problem; that the application of the dialectic method in understanding the development of the machine also helps us to understand the technological process. If, he continued, we see the effectiveness of a machine diminishing, we must " logically search " for new methods to new results, and although we may sometimes find it possible to prolong the effective value of a machine, this does not eliminate the basic need for a " new jump." This problem, he said, is solved in the United States by " human engineers," that is, by men able to deal in the dual fields of mechanical and human systems. Concerning technology in general, he pointed out that while automation frees man from harsh physical labor, it does also " bring out new forms of fatigue," and this is a new problem which must be solved. The psychological involvement of the engineer, he said, represents the same problem in America that it does in Europe.

Mr. Wilkinson pointed out that Professor Zvorikine's remarks were " reminiscent of Ellul's discussion " of man's relation to the machine and suggested that the problem put by the relationship does not seem to be solved any better in Russia that it is in the United States, that in both cases " man accommodates to the machine."

Mr. Theobald said that he would still like to know whether, in the development of a system to service technology, the laws of technology or of humanity will prevail. If the laws are to be dictated " by the system " itself, he said, then we may have Ellul's closed circle. Mr. Calder noted that this had been a " common dilemma " throughout most of the Conference.

Mr. Goldschmidt asked Mr. Zvorikine to deal next with his earlier question about the transfer of technology from one area to another in Russia. He suggested, for example, that the Russian experience in the transformation of Uzbek would be relevant to his question. The speaker replied that Russia has, of course, had much experience in this field; that until recently " the great Asiatic republics of the U.S.S.R. were relatively undeveloped " and that the Communist government went into them " boldly to create up-to-date conditions." The local people adjusted quite easily and rapidly to the technologies thus brought to them, he said, and " no special problems " seemed to be involved in the movement. Mr. Tyler suggested, however, that advance education of the people who would be required in the new industries had been an important step. Mr. Zvorikine agreed, and pointed out that it had also been necessary to send some labor cadres from the developed areas in Russia into the Asiatic republics. The entire program, he said, was tied to the effort to elevate the common culture.

Mr. Goldschmidt said it had been his understanding that although in Uzbek the Communists " may have gone in boldly " and mixed people " from outside " with those from the local areas, there were also some places in the Asian republics in which the approach was less bold and the effort was, instead, on the development of a local process of improvement. The experience, he said, could well be important in regard to those internationally scaled operations in which boldness might be less helpful than the "social engineering" approach. To this Mr. Zvorikine replied that the fast development of underdeveloped countries demands large investments of capital and that the Russian government invested more capital in the Asian republics than it did in Central Russia during the period under discussion. Further, he said, the government had to undertake a rapid school-building program. "No underdeveloped country will reject" that kind of a program, he insisted, though he did concede that older people in the republics had "grumbled" about the new technological conditions. Helpfully, he said, the youth of the area "adjusted so quickly," that in a very few years it was possible to "create amazing cadres of talented artists." Mr. Goldschmidt said that he had been trying to get at such problems as those related to, for instance, illiteracy—problems that must be faced in a basic way before deciding to begin the development of an undeveloped territory by transferring relatively high-level techniques to it. He said he agreed with Zvorikine about the value of capital, but felt that this was not a suitable answer to his question since capital, too, is only a tool which requires adaptation to each situation.

Professor Zvorikine agreed that the first problem to be faced in developing the Asiatic republics was the elimination of illiteracy, that this indeed had been a big problem in all of Russia after the Revolution, and said that great success had accompanied the effort to eradicate it. When the government sent advance labor cadres into the Asiatic territories, he said, they and the local people quickly found a basis for a common culture. Mr. Goldschmidt asked if the laborers sent to Uzbek took their families with them, and the Academician said they did. Mr. Goldschmidt asked, then, how long they were expected to stay in their new area, and Professor Zvorikine replied that "usually they just stayed there; conditions are good."

The Technical Act

THE ACT OF INVENTION: CAUSES, CONTEXTS, CONTINUITIES AND CONSEQUENCES

LYNN WHITE, JR.*

The rapidly growing literature on the nature of technological innovation and its relation to other activities is largely rubbish because so few of the relevant concrete facts have thus far been ascertained. It is an inverted pyramid of generalities, the apex of which is very nearly a void. The five plump volumes of *A History of Technology*,[1] edited under the direction of Charles Singer, give the layman a quite false impression of the state of knowledge. They are very useful as a starting point, but they are almost as much a codification of error as of sound information.[2] It is to be feared that the physical weight of these books will be widely interpreted as the weight of authority and that philosophers, sociologists, and others whose personal researches do not lead them into the details of specific technological items may continue to be deceived as to what is known.

Since man is a hypothesizing animal, there is no point in calling for a moratorium on speculation in this area of thought until more firm facts can be accumulated. Indeed, such a moratorium—even if it were possible—would slow down the growth of factual knowledge because hypothesis normally provokes counter-hypotheses, and then all factions adduce facts in evidence, often new facts. The best that we can do at present is to work hard to find the facts and then to think cautiously about the facts which have been found.

In view of our ignorance, then, it would seem wise to discuss the problems of the nature, the motivations, the conditioning circumstances, and the effects of the act of invention far less in terms of generality than in terms of specific instances about which something seems to be known.

1. The beginning of wisdom may be to admit that even when we know some facts in the history of technology, these facts are not always fully intelligible, i. e., capable of " explanation," simply because we lack adequate contextual information. The Chumash Indians of the

* Lynn White, jr., is Professor of History at the University of California at Los Angeles and President of the Society for the History of Technology. His most recent book is *Medieval Technology and Social Change* (Oxford, 1962).

coast of Santa Barbara County built plank boats which were unique in the pre-Columbian New World: their activity was such that the Spanish explorers of California named a Chumash village " La Carpintería." [3] A map will show that this tribe had a particular inducement to venture upon the sea: they were enticed by the largest group of off-shore islands along the Pacific Coast south of Canada. But why did the tribes of South Alaska and British Columbia, of Araucanian Chile, or of the highly accidented eastern coast of the United States never respond to their geography by building plank boats? Geography would seem to be only one element in explanation.

Can a plank-built East Asian boat have drifted on the great arc of currents in the North Pacific to the Santa Barbara region? It is entirely possible; but such boats would have been held together by pegs, whereas the Chumash boats were lashed, like the dhows of the Arabian Sea or like the early Norse ships. Diffusion seems improbable.

Since a group can conceive of nothing which is not first conceived by a person, we are left with the hypothesis of a genius: a Chumash Indian who at some unknown date achieved a break-away from log dugout and reed balsa to the plank boat. But the idea of " genius " is itself an ideological artifact of the age of the Renaissance when painters, sculptors, and architects were trying to raise their social status above that of craftsmen.[4] Does the notion of genius " explain " Chumash plank boats? On the contrary, it would seem to be no more than a traditionally acceptable way of labeling the great Chumash innovation as unintelligible. All we can do is to observe the fact of it and hope that eventually we may grasp the meaning of it.

2. A symbol of the rudimentary nature of our thinking about technology, its development, and its human implications, is the fact that while the *Encyclopaedia Britannica* has an elaborate article on " Alphabet," it contains no discussion of its own organizational presupposition, alphabetization. Alphabetization is the basic invention for the classification and recovery of information: it is fully comparable in significance to the Dewey decimal system and to the new electronic devices for these purposes. Modern big business, big government, big scholarship are inconceivable without alphabetization. One hears that the chief reason why the Chinese Communist regime has decided to Romanize Chinese writing is the inefficiency of trying to classify everything from telephone books to tax registers in terms of 214 radicals of ideographs. Yet we are so blind to the nature of our technical equipment that the world of Western scholars, which uses alphabetization constantly, has produced not even the beginning of a history of it.

Fortunately, Dr. Sterling Dow of Harvard University is now engaged in the task. He tells me that the earliest evidence of alphabetization is found in Greek materials of the third century B. C. In other words, there was a thousand-year gap between the invention of the alphabet as a set of phonetic symbols and the realization that these symbols, and their sequence in individual written words, could be divorced from their phonetic function and used for an entirely different purpose: an arbitrary but very useful convention for storage and retrieval of verbal materials. That we have neglected thus completely the effort to understand so fundamental an invention should give us humility whenever we try to think about the larger aspects of technology.

3. Coinage was one of the most significant and rapidly diffused innovations of Late Antiquity. The dating of it has recently become more conservative than formerly: the earliest extant coins were sealed into the foundation of the temple of Artemis at Ephesus c. 600 B. C., and the invention of coins, i. e., lumps of metal the value of which is officially certified, was presumably made in Lydia not more than a decade earlier.[5]

Here we seem to know something, at least until the next archaeological spades turn up new testimony. But what do we know with any certainty about the impact of coinage? We are compelled to tread the slippery path of *post hoc ergo propter hoc.* There was a great acceleration of commerce in the Aegean, and it is hard to escape the conviction that this movement, which is the economic presupposition of the Periclean Age, was lubricated by the invention of coinage.

If we dare to go this far, we may venture further. Why did the atomic theory of the nature of matter appear so suddenly among the philosophers of the Ionian cities? Their notion that all things are composed of different arrangements of identical atoms of some " element," whether water, fire, ether, or something else, was an intellectual novelty of the first order, yet its sources have not been obvious. The psychological roots of atomism would seem to be found in the saying of Heraclitus of Ephesus that " all things may be reduced to fire, and fire to all things, just as all goods may be turned into gold and gold into all goods." [6] He thought that he was just using a metaphor, but the metaphor had been possible for only a century before he used it.

Here we are faced with a problem of critical method. Apples had been dropping from trees for a considerable period before Newton discovered gravity: [7] we must distinguish cause from occasion. But the appearance of coinage is a phenomenon of a different order from the fall of an apple. The unprecedented element in the general life of sixth-century Ionia, the chief stimulus to the prosperity which provided leisure for the atomistic philosophers, was the invention of coinage: the age of barter was ended. Probably no Ionian was conscious of any connection between this unique new technical instrument and the brainstorms of the local intellectuals. But that a causal relationship did exist can scarcely be doubted, even though it cannot be " proved " but only perceived.

4. Fortunately, however, there are instances of technological devices

of which the origins, development, and effects outside the area of technology are quite clear. A case in point is the pennon.[8]

The stirrup is first found in India in the second century B. C. as the big-toe stirrup. For climatic reasons its diffusion to the north was blocked, but it spread wherever India had contact with barefoot aristocracies, from the Philippines and Timor on the east to Ethiopia on the west. The nuclear idea of the stirrup was carried to China on the great Indic culture wave which also spread Buddhism to East Asia, and by the fifth century the shod Chinese were using a foot stirrup.

The stirrup made possible, although it did not require, a new method of fighting with the lance. The unstirrupped rider delivered the blow with the strength of his arm. But stirrups, combined with a saddle equipped with pommel and cantle, welded rider to horse. Now the warrior could lay his lance at rest between his upper arm and body: the blow was delivered not by the arm but by the force of a charging stallion. The stirrup thus substituted horse-power for man-power in battle.

The increase in violence was tremendous. So long as the blow was given by the arm, it was almost impossible to impale one's foe. But in the new style of mounted shock combat, a good hit might put the lance entirely through his body and thus disarm the attacker. This would be dangerous if the victim had friends about. Clearly, a baffle must be provided behind the blade to prevent penetration by the shaft of the lance and thus permit retraction.

Some of the Central Asian peoples attached horse tails behind the blades of lances—this was probably being done by the Bulgars before they invaded Europe. Others nailed a piece of cloth, or pennon, to the shaft behind the blade. When the stirrup reached Western Europe c. 730 A. D., an effort was made to meet the problem by adapting to military purposes the old Roman boar-spear which had a metal crosspiece behind the blade precisely because boars, bears, and leopards had been found to be so ferocious that they would charge up a spear not so equipped.

This was not, however, a satisfactory solution. The new violence of warfare demanded heavier armor. The metal crosspiece of the lance would sometimes get caught in the victim's armor and prevent recovery of the lance. By the early tenth century Europe was using the Central Asian cloth pennon, since even if it got entangled in armor it would rip and enable the victor to retract his weapon.

Until our dismal age of camouflage, fighting men have always decorated their equipment. The pennons on lances quickly took on color and design. A lance was too long to be taken into a tent conveniently, so a knight usually set it upright outside his tent, and if one were looking for him, one looked first for the flutter of his familiar pennon. Knights riding held their lances erect, and since their increasingly massive armor made recognition difficult, each came to be identified by his pennon. It would seem that it was from the pennon that distinctive "connoissances" were transferred to shield and surcoat. And with the crystallization of the feudal structure, these heraldic devices became hereditary, the symbols of status in European society.

In battle, vassals rallied to the pennon of their liege lord. Since the king was, in theory if not always in practice, the culmination of the feudal hierarchy, his pennon took on a particular aura of emotion: it was the focus of secular loyalty. Gradually a distinction was made between the king's two bodies,[9] his person and his "body politic," the state. But a colored cloth on the shaft of a spear remained the primary symbol of allegiance to either body, and so remains even in polities which have abandoned monarchy. The grimly functional rags first nailed to lance shafts by Asian nomads have had a great destiny. But it is no more remarkable than that of the cross, a hideous implement in the Greco-Roman technology of torture, which was to become the chief symbol of the world's most widespread religion.

In tracing the history of the pennon, and of many other technological items, there is a temptation to convey a sense of inevitability. However, a novel technique merely offers opportunity; it does not command. As has been mentioned, the big-toe stirrup reached Ethiopia. It was still in common use there in the nineteenth century, but at the present time Muslim and European influences have replaced it with the foot stirrup. However, travellers tell me that the Ethiopian gentleman, whose horse is equipped with foot stirrups, rides with only his big toes resting in the stirrups.

5. Indeed, in contemplating the history of technology, and its implications for our understanding of ourselves, one is as frequently astonished by blindness to innovation as by the insights of invention. The Hellenistic discovery of the helix was one of the greatest of technological inspirations. Very quickly it was applied not only to gearing but also to the pumping of water by the so-called Archimedes screw.[10] Somewhat later the holding screw appears in both Roman and Germanic metal work.[11] The helix was taken for granted thenceforth in western technology. Yet Joseph Needham of Cambridge University assures me that, despite the great sophistication of the Chinese in most technical matters, no form of helix was known in East Asia before modern times: it reached India but did not pass the Himalayas. Indeed, I have not been able to locate any such device in the Far East before the early seventeenth century when Archimedes screws, presumably introduced by the Portuguese, were used in Japanese mines.[12]

6. Next to the wheel, the crank is probably the most important single element in machine design, yet until the fifteenth century the history of the crank is a dismal record of inadequate vision of its potentialities.[13] It first appears in China under the Han dynasty, applied to rotary fans for winnowing hulled rice, but its later applications in the Far East were not conspicuous. In the West the crank seems

to have developed independently and to have emerged from the hand quern. The earliest querns were fairly heavy, with a handle, or handles, inserted laterally in the upper stone, and the motion was reciprocating. Gradually the stones grew lighter and thinner, so that it was harder to insert the peg-handle horizontally: its angle creeps upward until eventually it stands vertically on top. All the querns found at the Saalburg had horizontal handles, and it is increasingly clear that the vertical peg is post-Roman.

Seated before a quern with a single vertical handle, a person of the twentieth century would give it a continuous rotary motion. It is far from clear that one of the very early Middle Ages would have done so. Crank motion was a kinetic invention more difficult than we can easily conceive. Yet at some point before the time of Louis the Pious the sense of the appropriate motion changed; for out of the rotary quern came a new machine, the rotary grindstone, which (as the Latin term for it, *mola fabri*, shows) is the upper stone of a quern turned on edge and adapted to sharpening. Thus, in Europe at least, crank motion was invented before the crank, and the crank does not appear before the early ninth century. As for the Near East, I find not even the simplest application of the crank until al-Jazarī's book on automata of 1206 A. D.

Once the simple crank was available, its development into the compound crank and connecting rod might have been expected quite quickly. Yet there is no sign of a compound crank until 1335, when the Italian physician of the Queen of France, Guido da Vigevano, in a set of astonishing technological sketches, which Rupert Hall has promised to edit,[14] illustrates three of them.[15] By the fourteenth century Europe was using crankshafts with two simple cranks, one at each end; indeed, this device was known in Cambodia in the thirteenth century. Guido was interested in the problem of self-moving vehicles: paddlewheel boats and fighting towers propelled by windmills or from the inside. For such constricted situations as the inside of a boat or a tower it apparently occurred to him to consolidate the two cranks at the ends of the crankshaft into a compound crank in its middle. It was an inspiration of the first order, yet nothing came of it. Evidently the Queen's physician, despite his technological interests, was socially too far removed from workmen to influence the actual technology of his time. The compound crank's effective appearance was delayed for another three generations. In the 1420's some Flemish carpenter or shipwright invented the bit-and-brace with its compound crank. By c. 1430 a German engineer was applying double compound cranks and connecting rods to machine design: a technological event as significant as the Hellenistic invention of gearing. The idea spread like wildfire, and European applied mechanics was revolutionized.

How can we understand the lateness of the discovery, whether in China or Europe, of even the simple crank, and then the long delay in its wide application and elaboration? Continuous rotary motion is typical of inorganic matter, whereas reciprocating motion is the sole movement found in living things. The crank connects these two kinds of motion; therefore we who are organic find that crank motion does not come easily to us. The great physicist and philosopher Ernst Mach noticed that infants find crank motion hard to learn.[16] Despite the rotary grindstone, even today razors are whetted rather than ground: we find rotary motion a bar to the greatest sensitivity. Perhaps as early as the tenth century the hurdy-gurdy was played with a cranked resined wheel vibrating the strings. But by the thirteenth century the hurdy-gurdy was ceasing to be an instrument for serious music. It yielded to the reciprocating fiddle bow, an introduction of the tenth century which became the foundation of modern European musical development. To use a crank, our tendons and muscles must relate themselves to the motion of galaxies and electrons. From this inhuman adventure our race long recoiled.

7. A sequence originally connected with the crank may serve to illustrate another type of problem in the act of technological innovation: the fact that a simple idea transferred out of its first context may have a vast expansion. The earliest appearance of the crank, as has been mentioned, is found on a Han-dynasty rotary fan to winnow husked rice.[17] The identical apparatus appears in the eighteenth century in the Palatinate,[18] in upper Austria and the Siebenbürgen,[19] and in Sweden.[20] I have not seen the exact channel of this diffusion traced, but it is clearly part of the general Jesuit-inspired *Chinoiserie* of Europe in that age. Similarly, I strongly suspect, but cannot demonstrate, that all subsequent rotary blowers, whether in furnaces, dehydrators, wind tunnels, air conditioning systems, or the simple electric fan, are descended from this Han machine which seems, in China itself, to have produced no progeny.

8. Doubtless when scholarship in the history of technology becomes firmer, another curious device will illustrate the same point. To judge by its wide distribution,[21] the fire piston is an old invention in Malaya. Dr. Thomas Kuhn of the University of California at Berkeley, who has made careful studies of the history of our knowledge of adiabatic heat, assures me that when the fire piston appeared in late eighteenth-century Europe not only for laboratory demonstrations but as a commercial product to light fires, there is no hint in the purely scientific publications that its inspiration was Malayan. But the scientists, curiously, also make no mention of the commercial fire pistons then available. So many Europeans, especially Portuguese and Netherlanders, had been trading, fighting, ruling, and evangelizing in the East Indies for so long a time before the fire piston is found in Europe, that it is hard to believe that the Malayan fire piston was not observed and reported. The realization of its potential in Europe was considerable, culminating in the diesel engine.

9. Why are such nuclear ideas sometimes not exploited in new and wider applications? What sorts of barriers prevent their diffusion? Why, at times, does what appeared to be a successful technological item fall into disuse? The history of the faggoted forging method of producing sword blades [22] may assist our thinking about such questions.

In late Roman times, north of the Alps, Celtic, Slavic, and Germanic metallurgists began to produce swords with laminations produced by welding together bundles of rods of different qualities of iron and steel, hammering the resulting strip thin, folding it over, welding it all together again, and so on. In this way a fairly long blade was produced which had the cutting qualities of steel but the toughness of iron. Although such swords were used at times by barbarian auxiliaries in the Roman army, the Roman legions never adopted them. Yet as soon as the Western Empire crumbled, the short Roman stabbing sword vanished and the laminated slashing blade alone held the field of battle. Can this conservatism in military equipment have been one reason for the failure of the Empire to stop the Germanic invasions? The Germans had adopted the new type of blade with enthusiasm, and by Carolingian times were manufacturing it in quantities in the Rhineland for export to Scandinavia and to Islam where it was much prized. Yet, although such blades were produced marginally as late as the twelfth century, for practical purposes they ceased to be used in Europe in the tenth century. Does the disappearance of such sophisticated swords indicate a decline in medieval metallurgical methods?

We should be cautious in crediting the failure of the Romans to adopt the laminated blade to pure stupidity. The legions seem normally to have fought in very close formation, shield to shield. In such a situation, only a stabbing sword could be effective. The Germans at times used a "shield wall" formation, but it was probably a bit more open than the Roman and permitted use of a slashing sword. If the Romans had accepted the new weapon, their entire drill and discipline would have been subject to revision. Unfortunately, we lack studies of the development of Byzantine weapons sufficiently detailed to let us judge whether, or to what extent, the vigorously surviving Eastern Roman Empire adapted itself to the new military technology.

The famous named swords of Germanic myth, early medieval epic and Wagnerian opera were laminated blades. They were produced by the vast patience and skill of smiths who themselves became legendary. Why did they cease to be made in any number after the tenth century? The answer is found in the rapid increase in the weight of European armor as a result of the consistent Frankish elaboration of the type of mounted shock combat made possible by the stirrup. After the turn of the millenium a sword in Europe had to be very nearly a club with sharp edges: the best of the earlier blades was ineffective against such defenses. The faggoted method of forging blades survived and reached its technical culmination in Japan [23] where, thanks possibly to the fact that archery remained socially appropriate to an aristocrat, mounted shock combat was less emphasized than in Europe and armor remained lighter.

10. Let us now turn to a different problem connected with the act of invention. How do methods develop by the transfer of ideas from one device to another? The origins of the cannon ball and the cannon may prove instructive.[24]

Hellenistic and Roman artillery was activated by the torsion of cords. This was reasonably satisfactory for summer campaigns in the Mediterranean basin, but north of the Alps and in other damper climates the cords tended to lose their resilience. In 1004 A. D. a radically different type of artillery appeared in China with the name *huo p'ao*. It consisted of a large sling-beam pivoted on a frame and actuated by men pulling in unison on ropes attached to the short end of the beam away from the sling. It first appears outside China in a Spanish Christian illumination of the early twelfth century, and from this one might assume diffusion through Islam. But its second appearance is in the northern Crusader army attacking Lisbon in 1147 where a battery of them were operated by shifts of one hundred men for each. It would seem that the Muslim defenders were quite unfamiliar with the new engine of destruction and soon capitulated. This invention, therefore, appears to have reached the West from China not through Islam but directly across Central Asia. Such a path of diffusion is the more credible because by the end of the same century the magnetic needle likewise arrived in the West by the northern route, not as an instrument of navigation but as a means of ascertaining the meridian, and Western Islam got the compass from Italy.[25] When the new artillery arrived in the West it had lost its name. Because of structural analogy, it took on a new name borrowed from a medieval instrument of torture, the ducking stool or *trebuchetum*.

Whatever its merits, the disadvantages of the *huo p'ao* were the amount of man-power required to operate it and the fact that since the gang pulling the ropes would never pull with exactly the same speed and force, missiles could not be aimed with great accuracy. The problem was solved by substituting a huge counterweight at the short end of the sling-beam for the ropes pulled by men. With this device a change in the weight of the caisson of stones or earth, or else a shift of the weight's position in relation to the pivot, would modify the range of the projectile and then keep it uniform, permitting concentration of fire on one spot in the fortifications to be breeched. Between 1187 and 1192 an Arabic treatise written in Syria for Saladin mentions not only Arab, Turkish, and Frankish forms of the primitive trebuchet, but also credits to Iran the invention of the trebuchet with swinging caisson. This ascription, however, must be in error; for from c. 1220 onward oriental sources frequently call this engine *magribī*, i. e., "Western." Moreover, while the counterweight artillery has not yet been documented for Europe before 1199, it quickly displaced the older forms of artillery in the West, whereas this new and more effective type of siege machinery became dominant in the Mameluke army only in the second half of the thirteenth century. Thus the trebuchet with counterweights would appear to be a European improvement on the *huo p'ao*. Europe's debt to China was repaid in 1272 when, if we may believe Marco Polo, he and a German technician, helped by a Nestorian Christian, delighted the Great Khan by building trebuchets which speedily reduced a besieged city.

But the very fact that the power of a trebuchet could be so nicely regulated impelled Western military engineers to seek even greater exactitude in artillery attack. They quickly saw that until the weight of projectiles and their friction with the air could be kept uniform, artillery aim would still be variable. As a result, as early as 1244 stones for trebuchets were being cut in the royal arsenals of England calibrated to exact specifications established by an engineer: in other words, the cannon ball before the cannon.

The germinal idea of the cannon is found in the metal tubes from which, at least by the late ninth century, the Byzantines had been shooting Greek fire. It may be that even that early they were also shooting rockets of Greek fire, propelled by the expansion of gases, from bazooka-like metal tubes. When, shortly before 673, the Greek-speaking Syrian refugee engineer Callinicus invented Greek fire, he started the technicians not only of Byzantium but also of Islam, China, and eventually the West in search of ever more combustible mixtures. As chemical methods improved, the saltpeter often used in these compounds became purer, and combustion tended toward explosion. In the thirteenth century one finds, from the Yellow Sea to the Atlantic, incendiary bombs, rockets, firecrackers, and fireballs shot from tubes like Roman candles. The flame and roar of all this has made it marvellously difficult to ascertain just when gunpowder artillery, shooting hard missiles from metal tubes, appeared. The first secure evidence is a famous English illumination of 1327 showing a vase-shaped cannon discharging a giant arrow. Moreover, our next certain reference to a gun, a " pot de fer à traire garros de feu " at Rouen in 1338, shows how long it took for technicians to realize that the metal tube, gunpowder, and the calibrated trebuchet missile could be combined. However, iron shot appear at Lucca in 1341; in 1346 in England there were two calibres of lead shot; and balls appear at Toulouse in 1347.

The earliest evidence of cannon in China is extant examples of 1356, 1357, and 1377. It is not necessary to assume the miracle of an almost simultaneous independent Chinese invention of the cannon: enough Europeans were wandering the Yuan realm to have carried it eastward. And it is very strange that the Chinese did not develop the cannon further, or develop hand guns on its analogy. Neither India nor Japan knew cannon until the sixteenth century when they arrived from

Europe. As for Islam, despite several claims to the contrary, the first certain use of gunpowder artillery by Muslims comes from Cairo in 1366 and Alexandria in 1376; by 1389 it was common in both Egypt and Syria. Thus there was roughly a forty-year lag in Islam's adoption of the European cannon.

Gunpowder artillery, then, was a complex invention which synthesized and elaborated elements drawn from diverse and sometimes distant sources. Its impact upon Europe was equally complex. Its influences upon other areas of technology such as fortification, metallurgy, and the chemical industries are axiomatic, although they demand much more exact analysis than they have received. The increased expense of war affected tax structures and governmental methods; the new mode of fighting helped to modify social and political relationships. All this has been self-evident for so long a time that perhaps we should begin to ask ourselves whether the obvious is also the true.

For example, it has often been maintained that a large part of the new physics of the seventeenth century sprang from concern with military ballistics. Yet there was continuity between the thought of Galileo or Newton and the fundamental challenge to the Aristotelian theory of impetus which appeared in Franciscus de Marchia's lectures at the University of Paris in the winter of 1319-20,[26] seven years before our first evidence of gunpowder artillery. Moreover, the physicists both of the fourteenth and of the seventeenth centuries were to some extent building upon the criticisms of Aristotle's theory of motion propounded by Philoponus of Alexandria in the age of Justinian, a time when I can detect no new technological stimulus to physical speculation. While most scientists have been aware of current technological problems, and have often talked in terms of them, both science and technology seem to have enjoyed a certain autonomy in their development.

It may well be that continued examination will show that many of the political, economic, and social as well as intellectual developments in Europe which have traditionally been credited to gunpowder artillery were in fact taking place for quite different reasons. But we know of one instance in which the introduction of firearms revolutionized an entire society: Japan.[27]

Metallurgical skills were remarkably high in Japan when, in 1543, the Portuguese brought both small arms and cannon to Kyushu. Japanese craftsmen quickly learned from the gunsmiths of European ships how to produce such weapons, and within two or three years were turning them out in great quantity. Military tactics and castle construction were rapidly revised. Nobunaga and his successor, Hideyoshi, seized the new technology of warfare and utilized it to unify all Japan under the shogunate. In Japan, in contrast to Europe, there is no ambiguity about the consequences of the arrival of firearms.

But from this fact we must be careful not to argue that the European situation is equally clear if only we would see it so.

11. In examining the origins of gunpowder artillery, we have seen that its roots are multiple, but that all of them (save the European name *trebuchet*) lie in the soil of military technology. It would appear that each area of technology has a certain self-contained quality: borrowings across craft lines are not as frequent as might be expected. Yet they do occur, if exceptionally. A case in point is the fusee.

In the early fifteenth century clock makers tried to develop a portable mechanical timepiece by substituting a spring drive for the weight which powered stationary clocks. But this involved entirely new problems of power control. The weight on a clock exerted equal force at all times, whereas a spring exerts less force in proportion as it uncoils. A new escapement was therefore needed which would exactly compensate for this gradual diminution of power in the drive.

Two solutions were found, the stackfreed and the fusee, the latter being the more satisfactory. Indeed, a leading historian of horology has said of the fusee: "Perhaps no problem in mechanics has ever been solved so simply and so perfectly." [28] The date of its first appearance is much in debate, but we have a diagram of it from 1477. [29] The fusee equalizes the changing force of the mainspring by means of a brake of gut or fine chain which is gradually wound spirally around a conical axle, the force of the brake being dependent upon the leverage of the radius of the cone at any given point and moment. It is a device of great mechanical elegance. Yet the idea did not originate with the clock makers: they borrowed it from the military engineers. In Konrad Keyser's monumental, but still unpublished, treatise on the technology of warfare, *Bellifortis*, completed c. 1405, we find such a conical axle in an apparatus for spanning a heavy crossbow. [30] With very medieval humor, this machine was called "the virgin," presumably because it offered least resistance when the bow was slack and most when it was taut.

*   *   *   *   *

In terms of eleven specific technological acts, or sequences of acts, we have been pondering an abstraction, the act of technological innovation. It is quite possible that there is no such thing to ponder. The analysis of the nature of creativity is one of the chief intellectual commitments of our age. Just as the old unitary concept of "intelligence" is giving way to the notion that the individual's mental capacity consists of a large cluster of various and varying factors mutually affecting each other, so "creativity" may well be a lot of things and not one thing.

Thirteenth century Europe invented the sonnet as a poetic form and the functional button [31] as a means of making civilized life more nearly possible in boreal climes. Since most of us are educated in terms of traditional humanistic presuppositions, we value the sonnet but think that a button is just a button. It is doubtful whether the chilly northerner who invented the button could have invented the sonnet then being produced by his contemporaries in Sicily. It is equally doubtful whether the type of talent required to invent the rhythmic and phonic relationships of the sonnet-pattern is the type of talent needed to perceive the spatial relationships of button and buttonhole. For the button is not obvious until one has seen it, and perhaps not even then. The Chinese never adopted it: they got no further than to adapt the tie-cords of their costumes into elaborate loops to fit over cord-twisted knobs. When the Portuguese brought the button to Japan, the Japanese were delighted with it and took over not only the object itself but also its Portuguese name. Humanistic values, which have been cultivated historically by very specialized groups in quite exceptional circumstances, do not encompass sufficiently the observable human values. The billion or more mothers who, since the thirteenth century, have buttoned their children snugly against winter weather might perceive as much of spirituality in the button as in the sonnet and feel more personal gratitude to the inventor of the former than of the latter. And the historian, concerned not only with art forms but with population, public health, and what S. C. Gilfillan long ago identified as "the coldward course" of culture,[32] must not slight either of these very different manifestations of what would seem to be very different types of creativity.

There is, indeed, no reason to believe that technological creativity is unitary. The unknown Syrian who, in the first century B. C., first blew glass was doing something vastly different from his contemporary who was building the first water-powered mill. For all we now know, the kinds of ability required for these two great innovations are as different as those of Picasso and Einstein would seem to be.

The new school of physical anthropologists who maintain that *Homo* is *sapiens* because he is *faber*, that his biological differentiation from the other primates is best understood in relation to tool making, are doubtless exaggerating a provocative thesis. *Homo* is also *ludens*, *orans*, and much else. But if technology is defined as the systematic modification of the physical environment for human ends, it follows that a more exact understanding of technological innovation is essential to our self-knowledge.

REFERENCES

[1] (Oxford, 1954-58).

[2] Cf. the symposium in *Technology and Culture*, I (1960), 299-414.

[3] E. G. Gudde, *California Place Names*, 2nd ed. (Berkeley and Los Angeles, 1960), 52; A. L. Kroeber, "Elements of Culture in Native California," in *The California Indians*, ed. R. F. Heizer and M. A. Whipple (Berkeley and Los Angeles, 1951), 12-13.

[4] E. Zilsel, *Die Entstehung des Geniebegriffes* (Tübingen, 1926).

[5] E. S. G. Robinson, "The Date of the Earliest Coins," *Numismatic Chronicle*, 6th ser., XVI (1956), 4, 8, arbitrarily dates the first coinage c. 640-630 B. C. allowing "the Herodotean interval of a generation" for its diffusion from Lydia to the Ionian cities. But, considering the speed with which coinage appears even in India and China, such an interval is improbable.

D. Kagan, "Pheidon's Aeginetan Coinage," *Transactions and Proceedings of the American Philological Association*, XCI (1960), 121-136, tries to date the first coinage at Aegina before c. 625 B. C. when, he believes, Pheidon died; but the argument is tenuous. The tradition that Pheidon issued a coinage is late, and may well be no more than another example of the Greek tendency to invent culture-heroes. The date of Pheidon's death is uncertain: the belief that he died c. 625 rests solely on the fact that he is not mentioned by Strabo in connection with the war of c. 625-600 B. C.; but if Pheidon, then a very old man, was killed in a revolt of 620 (cf. Kagan's note 21) his participation in this long war would have been so brief and ineffective that Strabo's silence is intelligible.

[6] H. Diels, *Fragmente der Vorsokratiker*, 6th ed. (Berlin, 1951), 171 (B. 90).

[7] The story of the apple is authentic: Newton himself told William Stukeley that when "the notion of gravitation came into his mind [it] was occasion'd by the fall of an apple, as he sat in a contemplative mood"; cf. I. B. Cohen, "Newton in the Light of Recent Scholarship," *Isis*, LI (1960), 490.

[8] The materials on pennons, and other baffles behind the blade of a lance, are found in L. White, jr., *Medieval Technology and Social Change*, (Oxford, 1962), 8, 33, 147, 157.

[9] See the classic work of Ernst Kantorowicz, *The King's Two Bodies*, (Princeton, 1957).

[10] W. Treue, *Kulturgeschichte der Schraube*, (Munich, 1955), 39-43, 57, 109.

[11] F. M. Feldhaus, *Die Technik der Vorzeit, der Geschichtlichen Zeit und der Naturvölker*, (Leipzig, 1914), 984-987.

[12] E. Treptow, "Der älteste Bergbau und seiner Hilfsmittel," *Beiträge zur Geschichte der Technik und Industrie*, VIII (1918), 181, fig. 48; C. N. Bromehead, "Ancient Mining Processes as Illustrated by a Japanese Scroll," *Antiquity*, XVI (1942), 194, 196, 207.

[13] For a detailed history of the crank, cf. White, *op. cit.*, 103-115.

[14] A. R. Hall, "The Military Inventions of Guido da Vigevano," *Actes du VIIIe Congrès International d'Histoire des Sciences*, (Florence, 1958), 966-969.

[15] Bibliothèque Nationale, MS latin 11015, fols. 49^r, 51^v, 52^v. Singer, *op. cit.*, II, figs. 594 and 659, illustrates the first and third of these, but with wrong indications of folio numbers.

[16] H. T. Horwitz, "Uber die Entwicklung der Fahigkeit zum Antreib des Kurbelmechanismus," *Geschichtsblätter fur Technik und Industrie*, XI (1927), 30-31.

[17] White, *op. cit.*, 104 and fig. 4. For what may be a slightly earlier specimen, now in the Seattle Art Museum, see the catalogue of the exhibition *Arts of the Han Dynasty* (New York, 1961), No. 11, of the Chinese Art Society of America.

[18] I am so informed by Dr. Paul Leser of the Hartford Theological Foundation.

[19] L. Makkai, in *Agrártörténeti Szemle*, I (1957), 42.

[20] P. Leser, "Plow Complex; Culture Change and Cultural Stability," in *Man and Cultures: Selected Papers of the Fifth International Congress of Anthropological and Ethnological Sciences*, ed. A. F. C. Wallace (Philadelphia, 1960), 295.

[21] H. Balfour, "The Fire Piston," in *Anthropological Essays Presented to E. B. Tylor*, (Oxford, 1907), 17-49.

[22] É. Salin, *La Civilisation Mérovingienne*, III (Paris, 1957), 6, 55-115.

[23] C. S. Smith, "A Metallographic Examination of Some Japanese Sword Blades," *Quaderno 11 del Centro per la Storia della Metallurgia*, (1957), 42-68.

[24] White, *op. cit.*, 96-103, 165.

[25] *Ibid.*, 132.

[26] A. Maier, *Zwei Grundprobleme der scholastischen Naturphilosophie*, 2nd ed. (Rome, 1951), 165, n. 11.

[27] D. M. Brown, "The Impact of Firearms on Japanese Warfare, 1543-98," *Far Eastern Quarterly*, VII (1948), 236-253.

[28] G. Baillie, *Watches*, (London, 1929), 85.

[29] Singer, *op. cit.*, III, fig. 392.

[30] Göttingen University Library, Cod. phil. 63, fol. 76^v; cf. F. M. Feldhaus, "Uber den Ursprung vom Federzug und Schnecke," *Deutsche Uhrmacher-Zeitung*, LIV (1930), 720-723.

[31] Some buttons were used in antiquity for ornament, but apparently not for warmth. The first functional buttons are found c. 1235 on the "Adamspforte" of Bamberg Cathedral, and in 1239 on a closely related relief at Bassenheim; cf. E. Panofsky, *Deutsche Plastik des 11. bis 13. Jahrhundert*, (Munich 1924), pl. 74; H. Schnitsler, "Ein unbekanntes Reiterrelief aus dem Kreise des Naumburger Meisters," *Zeitschrift des Deutschen Vereins fur Kunstwissenschaft*, I (1935), 413, fig. 13.

[32] In *The Political Science Quarterly*, XXXV (1920), 393-410.

The Technical Act

THE CHANGING TECHNICAL ACT

A. RUPERT HALL *

Modern technology seems to spring from four major roots, which I define in the order of their historical importance: the reorganization of labor, the use of machines in manufacture, the exploitation of man-made materials, and the application of new sources of energy. Each of these roots extends far back beyond the modern industrial period. There are indications of factory-like conditions of labor in the Middle Ages, perhaps even in the Roman period. Simple machines—the potter's wheel and the lathe, not to mention the plough and water-raising wheels—are almost as old as any form of civilized technology. Man-made materials like fired clay, glass, and concrete are hardly less primeval. As for new sources of energy, one (the weight of falling water) was discovered in Roman times, though it seems to have made a slow start, while a second (the force of the wind) came into common use during the high Middle Ages. The great potentialities latent in industrial technology were by no means wholly ignored in the pre-industrial age, so that any simply negative characterization of that era—that machines were not employed in manufacture, that man-made materials were not developed, and so on—would be false. For the most part, then, in defining the distinction between modern and craft technology we tend, after a little thought, to admit that it resides in multiplicity and complexity. Modern technology uses more machines and more man-made materials; both are far more complex in their nature and production than were the crude lathes and dusky glass of the pre-industrial epoch.

I shall return to this question later in order to indicate that there is a possible difference of principle implicit in the two stages of technology, though what we conventionally call the Industrial Revolution was well under way before it became clear. If such a difference of principle can be found it is obviously more significant than questions of relative multiplicity and complexity.

To begin with, however, I shall touch on the first root I mentioned, the reorganization of labor. Historians are by no means as clear as they would like to be on the relationship between the social status of the craftsman and technological change. That social structure has no

* A. Rupert Hall is Professor of History and Logic of Science at Indiana University and author of *The Scientific Revolution* (Boston, 1954).

relation at all to the demonstration of craft skills can hardly be doubted; all types of society have possessed such skills. The problem is to determine whether or not different pre-industrial societies have promoted changes in such skills and development of new ones more or less rapidly. It would be a nice task, for example, to compare the alleged sterility in new techniques often attributed to the existence of slavery with that equally associated with the conservatism of guilds of free craftsmen.

We have a laudable moral prejudice in favor of freedom. But I shall try to show, by considering first some aspects of technological history in antiquity, and then returning to the reorganization of labor associated with the beginnings of modern technology, that direction rather than pure freedom may be a condition of progress in techniques.

Direction varies in its object, and its results vary accordingly. In the relatively unfree societies of antiquity in which the craftsman might be more than a slave but still less than a citizen, direction was applied towards satisfying the wants of the few rather than the needs of the many. Weapons and armor, faience and glass, jewelry and hammerwork, fabrics and medals—the splendid objects in museums that we rightly admire as the masterpieces of ancient technology were no more typical of their respective societies than is a Rolls-Royce today. And just as a Rolls may go with a Renoir, so Pliny tells us that rich Romans vied in their ownership of costly works of craft as they did in their display of works of art; indeed the distinction was shadowy, as our language yet reminds us. Nor was this only because the painter and sculptor were craftsmen of a sort; equally the smith's and the glassblower's achievements were weighed in an aesthetic balance.

Here was one clear road *via* patronage to success and wealth; here was one sharp spur to invention. It was a road equally clear to Michelangelo and Cellini two thousand years later. However much the craftsman, the sooty empiric, was despised by philosophers in antiquity there is no reason to doubt that his finest products were cherished—and rewarded.

In contrast the prospects for bread-and-butter business were unattractive. A large part of such production took place about the hearth for the needs of the family—an ill site for invention though not an impossible one. The peasant grew his barley and tended his olives with traditional implements; his wife spun and wove. The traditional specialist crafts of the village—carpentry, tanning, blacksmithing, and potting—are intensely conservative rituals, in which changes occur over thousands of years indeed, but hardly before the eyes. The village is locked in its own self-sufficiency; it cannot market because it lacks the means to produce, and it cannot buy the means to produce because it has nothing to sell. The empty purposes of the state draw off its small surpluses and, too frequently, its human strength also.

It would be as frivolous to ask why the majority of Greeks or

Romans contributed so little to technological progress as to ask the same question of an Indian villager or an Egyptian fellahin. It was impossible that they should, except on the archaeological time scale. And it was almost as impossible that the townspeople should do so either, though there is good evidence that interesting things could occur when cities became large enough. The most commonplace of these urban techniques is that of water supply and sanitation, a form of engineering that appeared in virtually every ancient city-state. The technological problems were not very different from those that most of these states had surmounted in their efforts to furnish defense and buildings of suitable ostentation for their rulers and their gods; quarrymen could drive tunnels for water and masons construct aqueducts or sewers. Without sanitation and water supply the city would have been unbearable. But the city was—even until yesterday—perfectly bearable without modern technology; it did not require machines, or man-made materials, or new sources of energy. A city constitutes a potential mass-market but it is not necessarily supplied by mass production; on the contrary the most obvious explanation of why a city exists is that it is a place where a multitude of little tradesmen take in each other's washing. You make my shoes, and I'll make your pots.

Only for the production of food did the ancient city make any step towards mass-production, and then only late in antiquity. While the household normally ground grain to supply its own need for bread, in Rome, Pompeii, Athens, and perhaps other cities there appeared in the first century A.D. millers who invested in large rotary mills, driven first by donkeys and later by water-wheels. Although the best literary account of a complex water-mill with vertical wheel and right-angle gearing, that of Vitruvius (*temp.* Augustus), comes from Rome and although Rome was more dependent on her Tiber-driven mills than any other city, the basic invention was not made in the cities but rather in some region of swift streams, perhaps more than once. The economic peculiarity that persuaded urban populations to buy its flour ground is unknown, but the logic of the technological sequence woman-donkey-water is clear enough.

Imperial Rome was unique. But there was one other population of comparable magnitude in the Empire—the army. The army, like the city, required flour, and if it often ground its own in handmills. There was an enormous installation at Barbegal, near Arles, a cascade of paired water-mills, that was almost certainly designed to feed the troops in Gaul. The army also required wine and oil, commodities to be transported by sea in large earthenware vessels which may well have been made in handicraft factories, as may the army's shoes and weapons also. As with the Pyramids, increase in scale of production can (it seems) have been bought only by increasing the numbers of workers—except in the case of flour.

But there was one military exercise to which this simplest possible method of multiplication was hardly applicable: multiplying manpower is an ineffective way of hurling large projectiles against a fortification. The obvious first step was to take a proven device for this purpose, the bow, and enlarge it; accordingly the crossbow (which is merely a device for applying leverage against a bow too stiff for human arms to bend) was known in antiquity. A less obvious improvement upon it was the torsion catapult or *ballista*, which became the standard ordnance of the Roman forces. After the waterwheel the *ballista* was the most remarkable machine of the ancient world, about which the Greek engineers wrote far more than they did about all other machines put together.

Such machines—one for peace and one for war—were special cases. The Roman water-mill was a response to an exceptional urban economy; the *ballista* satisfied the exceptional demands of the military tactician. Neither was typical of ancient technology, no more than were Hero's ingenious mechanical toys, so pathetic an answer to the question: "What can machines do?" Making a bow in the direction of the Roman model farm, with its roller-crusher and screw-press, one has to move indoors to glimpse the true excellence of ancient technology. Here the effect of the direction from above that I mentioned just now becomes evident in superb furniture, fine pottery and glass, glorious textiles. The effect of a thousand years and more of technological advance was above all manifest in magnificent interior decorating. I am far from suggesting that this was a product of deliberate choice, or of the oppression of the poor by the rich—though this occurred. Nor had it anything to do with the free or servile status of the craftsman. It was simply a question of what was possible and what impossible. Just as the Roman could, and did, borrow the secrets of sericulture from the Chinese whereas he could never have borrowed the secrets of making cellulose acetate even had they been accessible to him, so he could devise or borrow a loom on which to make brocades although the plans of an automatic loom would have availed him nothing. Luxurious productions of certain kinds, which require only much time and patience in addition to the possession of basically simple empirical skills, are possible when the manufacture of cast steel by the ton or of barrels of petroleum is quite impossible. And the converse is, of course, equally true.

Thus a non-industrial society, until it begins to transcend its own limitations (as Rome did with the water-mill), is compelled to follow a single line of development, towards the perfection of craft into art. Improvement of technique in this sense consists in the production of fewer, finer pieces; it cannot entail the multiplication of indifferent, serviceable goods. In some instances, of course—as with the Japanese sword-blades studied by C. S. Smith—increased utility is fully commensurate with the attainment of the artistic effect upon which the effort is expended, though a gaspipe musket may well be a better weapon than a samurai sword. But for the most part beauty was the sole reward, since the most exquisite product of pre-industrial technology, a porcelain cup, holds water no better than a plastic monstrosity at whose birth the whole might of industrial civilization has presided.

How is this progress of pre-industrial technology towards perfection and from perfection to decadence transcended—or more accurately, how was it once transcended, in Europe? Partly by accident, for it seems sheerest political accident that Rome became mistress of the world and so for devious reasons the home of the first prime-mover and the first manufacturing machine. Similarly it was sheer accident that western Europe was overrun by forest peoples with remote eastern connections, who brought with them such odd but useful things as soap, beer, and barrels to keep it in.

Partly it was because the new peoples of Europe—rough, warlike, seafaring—thrust aside the urbane civilization that Rome had extended to Britain and the Rhine; they by no means despised its products, which they continued to import from the East, but they supported no class of superior native craftsmen. Their ingenuity turned not to the exquisite but to the useful. The close of the so-called Dark Ages found them already master of such simple but crucial inventions as the horse-collar, the flail, and the crank. If the crafts of Europe in the tenth century were, for the most part, crude rather than elegant, they were certainly far from stagnant.

To introduce an ethnological explanation at this point would be meretricious. The truth is rather that while the ancient empires seem to have suffered from over-population (or, which is the same thing, incapacity to organize their populations productively), medieval Europe experienced under-population. At least this was so in certain cyclical phases, periods in which (for instance) labor-services in agriculture were strictly enforced, contrary to the secular trend towards their commutation into money payments. Manorial lords kept a shrewd eye on the management of their estates, for they were not absentee town-dwellers cultivating civilized amenities. It was their policy, again, not the natural course of technological development, that ensured the spread of the water- and wind-mill across Europe; the seigneurial mill was a source of revenue, and the villeins who would have preferred to grind their corn free of charge at their own hearths were sternly discouraged from doing so. In this case at least feudalism early favored the machine. And when in later times the manor might possibly maintain not only a corn-mill but a fulling-mill, an ironworks, or a coalmine all this was to the lord's profit, and sometimes a result of his enterprise. Thus, very gradually, production for commerce of coarse essential commodities like foodstuffs, hides, iron and tin, salt and stone, wool and cloth, became the basis for prosperity, a fact clearly seen by the English kings, for example, in their fiscal policies. Some of the old village manufactures were becoming staples of international trade, and, it seems, the thrust of technological innovation began to shift, accordingly, away from the refinements of objects of luxury to the quantity production of common necessities. And the deployment of labor changed also.

What happened may best be seen in the history of the religious houses, ever better managed than lay estates and enjoying the advantages of immortality. They realized early the financial merits of massive production whether, as typically in England, of wool, or as in some of the French monasteries, of manufactures. In due course the latter evolved, as means suggested themselves, into proto-factories making large use of water power. For the religious had the security of continuity in their entrepreneurial ventures, and if they lived under a conscientious injunction against idleness they were intelligent enough (as Lynn White has pointed out) to understand, like Tibetans, that wheels can pray. There is much evidence (not least under the name of Theophilus Presbyter) to remind us that there was also religious skill in the more delicate crafts dedicated to the glory of God; but it was their output of crude wares that made the monasteries wealthy.

In a sense the very crudity of European manufacture created the opportunity for technological innovation, the same opportunity for the multiplication of serviceable, unpretentious articles that this country enjoyed in the eighteenth and early nineteenth centuries. While Europe was for so long inferior to the East in the more subtle handicrafts—sericulture and figured weaving, the blending of steel, the glazing of faience, and so forth—just as it also lacked such varieties of food as sugar, rice and citrus fruits which were known in the Levant, nevertheless it was running ahead in methods of basic production. The East continued to excel and even to advance further in those difficult manufactures which of necessity could only be practiced by a few rare craftsmen; the West was pushing ahead with manufactures that lent themselves to mechanization and quantity production. Here were two kinds of technological development strongly contrasted. Slowly but inexorably in the West commerce supplanted household manufacture (though centuries were to pass before the latter died out altogether), and commerce was supplied by highly organized textile industries, leather trades, metal-working, and so on, which by the end of the Middle Ages had confirmed their specialized skills by the use of water power in such operations as fulling cloth, sawing timber, or hammering wrought iron. As a consequence when the more artistic crafts did begin to flourish in Europe from the fourteenth century onwards, these were too practiced on a relatively large scale, virtually in factory units which employed water power for reeling silk at Florence or turning the potters' wheels at Deruta. In Western Europe even the luxury trades were from the first tinged by the notion of quantity production.

Given the profit motive and commerce as a means of exchange, the use of machinery furnished one way of swelling the volume of production while reducing relative costs. Yet although the machine was important it was not the only factor making for technical change, nor could it have exercised a decisive effect unless certain conditions had prevailed. Machinery required both the organization of labor into relatively large units and craft specialization. If every joiner sawed his own timber the sawmill would be unprofitable, just as the fulling-mill could only be economic when fulling had become an independent stage in the manufacture of cloth. Such a specialization, with direct gains in efficiency, had in fact already proceeded far before mechanization had seriously affected medieval industry. There was a consistent medieval tendency for every distinct technique to become identified with a separate craft guild, resulting it is true in some economic wastefulness (since the same material had to be transported from one little workshop to another), but with at least a potential gain in technological efficiency. Whenever one or more stages in the whole process could be mechanized this potential gain could be fully realized.

This organization of manufacture was the essential foundation for technological improvements tending towards mass-production. In fact it contained the germ of the reorganization of labor that was the distinguishing feature of the first stages of the classical industrial revolution. Already before the end of the Middle Ages the type-figure of guild craftsmanship, the independent master, was an evanescent figure; a large proportion of the whole volume of production came from the hands of wage earners or pieceworkers. It remained only to assemble a body of such workers under one roof to constitute a factory, a step taken in the cloth trade as early as the sixteenth century. The reorganization was complete when, within the factory, the medieval fractioning of trades was extended into that division of labor applauded by Adam Smith as the foundation of modern industry.

When Adam Smith wrote it was still possible to underestimate the significance of technical change, of new machines and new processes. Then the scale of the new industries—London brewing, Wedgwood's Etruria, or the hammer trades of the Black Country—was more impressive than their technical differentiation from what had gone before. The technology of the era just before Watt (as we see it for example in Diderot's *Encyclopédie*), itself the product of more than a century of fairly rapid evolution, was already well advanced towards mechanization and infiltrated by new processes. The late seventeenth and eighteenth centuries were accustomed to technological progress—had striven consciously to accelerate it—so that what was impressive about 1780 was less novelty in manufacture than its new magnitude, and the orderly management of its massive labor force. This was the firm foundation on which future engineers and chemists were to build.

It is true that the history of industry is distinct from that of machines and processes. But the two constantly interlock. If one may postulate a secular spirit of commercial expansiveness (the expectation that increased profits will follow from increased production), then it is a fair assumption that such a spirit will stimulate both the rational organization of labor *and* the substitution of more efficient means for less efficient—including the replacement of men by machines. These two tendencies are complementary rather than antithetic. Modern technology does require the factory rather than the handicraft system, and vice-versa. High production requires less wasteful and quicker methods: when a mine produces hundreds of tons per week a horse-pump is no longer good enough; when bleaching hundreds of pieces at a time an efficient replacement for sunlight and sour milk must be found.

For these reasons, it seems, the conscious search for inventions, for improvements in the "technical act," is much older in Europe than is customarily recognized. As I indicated at the beginning, the roots of modern technology are implicit in pre-industrial manufacture; in the Middle Ages they were not yet clearly distinguished and the aim of material progress was still confused, and even mingled with mysticism and magic. Yet by the fifteenth century there is indisputable evidence that there were men possessing a firm notion of what technological progress is, and of how to forward it. It is hard to believe, for example, that the clock escapement of the fourteenth century was other than a mechanism deliberately designed as a unity by some anonymous inventor, as were the paddle-wheel boat and the less successful windmill-car. As for later times, the purposeful ingenuity of the sixteenth and seventeenth centuries is too obvious to require demonstration, while the ideal of technological progress was (among other things) formulated once for all by Francis Bacon.

In so far as we are entitled to draw any inference about the direction given to technological progress by Bacon explicitly and by anonymous and known inventors implicitly, it seems to be of a constant kind: towards the amelioration of human life, as Bacon said, by mastering new natural powers and reducing the burden of human labor. J. U. Nef particularly has brought out the sense in which the coal-burning revolution of sixteenth and seventeenth century England consistently favored the massive production of somewhat indifferent goods; English glass was never as fine as the Venetian; nor was coal-smelted iron as excellent as the charcoal-smelted Swedish metal. This development Nef has contrasted with that occurring in contemporary France, where court and nobility encouraged not the great producers but the most skilled and artistic craftsmen—glass-blowers and mirror-polishers, gilders and turners, tapestry- and lace-makers, porcelain makers, and so on. For seventeenth century France, partly through the policy of Richelieu and Colbert, continued that naturalization and extension of fine craftsmanship begun some centuries before in Italy, where the crafts of elegance had flowered during the Renaissance.

Nef's antithesis is just; it defines exactly the distinction between the art of technology (which has prospered in many forms, in many societies, at different times) and that particular path of technological evolution which Europe alone has followed, aiming steadily at quantity production and reduction of labor. Nef seems to me mistaken, however, in his assumption that this distinction appeared for the first time in Elizabethan England and was associated with coal-burning. In my view, rather, it is traceable through medieval technology and is linked first with mechanization. Instead, then, it was the reappearance in Renaissance Italy of the art of technology as the ideal of industry that should be considered the aberration, which the French pursued and the cruder English avoided.

What, once more, were the salient characteristics of the medieval technical advance? First, a relatively heavy (though still inadequate) production of foodstuffs with an emphasis on grains and fish, combined with the improvement of methods of preservation. Secondly, a more lavish exploitation of mineral resources, of such metals as iron, tin, copper, zinc, and even mercury; of coal, beginning in the thirteenth century; and later still of clay, as earthenware and bricks. Deposits of fuller's earth, chalk, alum, vitriol, sulphur, and other chemicals were also actively worked. Nor should the northwestern European abundance of sound large timber be forgotten, as it was essential to shipbuilding, housing, and industry. Lastly there was the development of machinery, for which again wood provided the major material. The historical origins of the medieval technical tradition are to be found in the ancient empires (whose heritage did not survive entire) and in the native methods of the Germanic peoples; its modifications are to be traced partly to borrowings from the East, still more to indigenous invention.

It is when we consider this last—invention—that we hit upon the great defect of medieval technology. Completely lacking a *rationale* it could proceed only blindly, the inventor working by analogy, or upon the bases of crude and casual observation, or by sheer chance. As had been the case throughout the whole course of human history hitherto, there was no body of knowledge nor set of substantiated theories to which the technologist could appeal for guidance or suggestion. Even to speak of " a technologist " in a pre-nineteenth century context is an anachronism, since until then a man who had both a practical knowledge of any one craft and a wide general knowledge, or even literacy, was a rare being. Craft knowledge was craft secret, and as a potential innovator the craftsman suffered not only from lack of familiarity with any theoretical notions that might be abroad, but from the teaching of an ingrained, narrow specialization that there was only one possible way of doing things rightly.

The remoteness of the possibility that major technical improvements will be hit upon by chance or even through pursuit of analogies was sufficiently stressed by Sir Francis Bacon some 350 years ago. It may be less obvious, however, that nullity of theoretical insight is far more hampering to the radical, utilitarian development of technology upon the three roots I have mentioned before than it is to the refinement of the art of technology. Yet if it were not so it would be difficult to explain either why masterpieces of craftsmanship have been produced by primitive techniques, or why, when we seek to emulate such work today, we must turn to the few remaining exponents of such craft skills. The point is identical with that made in connection with the progress of technology in antiquity. Empiricism can culminate in a Ming vase; it can never culminate in a plastic cup. The difference is perhaps like that between a poet and a philologist, or a calculating prodigy and a mathematician. The nature of things just is such that hazard or trial-and-error can confer mastery of some techniques but not that of others. It is true that empirical techniques may involve obscure physiochemical properties and hence require sophisticated scientific theory for their explanation; nevertheless they are always operationally rather simple and in general controllable by fairly straightforward tests. Now, considering the three roots of modern technology, it is manifest that in each respect the limits of empiricism are soon reached. When the design of machinery is wholly unaided by theory its products are clumsy, inefficient, and slow; analysis of the action of machines is essential to the realization of their full potential. Moreover machine-building is dependent on the other two roots, and that new materials and new sources of power require for their realization some command of physics and chemistry can hardly be doubted.

If this account is correct, then, it should be possible to predict that most developed societies will make some progress along each of the three material roots of modern technology but that their progress will cease unless, at some point, it becomes possible for the society to draw upon theoretical, scientific knowledge. At that point it should be possible to discern, in a fully successful society, the transition of empirical craftsmanship into applied science. This is the difference in principle that I mentioned at the beginning.

Such a prediction is verifiable. Advanced, non-scientific societies like those of the ancient world, of China and of medieval Europe did make progress along these three roots; each made some use of machines for production, for example, but all failed to construct precisely engineered, high-speed machines. Their machinery was cumbersome and inefficient, although these societies could (for instance) make excellent castings in bronze. Conversely, we can clearly trace certain critical steps in early modern technological history to the influence of science: in the devising of the steam engine, for example, and in the chemical industry. The confirmation of this tendency since the seventeenth century requires no emphasis. Verification of the prediction upon the European scene is complicated by the rough equality between the rates of development of science and technology between (say) 1500 and 1800. It is the more difficult to weigh the impact of the former upon the latter because science was becoming mature precisely at the moment when techniques were reaching the limits of empiricism. To give an example: did Watt's separate condenser owe anything to Black's discovery of latent heat? The engineer denied the scientist's claim that it did. And while it is true that Black's researches might have assisted Watt, it is no less true that Watt could—and probably did —by very plausible reasoning have hit upon his solution for the imperfection of the Newcomen engine without possessing Black's theoretical formulation of the reason for it. As is well known, practical thermodynamics (if I may so put it) was to remain for another generation ahead of the theoretical science.

The late eighteenth century was the point in time at which the curve of diminishing returns from pure empiricism dipped to meet the curve of increasing returns from applied science. This point we can fix fairly exactly, and so we may be sure that if science had stopped dead with Newton, technology would have halted with Rennie, or thereabouts. The great advances of later nineteenth century technology owe everything to post-Newtonian science. If this may be agreed, then it will follow that a limit for a purely empirical technology will be roughly the level of Agricola. As even sixteenth century technology had some indebtedness to the theoretical frame of mind, perhaps even this is an over-optimistic guess. For, in the first place, even pre-industrial engineering owed something to geometry. In particular the idea of proportion (at root aesthetic) becomes in the engineering context mathematical: one might say that engineering is the Pythagorean craft. Hence Greek engineers described the construction of a *ballista* not in absolute measures but in proportions, in much the same way that Greek architects prescribed proportions for buildings. Again, it is a plausible guess that at least some mechanical devices—the screw, the gear, perhaps the cam and tappet, and the piston and cylinder combination—were of theoretical rather than craft origin. The possibility that intellectual curiosity exerted some minor influence on agricultural practices cannot be excluded either. Whether the chemical crafts borrowed in any serious sense from theoretical concern with the transformation of substances depends so largely upon the definition of alchemy as science or craft that the question is highly dubious; but a strong case has been made out for considering distillation, at least, as a gift of the philosophers to the artisans. Certainly it is indisputable that in later times seafaring was constantly infused by scientifically-derived techniques of navigation, quite apart from its dependence upon mathematical cartography. Thus the indebtedness of the late medieval world to its intellectual history in many aspects of its material civilization is unquestionable, though indeed the specific contribution that learning and science had made, as contrasted with that of generations of unlettered craftsmen, was as yet pitifully small.

How far did the situation change in the next three centuries, from the sixteenth century to the time the cross-over point and the heyday of the classical industrial revolution have been reached, or passed? The beginning of the modern age coincided with the lifetime of Leonardo da Vinci, whom some authorities have judged to be one of the greatest mechanical geniuses of all time, although his inventiveness had little or no practical effect. In the next generation Biringuccio and Agricola wrote elaborate accounts of mechanical devices, mining, metallurgy and chemical industry; the succeeding generation again brought in the machine-books of Ramelli, Zonca, and others. Emphatically, technology had emerged out of darkness—which, by the way, the recent more intensive study of medieval sources has proved was never complete. Agricola clearly perceived that practical men, miners, mechanicians, workmen engaged in chemical processes, had a more intimate and deeper knowledge of nature than the cabinet-philosophers. This was to be a major didactic theme of the following century; it is perhaps needless to add that in a more limited way Paracelsus had taken the same line even earlier. At the same time Agricola made occasional rather diffident attempts to rationalize for his readers the accounts of his crude, suffering artisans; there were a few times when he felt that he had a theoretical command over his material. Yet for the most part Agricola was content, like all the other technological writers of the sixteenth century, to describe rather than interpret, and this reflects no discredit upon them, when even Galileo confessed that he was troubled to explain many mechanical practices and observations.

None of these writers was a major innovator; the anonymity of technological development was to endure into the seventeenth century. While we note the significant attention of these writers to the essentials—power (of wind and water), mechanization, and chemical techniques—we note too their humility. Their emphasis was still on the present fruits of the ingenuity of craftsmanship and on its future promise; they did not foresee technical improvement as the consequence of a superior intellectual system. That more audacious claim followed upon the first successes of the scientific revolution in the seventeenth century, marching with the new philosophers' assertion of a knowledge of nature that was certain because experimental and mathematical. Bacon's proclamation of the technological utility of science was echoed through his century and reflected in attempts to solve the problem of determining longitude at sea, programs for agricultural reform, a very few attempts to apply mathematical analysis to machines, endeavors to treat problems of river control and land drainage scientifically, interest in the art of war (especially ballistics), and above all in the continued effort to perfect medicine through chemical and biological investigations.

These were noble ambitions though their immediate fruits were small. So many problems, even mechanical ones, defied the feeble tools of young science; so many of its recommendations were vainly idealistic in the then state of manufacture and agriculture. Curiously enough the internal displacement occurring at this time within techniques that has commanded most attention since—the substitution of coal for wood as a fuel in northwestern Europe—was almost completely missed by the scientists. At a time of many patents for " charking " of coal and for its use in the smelting of iron, this metallurgical problem too was neglected by the scientists, the first scientific study of ferrous metallurgy being Reaumur's in 1722. On the other hand the idea of rarefying matter by heat and then compelling the atmospheric pressure to do work was certainly originated among the scientific group, though the successful implementation of this idea was accomplished by practical men, Savery and Newcomen.

The fact is that seventeenth century scientists were not misled by their own fairly consistent propaganda in favor of the public support of science on the ground of its usefulness. Rather they worked toward the solution of traditional problems of planetary motion and the structure of the universe, the motions of bodies and chemical combination, physiology and embryology and so forth, so that when we speak of seventeenth century mechanics we mean not a theory of machines but a mathematical science of motion. This was well, for neither science nor technology could have flourished if Galileo, Descartes, and Newton had regarded merely " lucriferous experiments," which Bacon (to do him justice) had ranked lower than " luciferous " ones.

For in technology, despite the tremendous gains in mathematical and experimental science, the next major steps were almost as empirical as the last. It was coal that made the steam engine practicable—and it was the engineers who perceived this, and who took advantage of it. Coal, again, made cast iron available as a constructional material, through the persistence of a practical smelter. The same ingenuity that had created the spinning wheel and the clock went on to devise the eighteenth century's textile machinery. And so on. The new world of eighteenth-century technology from which wood was fast vanishing was almost as scientifically unpremeditated, and indeed, almost as scientifically crude, as that which it replaced. It was a world with more power than its forerunner but hardly with more subtlety; such a world in fact as the same kind of " technical act " would create, working with coal and with iron rather than with wood. That road carriages should be placed on railroad tracks was not simply a defect of design, nor was the casting of Gothic ornament in iron merely a freak of taste; both symbolize (like the horseless broughams of the twentieth century) a deeper technological uncertainty, an ambivalent desire not so much to create a new technical act as to protract an old one into a world where it no longer belongs. There is a sense—a very extended sense admittedly—in which no small part of technology was still medieval into the early railway age—was not the railroad itself a medieval invention? The Middle Ages had cast the bronze bell and the iron gun; moreover they had set up the blacksmith as mechanician and engineer, a position from which he was not wholly displaced when the twentieth century opened. True, there were scientifically minded engineers also, like Smeaton and Watt, but on balance it seems that the main drive towards science in techniques came, at this time, from another quarter than engineering.

Here A. and N. Clow have demonstrated an excellent thesis. The late eighteenth and early nineteenth century revolution in chemical industry was a significant one, immediately and indirectly. Immediately, chiefly because it complemented the vast increase of production of textiles. Indirectly, because it began the introduction of chemcial science into industry and made possible—economically and organizationally—the greater dependence of such manufactures upon science that occurred later, with aniline dyes, explosives, synthetic drugs, and so forth. But the point to be insisted upon here is that wherever this happened—in France, England, and Scotland especially—the new processes for making acids, bleaches, soda and a few other basic chemicals were designed upon a theoretical foundation in science. A poor foundation, it is true, hence some of the early processes were mightily inefficient. But they were not accidental. They were straightforward examples of applied science, however crude, and as such hard to duplicate as yet in any other branch of technology.

To pursue the story of the application of science to industry would be to traverse familiar ground, although the details, especially in the earliest stages of uncertainty in the shift from empiricism to theoretically-based procedures, are worthy of close examination. But at least the course open to the nineteenth century is broadly clear; it could only move forward toward Edison, Parsons, and Marconi. And whatever else the science of technology produced, at least it could not cause a reversion to that art of technology which had yielded the masterpieces of earlier ages; partly because science is irrelevant to the masterpieces of craftsmanship, still more because reliance on science is only worthwhile when production is on the largest scale. Science is the best key to material progress, but it is also a costly one. Hence scientific technology has tended toward creating a rough egalitarianism of wealth and well-being in those societies in which it has flourished best, while at the same time exaggerating in that respect the disparity between such societies and others which have not learned to exploit it.

For a conclusion, this argument may be traversed backwards. Science—the body of theoretical knowledge from which it may be predicted what effects can be obtained, and by which methods—is essential to modern technology both for arriving at the point which the midtwentieth century has reached and passing beyond it. But for the possibility to exist that science may be so applied there is required, first, a certain measure of craft skill (without which, indeed, it is hardly to be imagined that science itself could have advanced to the necessary confidence) and, second, an industrial framework within which the kinds of changes that may be effected by science are not only useful but acceptable. Scientific knowledge is of little material value if the object of technological proficiency is the manufacture of objects of luxury; hence in backward contemporary societies the arbitrary installation of a few modern industrial plants, without modification of the basic economy, has little more result than to allow the rich to adopt Cadillacs and television in place of more barbarous means of ostentation. Hence the application of science to industry can only occur creatively after technological progress has become identified with the easy and copious manufacture of goods, that is, with quantity rather than quality. In Europe this shift of inventive emphasis is associated with the empirical development of power resources and of machinery, but these were not necessarily its causes. For the mere employment of some such resources and machines for even a number of productive processes is not a sufficient condition for transition to the proto-scientific or classical " industrial revolution " stage of technology (as the histories of the ancient empires and China demonstrate), though it may be a necessary condition for this transition. No less essential are the progressive reorganization of labor for quantity production and the expansive spirit in industry and commerce, to break down the stultifying effect of the village economy and the village craft and to foster that type of massively productive inventiveness that, in fact, brought Europe and Europe alone through the Middle Ages to the upper limits of empirical technology.

The Technical Act
COMMENTARY

RITCHIE CALDER *

Technology has been discussed here as the history of man, the toolmaking animal. But I would like to define technology as beginning at the point at which this toolmaking experience was taken and ordered. When the vague, sporadic and largely spontaneous technical development began to be organized, technical progress could be deliberately achieved. I agree with Alfred North Whitehead's pronouncement that the greatest invention of the nineteenth century was the invention of the method of invention. With that accomplishment the road to our present technological success was opened.

In these discussions we are looking for pointers for the projection of technology. We wish to plot our technical future, foresee its crises, and avoid its pitfalls. We are trying to chart a wide and largely unexplored area. But we have the essentials for making this projection. We perceive the direction we must take and have some understanding of today's problems through the lessons taught in the history of scientific development. As Sir Robert Watson-Watt pointed out, we are now seeking ways through the second Industrial Revolution. We can learn by going back and looking at the origins of the first.

The first Industrial Revolution generated in gatherings like the Lunar Society of Birmingham. This was a group of people who met to talk. They didn't use seminars or colloquies. There was no agenda. They assembled on the night of the full moon each month so Erasmus Darwin, Charles Darwin's grandfather, could drive back by post-chaise to Litchfield by moonlight. They called themselves the Lunar Society, and were called, inevitably, the Lunatics.

This extraordinary group included Benjamin Franklin, Erasmus Darwin, William Small, Josiah Wedgwood and Sir William Herschel, the Royal astronomer. Their discussions were completely unbuttoned. They ranged freely over any subject. This kind of interrelationship of people and ideas was the basis of the technological breakthrough. The end of the eighteenth century saw a tremendous yeasting of ideas which was not just the literal methodological development of technology. It was a surge of original thinking generated in the intellectual feedback between men like those in the Lunar Society. The society produced an environment in which this kind of thinking could develop.

The "Lunatics" were a fascinating body of men who participated in the birth of the Industrial Revolution in a curious history of interactions. William Small was a medical graduate of Edinburgh and a professor of natural philosophy at the University of Williamsburg. He was, in fact, Jefferson's professor. Jefferson has recorded that "no man so influenced my life as William Small." Small went to Birmingham to set up a medical practice with a letter from Franklin to a man

* Ritchie Calder, C. B. E., M. A., is Professor of International Relations at the University of Edinburgh. He has served the United Nations extensively as adviser to several agencies and member of Missions to Asia and the Arctic. His latest book is *After the Seventh Day* (Simon & Schuster, Inc., 1961).

named Bolton. Bolton had built a factory at Soho by the side of a stream. It was going to be a water-driven mill, but he ran into trouble because of a drought. He wanted to devise a method by which he could lift the tailrace of the stream back into the mill pond. Bolton wrote to Benjamin Franklin, then struggling with the Stamp Act, and asked for his guidance. Strangely enough Franklin was too busy. Small suggested that Bolton get hold of this fellow Watt in Glasgow. That was the introduction of Bolton to Watt and the beginning of the production of the steam engine. What is more, the steam engine would not have been possible if Wilkinson, the cannon baller, had not been a member of the Lunar Society. His lathes perfected the cylinders of the Watt steam engine.

There are many examples of the diverse impact of this society. Wedgwood contrived that Priestley be given a sinecure at Birmingham so he could conduct the experiments that eventually isolated oxygen. In Lunar Society discussions of oxidation Wedgwood realized that he needed non-ferrous clay for the white potteries of Etruria he subsequently produced. The Royal Society of London was reinvigorated by this small group. Lunar Society technologists were introduced and accepted into the jaded Royal association. In fact, Wedgwood was given his fellowship for a pyrometer. It set the Royal Society on the road toward specialization.

The atmosphere the Lunar Society provided and the relationships it fostered were essential to the initiation of technology. In those days science was free thinking and free moving. Creating similarly free conditions for the growth of scientific thought is now important to our rate of advance. More important, however, is building a solid underpinning of general scientific education to support the coming surges of technical progress.

In Britain it was unfortunately possible to develop mass production by the mechanization of illiteracy. Craftsmen or the landless proletariat could man the machines. Illiterate artisans could produce the results. Consequently the Industrial Revolution became a massive production system that neglected the scientific background that had made it possible. The relationship between science and technology was practically nonexistent. There was no technological transfer to pick up ideas and apply them.

It was a mistake Britain paid for. Once Britain had begun industrialization Europe responded with jealousy and apprehension. In Belgium the competition of British machine-made textiles caused widespread unemployment among Belgium's hand weavers. Up to 1828 the McMann Act prevented the disclosure of any technological methods to potential rivals. But the man who became King of Belgium in 1831 was Leopold I, the uncle of Queen Victoria. He was closely aware of developments in Britain and had a sharp interest in industrial development. When he assumed his kingdom he was confronted with unemployment and famine. In 1845 half a million were out of work because mass-produced linen had destroyed the hand linen trade. Leopold began public works including the building of roads and canals. The machinery required for the revival of the linen industry was introduced from Britain. Most important, primary schools were established and education was made compulsory. Technical schools and colleges and model workshops were set up and skilled instruction given in the latest methods of textile manufacture.

This breakthrough on the educational level formed the plateau for an industrial advance that leapfrogged over British development. One irony of this was that the first iron bridge built in Glasgow was built by Belgians. Britain was still going along with the mechanization of illiteracy approach to the Industrial

Revolution, while the educational breakthrough was happening all over Europe. Dyes were taken over by Germany and a whole dye and drug industry developed from it, because in Germany students dug into their classes and applied science to technology. This meant that at the first Industrial Exposition ever held Britain, who had a headstart to boast of, showed signs of being left behind. By the beginning of the century Britain was still riding high in production, but was trailing badly in the growing educational specializations.

Here we have in the lessons of the nineteenth century very profound lessons for today. Technology develops from pleateau to plateau. Its ability to make the next leap depends on the level of technical education, of training, supporting the plateau it has reached. General ignorance creates an impasse, an insurmountable obstacle to the advancement of science. Scientific education is the most important single factor in the acceleration of technological development.

But marching with scientific education must go education for control and direction. Control and direction does not mean putting the brakes upon scientific knowledge. It means exercising judgment over the development of technology. Priorities must be established to deploy our massive technological development to those things which are important, not only to man's curiosity but to man's survival. This is far more serious than the task of ensuring scientific progress. It is the paramount question we face today. For example, one big problem is to decide how technology should be handled in underdeveloped countries. We introduce these countries to higher plateaus of technology and may be precipitating them into something dangerous for their whole civilization and culture. These peoples should draw what they need for their way of life from the range and variety of technological advantages and not be subjected to what we, from our peak of advancement, think they ought to have. The problem is not one of techniques, but of understanding and direction.

The past has shown us some of the requirements of continuing scientific progress. A free and active intellectual environment is necessary for the germination of scientific ideas. Technological achievement must be supported by an ever higher general level of scientific comprehension and technical readiness. But technological success itself can carry us to disaster if it is not thoughtfully directed. It is to the problem of direction that we must turn our best talents.

The Technical Act
COMMENTARY

MELVIN KRANZBERG *

Is man the master or slave of technology? Before we can give a meaningful answer to that question we must learn more about both man and his technology. Man's self-knowledge has grown but slowly over the centuries; as for technology, we have only recently become aware of its significance and have made only the barest of beginnings in its systematic study. We know very few of the hard facts of the technical act—the motivations which impel the technologist, the creative impulses of the technical innovator, the forces which account for the acceptance or rejection of technical innovations—in brief, the what, why, and how of the technical act. Even when the facts are known there is frequently disagreement regarding their interpretation, for the area of our greatest ignorance lies in the realm of the interrelations of technological developments with society and culture.

There are two main reasons for our ignorance: one is founded upon the nature of our educational tradition; the other on the nature of technological development itself. Our education, particularly our historical education, concerns itself but little with technology, largely because our education has a classical bias. Reaching far back into Western culture, we find that Plato made a distinction between the mind and the hand: formulations of the mind were considered superior to the products of the hand. Our educational system has derived largely from the classical tradition exemplified by Plato. What might be termed snobbishness on the part of those who have written our history and who have directed our higher education has led them to regard man's technological development as something inferior to his intellectual history—as if the technical act occurred without the exercise of man's intellect!

Even when the Industrial Revolution of the eighteenth century thrust an awareness of the importance of technological development upon the consciousness of educated men very little scholarship was directed toward its investigation. Scholars, themselves products of a classical education, felt that they could not comprehend the workings of machines and hence believed themselves incapable of writing about the machine in any meaningful fashion. Only within the past few decades have scholars, both in this country and abroad, attempted to study the development of technology in a systematic fashion.

But our study of the facts of the technical process is inhibited not only by our educational tradition but also by a difficulty inherent in the nature of technological development—what we might call its "anonymity." Even if historians of an earlier period had been interested in chronicling technical development, the facts were not available. Several factors account for this. Technology developed

* Melvin Kranzberg is Professor of History and head of the Graduate Program in the History of Science and Technology at Case Institute of Technology. He is Secretary of the Society for the History of Technology and Editor-in-Chief of *Technology and Culture.*

first from an empirical, craft tradition. This was an oral tradition carried on by the lower orders of society who is most cases were illiterate and hence unable to write down the story of their technical arts. In addition, there were the requirements of secrecy; these men possessed special knowledge and skills which the requirements of the social situation kept them from broadcasting. Even when at a later date craftsmen became literate they tried to keep their secrets to themselves. In the fifteenth and sixteenth centuries, for example, inventors sought Papal letters patent so they could get credit for and profit from their inventions. But these letters patent deliberately described the inventions in extremely vague terms so as to keep the actual secret of manufacture privy to the inventor himself.

Only with the spread of the patent system in the eighteenth century did inventors actually seek publicity for their inventions. Yet even the patent system did not guarantee a supply of facts for the student. Many inventors kept their innovations secret, lest others modify and reap profits from them. At a later date came the development of the corporation, an anonymous personality which began acquiring the patents instead of the individual inventors. This, of course, left the scholar in the dark about the process through which the individual inventor actually formulated his device or technique. Finally, two factors in the current situation prevent us from knowing fully about the technical act. One of these is the requirement of military security; much technical innovation occurs under the aegis of the military and is usually kept secret from the rest of the world. The other is the team approach in industrial research and development laboratories. This increasingly important source of technical innovation makes it difficult for the scholar to determine the effective role of the individual on the team and to investigate the give-and-take which leads to the technical act.

Another element in this anonymity arises from the failure of machines to last. These artifacts of the innovator become obsolete; unlike old books which are kept in libraries so that the ideas of the philosophers, the theologians, and others are preserved, machines which represent the handiwork and creativity of the inventors are scrapped when they no longer fulfill their function. Perhaps archaeologists of the future will find some of our artifacts in the scrap heaps and try to figure out what the technical act must have been in the twentieth century.

Even where we can pierce this veil of anonymity and know the facts, we cannot agree on the exact nature of the technical act because we disagree on interpretation of the facts. For example, although I agree with Mr. Hall's statement regarding the change in the principle of the technical act from craft to science, we have a minor difference over the date of this transition. Mr. Hall envisages a point on a graph near the close of the eighteenth century wherein the descending curve of the empirical craft tradition meets the ascending curve of the new technology of applied science. Using a different set of indices, one could draw curves which would place that point well into the nineteenth century rather than at the close of the eighteenth. Here is perhaps one of those typical quibbles beloved by scholars; yet both Mr. Hall and I agree on the fact of the change from a craft to a scientific tradition. And we agree further that this transition has never been wholly complete, that empiricism still plays a large role in modern technology.

A similar disagreement arises among scholars over the problem of interpreting the degree of science involved in Watt's invention of the steam engine. Here Mr. Hall and I are in agreement in finding little evidence of the influence of science on that invention. A number of specialists have been debating this very topic in the scholarly journals; the facts, including statements by both Joseph Black and James Watt, are readily ascertainable. Yet so violent is the disagreement over the interpretation of these facts that the scholars have already generated more heat in their controversy than did Watt's original machine.

Another possible disagreement arises from Mr. Hall's statement that "what was impressive about 1780 was less novelty in manufacture than its new magnitude and the orderly management of its massive labor force." It is my impression that the novelty in manufacture was the factor which led to a change in magnitude and to a transformation in organization of work. Thus the introduction of new types of textile machinery brought about just those changes which Dr. Hall sets apart from the manufacturing process itself. These machines, larger than those formerly employed in the domestic or cottage industry of the past, were too complex, too cumbersome, and too costly to be installed by the peasant in his cottage. Here was a case of novelty in manufacture leading to the demise of the domestic industry and the growth of the factory system.

Still another factor which prevents our full understanding of the technical act is its increasing complexity. An illustration of how this acts as an obstacle to our comprehension of the technical process is afforded by the confusion surrounding the contribution of one of the distinguished participants in this Conference, Sir Robert Watson-Watt. His claim to be the inventor of radar has been disputed by others. How can honest men disagree on this point, particularly when radar is so recent and when we have ample evidence at hand from those who actually participated in its development? The answer is that radar, like a good many other modern innovations, is a highly complex aggregate of a series of innovations. The point at issue is: who adds the last little bit from "pre-radar" or "almost-radar" to create radar? The anthropologists face a similar problem when they try to distinguish man from pre-man or "almost man." To my way of thinking, Sir Robert's contribution was a synthesis—a slight increment added to much previous innovation which made possible the effective application of radar. This was truly a creative contribution, making him at the very least the British inventor of radar. Yet the fact that the work of Watson-Watt, like that of every other technologist, rests on prior technical art gives rise to dispute over priority of innovation.

In addition to obtaining the hard facts regarding the technological artifacts themselves, we must learn more about the creative processes of the technologist and we must study in depth the social context of technological development and the impact of technological change on the social *milieu*. Mr. White calls the study of the creative process one of the chief intellectual commitments of our age; we want to know more about the motivations, the stimuli, the hindrances, the processes of creativity in all fields of endeavor. Technological creativity shares certain characteristics with other forms of creativity but also possesses some traits which are *sui generis*. One characteristic which is found in technical creativity more than in other areas is serendipity. To avoid a complicated definition, serendipity means that when one is looking for one thing he discovers something else of value which he had not expected to find. This means that the technical act often results in unexpected bits of creative development which are not bound in any causal relationship with the motivations of the creator, thereby making more complex and difficult any study of technological creativity.

A related problem involving technical creativity is the general question of the relations of thought and action, or the gap between what one is trying to do and what one actually does. This is not simply a case of falling short of one's goal. Furthermore, the interrelatedness of idea and action is more subtle, infinitely more complex than can be explained by a simple cause and effect relationship based on chronological sequence. There is a feedback relationship between the idea and the act: the technical act often modifies or transforms the technical idea during the dynamic process of converting thought into action.

The gap between idea and act is closely related to the philosophical question of ends and means. Yet the questions of the ends justifying the means and the means conditioning the ends are scarcely relevant in the context of the technical act. What the technologist asks is: do the means effectively reach the ends? This approach, I think, is basic to the technical act. The technologist says if it works, it's right; if it fulfills its end, it's right. This is the philosophical justification of the " cut-and-try " approach of the craftsman and of the empirical outlook of the engineer. Many devices and techniques work satisfactorily without the technologist knowing how and why they work. Indeed, the technical act can be founded on a false technical idea, but it is not false as a technical act if it works. This pragmatic formulation has been implicit in technological development since the time of the first stone implements.

A critical problem in the study of creativity is the matter of motivation. Why do technologists invent? Because technology deals with material things and promotes our creature comforts, it is popularly believed that the stimulus to invent arises solely from crass materialistic motives. Yet I doubt if it could be demonstrated that engineers are more or less materialistic than other human beings. Some light may be shed on the engineer's creative impulse by Emerson's famous saying about building a better mousetrap. The operative phrase in that dictum as far as the technologist is concerned is not the world beating a path to one's door, and certainly not the mousetrap, but building a better one. Technologists have an inner compulsion to create. They like to tinker; they want to improve things.

Mr. White points out that creativity " may well be a lot of things and not one thing." One of the things is this inner compulsion, but there are many other factors which stimulate the creative impulse and which condition its application. The social scientists must investigate the socio-cultural interrelations of technology to determine the social context which stimulates or retards the technical act.

In many discussions on this point of the social impact of technology, the technologist, or even the machine itself, is made to appear solely responsible for the " technological order." Those who fail to comprehend that order—and hence fear and distrust it—regard the technologists as the villains of the piece. As a matter of fact, technologists are too innocent, too unaware of the impact of their activities. Innovators cannot foretell all the socio-cultural effects of their innovations; they cannot even foresee all the technical effects. Frederick Winslow Taylor, one of the original proponents of scientific management, was opposed to the speedup. Favoring cooperation between management and labor, he failed to forsee that the industrial methods he introduced would greatly increase the organizational role of management and thereby deprive the worker of much initiative and participation in the work process, nor that economic pressures would make the speedup imperative. Similarly, Henry Ford, writing on mass production in the *Encyclopaedia Britannica*, foretold effects which now seem at variance with the actual results obtained. He expected that mass production would make finance the handmaid instead of the mistress of product industry; that mass production would give the product " the highest standard of quality ever attained in output of great quantity "; and that mass production would lead to a higher degree of mass intelligence. Here is the technologist unable to foresee either the technical or socio-cultural consequences of his actions.

But why should we expect the successful technologist to be a prophet or a social scientist able to predict on a statistical basis? Sir Robert Watson-Watt's well-intentioned suggestion that technologists take Hippocratic oaths to prevent them from misapplying their innovations would seem to have little relevance to the actual situation. There are already ethical codes for professional engineers, but even with the best of intentions the technologist—or anyone else, for that matter—cannot always foresee the results. Before we can control, direct, or regulate the direction of the " technological order," we must know much more about the technical act—its sources, its nature, its impact. To accomplish this, we must study the relations of technology with all aspects of society and culture. For technology does not exist in a vacuum; it develops in a social context, as do all other human activities. Instead of being a mechanical master which determines man's destiny, or a Frankenstein's monster which threatens to destroy its creator, technology has always been, and still remains, an essential part of man. The question, therefore, is not whether man can master technology but whether man can master himself.

The Technical Act

A REPORT OF THE DISCUSSION

WARREN E. PREECE

Morning Session

Mr. Stover presided. In summarizing the morning presentations, he reminded the Conference that Mr. Kranzberg had said that a study of technology in historical context is necessary if we are to understand it and that Mr. Calder had said we should "go to history," to look, for example, at the first Industrial Revolution to find clues which might guide us in attempting to control the second. In view of the importance which both speakers attached to history, he asked whether the rate at which technology is leading us into a revolutionized world would leave sufficient time for the study required.

Mr. White pointed out that we must recognize that history is not "really a guide to action" because in fact the novel elements of any new situation far outweigh those elements which the new situation may share in common with older ones. Thus, he said, the key to wisdom and wise actions may actually lie in understanding the novelty of the present as well as in understanding the history of the past. The function of history, he suggested, is to clarify group memory, and it is important that we be aware that this memory includes factors such as pride, myth, etc. Continuing, he warned that the history of technology will not give us a guide for the salutary control of technology but said that, despite this, the more we know with certainty about the history of technology the better chance we will have of analyzing the current situation correctly. In our analysis, he submitted, it is not necessary to wait until we know everything that is to be known, but, at the same time, we should not try to do too much while standing in the presence of ignorance.

Fr. Ong said he agreed with Mr. White concerning the importance of seeing "the full human dimensions of technology," and pointed out that since technology builds on memory, our plan for controlling it must recognize that our planning ability is itself at any one time a correlative of our memory.

Expressing fears that our view of technology is "fearfully foreshortened," Mr. White said that though he would concede that a change of quantity can equal a change of quality, he would still suggest that it is important to recognize that man has dealt with the problem of technology longer and more intensely than many appear to recognize.

Suggesting that one of the ways in which we have foreshortened our view of technology is in the ascription of a quite recent date to the so-called transition from "empirical" to "scientific" technological traditions, Mr. White said it is not even certain that the assumption of an at-one-time "empirical basis" is accurate. He pointed out, for example, that in the tenth century significant changes in glassmaking resulted from discoveries which appear to have had in them many elements of science, and that the very earliest craftsman possessed skills which were marked by a high degree of sophistication. He urged, therefore, that we not rule out the possibility of a very early "scientific" technology.

140

Continuing in the same vein, Mr. White warned against overemphasizing the so-called "invention of invention" as a decisive new factor in technology. He pointed out that in our own culture innovations recognizable as "deliberate inventions" occurred at least as far back as the thirteenth century and that there was even then frequent contact between the craftsman and the learned man. It would appear, Mr. White suggested, that even the term "the first industrial revolution" may not be clear enough, particularly in so far as it is generally used to refer to the application of power to a manufacturing process with "important results for the economy." If this is to be the distinguishing element of the first revolution, he said, then that revolution can perhaps be located as far back as the eleventh century if not in the tenth with the invention of the windmill. He emphasized that the point he was trying to make was that the whole notion of process and impact are older than most people recognize and that though this fact may not modify our sense of what we now want to do about technology, it is a fact that we have survived a long history of technology and have built a fund of experience to draw on.

Mr. Goldschmidt asked how technology of the tenth and eleventh centuries could have spread rapidly enough to have had an economic impact if Mr. Kranzberg and Mr. Calder were right about the "secrecy" of early technology. Mr. While said that the spread was in part simply the result "of a lot of people scuttling around" the world. Mr. Meier suggested that this kind of travel is the habit of craftsmen in general and Mr. Calder pointed out that the early crafts were in fact "extremely international." Mr. White commented further that he had not found in his research any evidence of craft secrecy in the Middle Ages or, in fact, before the seventeenth century. He also noted that he had found no evidence of organized opposition to technological change in the Middle Ages, except that which was expressed in order to guarantee the maintenance of the quality of production.

Fr. Ong suggested it was important in spreading technology in earlier ages that, since there was no great stress on literacy, the craft system, basically an oral system for the transmission of knowledge, developed and that this inevitably meant that the knowledge of a craft went wherever the practitioner of the craft did.

Mr. Gorman pointed out that there was a basic point at issue in the papers by Mr. White and Mr. Hall; that whereas Mr. White appeared to be urging that we not commit the "fallacy of the misplaced novelty," Mr. Hall was suggesting that the difference between our technology and that of an earlier time is more than the matter of mere complexity and was indeed a matter of kind springing from the introduction of a "scientific orientation" and approach into technology. He asked Mr. White if he would want to deny that at some time, regardless of when that time might be placed, there had been a major importation of science into technology. Mr. White said he would not deny the point; that, for instance, he could find no real connection between mathematics and physics and the technology of the Middle Ages. He said he would be inclined to put the change somewhere in the nineteenth century, but he emphasized that this would not be to deny an element of very great sophistication to the empirical tradition itself. Mr. Gorman argued then that it is significant that, regardless of when the change occurred, the change is indeed reflected in present-day technology.

Mr. Hall said that while many features of the technology of the Middle Ages are admittedly quite difficult to explain he would not think that an apparent ability to control an element in a process such as glassmaking should be taken to imply, for example, a knowledge of solid state physics. He emphasized, however, that neither had he meant to suggest that all early technology was crude or lacking in uniformity. Mr. Gorman noted again, then, that the important consideration would still be that there was a time at which a scientific method developed and had an impact on technology, and that it is not important to the purpose of the present Conference to be able to place the time precisely. Mr. White said that the connection may well have been the other way around; that the technology may have had an impact on science. Why was it, he asked, that no one seems to have wondered why a column of water in a suction pump " broke " until almost two centuries after the invention of the pump itself.

Mr. Kranzberg suggested that we need better criteria for " what constitutes an industrial revolution." He said in this context that he would not agree to locating the first industrial revolution in the eleventh century, despite at least one writer who has claimed that it took place in pre-history when agriculture was invented. To be meaningful, he submitted, we must think of the industrial revolution as a process involving technological and societal factors. Pointing out that an important difference of opinion might revolve around the question of (1) when a change occurred and (2) when the change had its impact, he said that if Mr. White is correct in assuming that the " origin " of an invention is the same thing as the invention itself, then it is necessary to hold that da Vinci really invented the aeroplane. He said he would prefer to fix the time of an invention in terms of when its application became feasible.

Continuing, Mr. Kranzberg said a further cause of difficulties among those at the Conference could be different views of man's relation to the machine and to nature. In this connection, he said, it is indicative of what has happened that whereas in an earlier day man was thought of as a machine operator, he is now coming to be thought of as a machine overseer.

Mr. Kranzberg pointed out in conclusion that anthropologists have said that invention requires " an opportunity, a need, and a genius." This, he suggested, makes the social milieu, in terms of its readiness to accept new invention, an important factor. Opportunity, he continued, is related to need, in that once a society has accepted any one invention it has also created a probable necessity for even another one. Since genius has been determined to be present among all people, he said, the crucial question about invention would seem to be the matter of " opportunity " within a socio-cultural context. What we need, he urged, is further research into the factors which allow for invention.

In asking for more comment on the material discussed earlier by Mr. Calder, Senator Benton pointed out that if we assume that we are living in an age of revolution created by technology, even as the first such revolution was also brought about by technology, then we should consider what dangers might be inherent in the attempt to export technology to the underdeveloped nations. Mr. Thai agreed, and pointed out that " it is disquieting " that in Germany and Japan it was the rapid imposition of imported technological change on feudal societies which apparently helped to stimulate the development of imperialism and aggressiveness.

Mr. Calder said it seemed to him that the essence of the problem was related to the matter of priorities; that much can be done technologically in the underdeveloped countries if we " just don't rush the gates." He suggested, for example, that it may be a serious mistake to encourage such nations to speed the domestic establishment of highly advanced research laboratories rather than sending their capable people to work in existing laboratories in more advanced lands. The exportation of talent, while not ideal, he said, is at least not likely to involve the distortion of the fabric of national life. Further, he urged that we should be circumspect in encouraging developing nations to create technologies which they will be unable to support. To do so, he insisted, would be to indulge in a dangerous form of industrial colonialism because we would be effectively lashing the fulfillment of their new needs to our own technology. He said he was particularly fearful about the consequent frustrations which would arise within the new nation if such a course were to be followed at the very time when it was most vulnerable to disruptive elements.

Senator Benton suggested that the problem which Mr. Calder had raised related significantly to the educational level of the recipient nation. Noting that in Brazil, for example, there are only seven technical schools, and that even these are not utilized to capacity because of the lack of adequately prepared entering students, he said, " Clearly, one of the big lags in the world is in education."

Mr. Calder agreed, and pointed out that the lag manifests itself in many ways; that, e. g., there is much concern for the loss which an underdeveloped nation sustains when it sends talented young people abroad for training, only to find that the trained man never returns to his homeland, in any useful sense, because there is no educational or technological base capable of supporting his work at the level of his training. He noted in this connection that some 1,400 Iranian students are now being educated in the United States, and that "practically none" of these will ever go back to Iran.

Mr. Goldschmidt warned that it is dangerous to generalize about the level of technology which underdeveloped nations should be encouraged to desire. He said, for example, that in Brazil the problem is one of finding ways to put a scientific underpinning beneath the technology and this might well require the creation of advanced domestic laboratories, since the fact is that most scientific work in the developed countries is simply not conducted in ways likely to be helpful to the underdeveloped countries. Talent exported from underdeveloped nations, Mr. Goldschmidt agreed, represents an enormous loss to the nation involved, and one of the things that the advanced nations should do is create places for " genius to go to work " within its own country.

Commenting that Mr. Goldschmidt had, on the previous day, pointed up the effects of technology as seen in the rapid automation of agriculture and suggesting that we are now beginning to see the impact of this transformation in economic consequences (higher prices, higher taxes, and political problems), social consequences (dramatized by the influx of unskilled, untrained labor into, for example, Chicago), political consequences (the accentuation of a system of rotten boroughs which prevents effective legislation), and cultural consequences, Mr. Ashmore asked what the historian of technology is able to say that bears on the problem other than that " it has happened before," too. Does history, he asked, reveal any evidence for believing that we will find the answers to technology in technology itself.

Senator Benton said that as a footnote to the Conference he would want personally to challenge the implication that technology is " a bad thing " and would insist that technology in, for instance, automating the farm, had been " a wonderful thing." The greatest single effect of technology, he said, has been the increased mobility of the people, that mobility which explains the great influx of former Southern farm families into Chicago, referred to by Mr. Ashmore. Recalling that his own ancestors had been " chained to impoverished farms " in Connecticut until a growing mobility had made it possible for most of the farm families to move out, he said that the new mobility also brought new people into the state and, " in Connecticut, we taught them."

Restating his belief that the main impact of technology has been on improved mobility, that 20 per cent of all of the people in the United States now move every year, whereas in the days of which he had first spoken " you simply couldn't get off of the farm," the Senator said he will always believe that it is a good thing that people can pick up and get off of a farm in Georgia and go to Chicago. He said he would insist that we need more optimism among the experts and that he would urge on the experts that they not lose sight of the new freedoms which the people have won through technology.

In answer to the specific question which Mr. Ashmore had asked, Mr. Hall pointed out that problems of population displacement have normally been met through social improvements, humanitarianism, and social legislation, and Mr. Meier suggested that the situation is probably more hopeful than Mr. Ashmore had recognized. He recalled, for example, that in the days of the New Deal, when " it was fashionable " to blame such things as delinquency on the environment, a five-year survey in Baltimore which involved continuing knowledge of new residents, 50 per cent of whom had been left in slum areas and 50 per cent of whom had been moved into better environmental areas, had to be abandoned after three and a half years because none of the control group in the slums could be identified any longer—that is, they " had all moved up and on."

Afternoon Session

In opening the afternoon meeting, Mr. Stover noted that the Conference seemed to agree that " the past is important " and that a proper understanding of the past can free us to be contemporary. It had also been suggested, he pointed out, that we can gain confidence about the future from the past. Yet, he said, we still need to clarify how the past can help us to understand the technological present. Since the *Britannica* wants to make clear to its readers what technology is, what it means, and what should be done about it, he said we need to know: (1) if the novelties in the current situation are the most important aspect of that situation, how novel is it, and (2) what questions should we be asking of history in order to establish its relevance to the present?

Mr. Theobald said that although he " would like very much to be encouraged " by Mr. White's belief that we are now merely at the furthest point on what has been a continuum, he could not agree; that such things as the fact that computers will soon be able to do much of our thinking for us, that biological control will be possible, and that greater self-knowledge will be a fact, lead him to assume that we are in sight of a distinctly new situation. Continuing, he said he would want to look more closely at the " play element " which earlier had been introduced as an alleged factor in man's wish to increase his power over nature, and he suggested that there would seem to be little play at all involved in the fact that 95 per cent of all technologists are today employed by either industry or the military. Industry, he argued, employs technologists to keep itself alive by creating new artificial scarcities in the form of new products which can revolutionize the way we live, and military technology is clearly required to repress " everything human " in the interests of getting a job done within an allotted time. In view of the influence of government and industry on technology, he submitted, we cannot assume that the rate of technological growth is a " natural function " or something " given," but must assume that it is a function of the money put into research and development by government or industry.

Since the technological act today is motivated by either the desire to kill an enemy or to make a profit, Mr. Theobald said, our situation would change immediately if the military and business requirements on which it rests were to vanish.

Mr. Real said he wanted to associate himself with Mr. Theobald's remarks concerning the close connection between technology and the military and would also agree that the technological situation today is "almost completely novel" because of the existence of a "systems system."

Mr. Kranzberg said, in relation to Mr. Stover's questions, that the uses of history are the uses of all education—that is, to answer the questions (1) how did things get the way they are and (2) what are we to do about it? He said, therefore, that history alone cannot give us any specific answers to today's problems, which is to say that "history does not repeat itself." For a fuller understanding of our own time, he urged, we must turn to the social sciences and the humanities.

Recalling his earlier remark that invention needs opportunity, necessity, and genius, Mr. Kranzberg said it is suggestive that most underdeveloped nations "can handle" the artifacts of advanced technology but not the underpinnings on which it rests. Urging that the role of the social scientist should be in part to tell us of the needs of the underdeveloped nations, he pointed out that India simply does not need the highly advanced "push-button technology" of our culture and the factories which it makes possible, but needs instead to find ways to employ large numbers of people efficiently. Regarding Mr. Theobald's remarks, Mr. Kranzberg said that technology is not, after all, neutral but that most technologists "are indeed innocent" and well-meaning people who do not think of themselves as "lackeys of the death industry." The technologist, he urged, is concerned only with learning whether given means will achieve given ends; as a technologist he should not be concerned with determining what ends should be met, since this job is rightly the work of society.

Mr. Piel suggested that Mr. Kranzberg had really sharpened the point made by Mr. Theobald and Mr. Real. Arguing that the technologist is very aware of the "moral burden" of his work "in the rat hole," he insisted that the issues of technology and its close connection to the military and to industry are related in that the issue of controlling technology is "profoundly raised" by the existence of war and profit and that war and profit are themselves interlocked. In support of his argument, he contended that the United States is heavily "over-armed by any reasonable measure," that it has five times as much atomic strength as it needs to destroy all of Russia, and that it keeps itself armed to this extent because of its need to subsidize a tottering economy. This means, Mr. Piel continued, that technology and its advances have outrun the viability and serviceability of our economic institutions and may, therefore, be said to threaten our continued existence. We need, he concluded, a wider and more rational social control of both. Mr. Kranzberg suggested that all that Mr. Piel was really saying was that we need more study of the social control of technology and this, indeed, had been his own point.

Mr. Ashmore asked Mr. Kranzberg if he agreed with Mr. Piel that the only reasons for the existence of defense technology and the expenditures made for it are those of propping the economy. Mr. Piel interrupted to say that this was not what he had meant to say; that his argument was that the United States has five times as much retaliatory strength as it needs and should therefore, in the interest of easing world tensions, unilaterally disarm four-fifths of its own strength, but that because of our economic dependence on the defense industry such action is unlikely. Mr. Ashmore insisted, however, that in asserting that there is " no rational need " for the present armaments level, Mr. Piel was dismissing all of those who defend these levels as militarily necessary and was, in effect, saying that Ellul is right and technology does create its own demonic tendencies.

Mr. Piel replied that he had been trying to say that Ellul's diagnosis is misapplied and does not explain the factors which now seem to direct technology. He said it is easy to see " the decerebration and dehumanization " of technology at work on people in the military industries. Mr. Ashmore said then that " no matter how you phrase it," it would seem that the demon must be " in technology somewhere." Mr. Piel said he thought that the demon lay in the existence of a " reckless operation " conducted for unrecognized motives. To this extent, he suggested, the demon is in the economic system rather than in technology. Mr. Gorman noted that " this demon " is sometimes referred to " in some circles " as the " internal contradiction of capitalism."

Continuing, Mr. Piel said that the forces which he had been trying to describe cannot helpfully be visualized in the usual " City Hall, good guy vs. crook " terms. Mr. Ashmore insisted, however, that Mr. Piel's analysis had suggested that there is a motivating power, " if not a crook or worse," in the system. Mr. Piel said then that the motivation comes from the necessity of maintaining full employment in an economic system which requires that employment be largely a matter of wages earned in the pursuit of private profit rather than " on public nonprofit-making payrolls."

Mr. Theobald pointed out that the economic profits of a firm grow when " it has something to sell which no one else has," or something " which people will buy even though they do not need it." This, he said, is the villain in the piece. Mr. Ashmore argued, however, that this was not responsive to his point, which had been that both Mr. Piel and Mr. Theobald appeared to be describing an entirely closed system operating as if by demonic forces responsible only to an inner logic and following its own rules. He said his question was, therefore, whether the operation is " conscious or unconscious." Mr. Theobald said that the " problem is not that simple "; that the fact is that if one is in business and hopes to keep his company going he must look around for things to make and this inevitably spurs technological development.

Mr. Calder said again that he believes the demon is " the faceless man at the elbow of the uninformed." The real problem of " the system," he said, is suggested by the fact that in Britain, for example, ever since the war whenever anyone has had an idea that might be useful to the government he has asked for £4,000 with which to have feasibility studies of it made; if these studies have indicated that the idea " can work," he has then asked for £40,000 for research projects on it with the result that someone in government has already become convinced that the idea is a good one and ought to be developed before " the other side gets it " and that this means that on the basis of incomplete research someone next asks for £400,000 with which to go ahead to " manufacture obsolete hardware." Certainly, he urged, we need someone in government able to call a halt somewhere in the cycle.

Conceding that there is in the United States, and perhaps in the West in general, a " security-mania " which tends to operate in such a way that any new idea which appears likely to bolster the feeling of security will be accepted, Mr.

Meier pointed out that in recent years there has been a growing awareness among technologists of the "incremental push toward the inevitable." As a result, he said, most technologists today want to "be able to investigate the system as a whole," and this explains such things as the fact that most military industrial suppliers when advertising for scientists and technologists proclaim opportunities to engage in "peace research."

Mr. Ashmore asked Mr. Meier if he was suggesting that people in positions of critical power are making bad decisions or that no one can make good decisions because of the system. Mr. Piel said that "most of them" are making the best decisions they can within the context of the system and its relations to the economy. He recalled in this connection that Keynes very early noted that private business interests inevitably resist any government program which seems likely to collide with their own private activities.

Mr. Hall suggested that Mr. Meier's remarks about the "incremental push" were well illustrated in the field of medical research, where many qualified people now insist that we simply "cannot wisely spend on medical research" all of the money which is being made available for it. Mr. Meier explained that medical research funds are almost always increased above the amounts requested because Congress feels that while it is appropriating so much money for defense it should keep the balance even by increasing expenditures for health.

Mr. Kranzberg said he was "not at all certain" that the relationship between technology, industry, and the military is as clear-cut as Mr. Piel and others had suggested. He argued, for instance, that in fact the military-technological solution to a problem frequently defeats the ideal of full employment as an economic end—that a missiles program costs more but creates fewer jobs than the construction of, perhaps, 10,000 heavy tanks. Recalling that the question for today's meeting was the technological act and its ends, he suggested that discussion should center on such things as whether or not the technological act controls its own ends, whether or not the technological act is controllable, and, if the answer to both is affirmative, how man may undertake to exercise control.

Regarding the moral question which had been interjected into the discussion, Fr. Clarke said that it is necessary "to situate technology within an entire context" before judging the morality involved. He said that he could not believe that we do not have, or cannot get, people in the Department of Defense who are capable of "seeing the whole picture" with more clarity than had been suggested by Mr. Piel, and he expressed fears that the result of the Piel-Theobald approach would be to leave all moral judgments to a "very few people at the top of a planning structure." Sociologists, people in operations research, "in fact, all of us," should be making moral judgments, he insisted. Mr. Kranzberg asked Fr. Clarke if he was suggesting that we cannot separate the information function from the policy function. Fr. Clarke agreed that this conclusion was implicit in his remarks, but said that primarily he had been trying only to say that it is not certain that working in a defense industry is necessarily unmoral *per se*; that the question deserves more discussion than it has received.

Mr. Goldschmidt said he was not enthusiastic about getting "still another 'ist'" to study the problem which the technologist has made. Arguing that the problem of morality relates to the basic values of people as people rather than to the values of people as workers, he pointed out that at the time the McMahon Act was being debated in Washington, "literally hundreds of young scientists from Los Alamos" turned up in Washington filled with moral concern about the atomic power which they had unleashed, but that the fact is that they were all in Washington " as people rather than as scientists." Mr. Kranzberg said that he would not want to suggest that technologists are not people; that, indeed, he thought it hopeful that most of the persons now involved in scientific education are trying consciously to make the scientists of tomorrow better " well-rounded men." The job is worth undertaking, he said, because, certainly, if the technological act is the product of technologists then the moral and spiritual values of technologists are immediately important.

Mr. Stover suggested that the point was related to the more general question of professional responsibility introduced by Sir Robert in his keynote remarks, and asked whether the history of craft guilds has " much to teach us here." Mr. White said that he did not think that it did, that although such guilds controlled the quality of products, the hours of labor, etc., the fact is that it is more " indicative of their character " that they generally " drank up their dues whenever the treasury was full." Their scale of operations, he said, was too small to be of assistance. In a general reply to Mr. Kranzberg's last point, he said he thought that only a small portion of the over-all problem of technology would respond to " merely redoing the engineer." The basic problem, he argued, is a matter of moral values; and, for example, it is not realistic to " pin all of our present arms race " on economic greed, or to ignore entirely the matter of fear. In dealing with technology, he said, we must deal with the whole population, rather than merely with the engineers. He suggested, further, that the fact is that most engineers " want to be civilized " and that it is the humanists in the Greek tradition who " have no intention of enlarging their view " to " include technology as a human activity."

Fr. Ong said he agreed with Mr. White's position on the " Greek tradition " and its refusal to " get its hands dirty." He suggested that technology is, after all, a human product; that we must be concerned with it as such and that this means that our concern must go beyond the technologist. He warned that the technologist cannot be " expected to do it alone " because his own job involves only a day-to-day dealing with a tiny element of the whole technology rather than with the whole of the technological process within a social context.

Going back to the questions Mr. Ashmore had raised earlier, Mr. Real suggested that " the guilt" for the whole technological-military-industrial situation is so pervasive that it is necessary to say " that all of us are guilty," that all of us are involved in the weapons business. The people in the Department of Defense, he said, are good people, but they are subject to Congress and Congress in turn is subject to " the people." Referring to the 1962 clash between Congressman Vinson and Secretary of Defense McNamara over the B-70 project, he suggested that the argument really was to determine who is going to put the war system together and that fear obviously has as much, or more, to do with this argument than greed. Mr. Piel said he suspected that the problem is more one of " mindlessness than of greed "; that it is inherent in the economic process. He said he recognizes the human desire for " oversafety " in the world situation and concedes that once a people has let itself get into an arms race it is hard for them to limit themselves to the minimum deterrent necessary (though, he suggested, the Russians seem to have been " better able to do this than we have "). He insisted, however, that the economic factor, the apparent inability, for instance, to shut down an unneeded defense plant, is a strong force.

Mr. Ashmore commented that the arguments Congressmen are likely to make against closing a defense plant seem to him to be " no more moving and no less irrelevant " than the arguments Senators make about preserving the family farm.

He suggested that the real problem is that such things as the surplus defense plant, the unneeded small farm, and the displaced person in Chicago or Bombay are all the result of the technological act and all represent a problem for which there does not seem to be a technological solution. Does history, he asked, offer any help in this matter, or do we need, perhaps, a political solution which will be shaped by, but independent of, technology? Mr. White commented that history, " sadly enough," seems to offer no consolation.

Mr. Hartner said that the legend of the man who knew of a panacea for every problem but had to keep it to himself, suggesting that an honest man is not necessarily either good or useful, and that of the emperor who destroyed a machine which could replace man lest the poor be deprived of their income, had major implications for the subject of the Conference.

Noting, to the contrary, that the Nobel Peace Prize itself was, and is, financed from profits which accrued from the invention and distribution of " the horrors of TNT," Mr. Hall suggested that too many people appear to believe that the scientist or technologist ought somehow to have better morals than society in general, if only because society is too likely to be carried along by science and technology, neither of which it is able to understand. Science, he insisted, is largely a reflection of the moral level of society.

Concerning the matter of the so-called neutrality of technology, the question of which, he said, had been implicit during most of the first two days of the Conference, Mr. Gorman suggested that, in the abstract, technology is morally, social, ethically, and politically neutral, and the judgments of the technologist are based largely on whether or not something will work, but that the really important fact is that technology cannot exist in the abstract and has to have a social existence. All of this means, he said, that the important question is: who is to control technology and, thus, give social direction to the technologist? Continuing, he suggested that judgments to be made concerning the practical decision to apply a scientific or technological invention involve factors which are social, political, moral, and ethical, rather than technical in character, and he pointed out that while there seems to be something in human nature which creates a " firm " social pressure toward the use of any technology which seems likely to be hopeful, there is no similar firm pressure toward that restraint which might be required by social, political, moral, or ethical determinations.

Mr. Theobald said that Mr. Gorman's remarks were obviously relevant to his own argument that a large part of our technology since World War II has been artificially induced. The major question now, he said, is whether or not these artificial inducements have put us in a situation in which we have to run merely to keep in place, or whether we can yet find ways to slow down enough to permit technology to become again something distinctively human.

Mr. Huxley pointed out that since the context within which technology exists is important, it might as well be admitted that the major context for almost everything now " is that of nationalism," and that for so long as nationalism is the idol we cannot hope to eradicate the adverse features which it inspires. Mr. Kranzberg argued, however, that such things as, for example, the increased possibilities of international communications which stem from new technology may actually help to moderate the effects of nationalism. Mr. Huxley replied to this that the fact, of course, is that " when we didn't communicate with Japan we didn't go to war with her, either."

Mr. Theobald said his primary question would be to ask whether, even if nationalism were to end tomorrow, we would yet be able to free ourselves from its effects and from the chains which it has created. Pointing out that the question as put pertains to Ellul's " autonomy " of technology, Mr. White said he doubted the fact of autonomy and believed, indeed, that history offers evidence to show that man can refuse, and at times has refused, to use every technological advance which is made available to him. Mr. Theobald replied that even if this has been true in the historical past it might not any longer be true in so far as " our artificial rate of progress " may now demand that we continuously accelerate merely to keep up.

In general comment on the discussion to this point, and particularly in relation to the question of the uses of history in understanding the technological act, Mr. Meier said that a study which he had conducted appeared to indicate that the creative scientist almost invariably knows more about the history of science than his " run-of-the-mill colleague " does; that he is more conscious of the evolution of ideas and knows from history " what is really novel," and what is, therefore, worth pursuing as distinct from that which has been worked on unsuccessfully before and so offers little hope of being useful. Continuing, he suggested that the notion of a " decision rule "—that is, a rule which says, in effect, that " if you don't know how to decide, then do it this way "—has some relation to the question of the control of technology and to the value of history. He pointed out that one of the interesting questions about a decision rule is the way in which it becomes " locked into a given institution," and he suggested that history may help us to find out what values lay behind any given decision rule. The technologist can be made more aware of these values of history in his work, Mr. Meier suggested, by training him first in " tracking down the individual components of a problem " and second by training him in the investigation of, for example, the probable nature of an organization which might use any given decision rule.

In reference to Mr. Gorman's earlier comments, Mr. Piel said he would insist that a moral judgment has to be involved somewhere in the technological problem and he would argue that society is itself heavily conditioned by, and involved in, technology. He suggested that it is useless to discuss technology as a platonic ideal existing in the abstract and meaningless to abstract moral judgment from the social context. The two things, he said, must come together, as they evolve together. He suggested, as an example, that it is only because technological tools for aiding the underdeveloped nations are available that aid to underdeveloped nations can even be considered as a moral issue. Mr. Gorman said he would not disagree and would assume that, except in a pathological situation, technology may condition the moral imagination in so far as, by its very nature, it starts out with the intention to be useful. Technology, he agreed, obviously makes possible visions that could not be imagined without technology, but, he continued, there is a difference in kind between the moral judgment and the technological judgment.

Mr. Wilkinson said he was convinced that the engineer must in the end work out the solution to his own salvation, that it will be uniformly " disastrous for everyone " if the humanists " rush in to solve all problems." He pointed out that in other conferences related to technology, as so far in this one, almost invariably the moral issue is raised " in a very timid way," presumably so that " someone may make Mr. Piel's speech " on morality but that, in fact, the content of the sermon itself inevitably furnishes Ellul with a set of " unrivaled paradigms " to support his thesis.

Nature, Science, and Technology †

TECHNOLOGY AS A SYSTEM OF EXPLOITATION

SCOTT BUCHANAN*

The current discussion of technology in books and journals, both learned and popular, can be heard as a desperate clamor for a definition of terms. The reader or listener would like to call a moratorium on argument until the authors come to terms with each other and hopefully with their common subject-matter, or less hopefully with their separate subject-matters. Each new author is tempted to respond to the clamor and legislate clear and distinct definitions. There may be wisdom at the present stage in refusing to yield to the clamor. There have been many definitions in the past that simply do not comprehend the problematic phenomena of the present. There are always attempts to make loose and general definitions that do not penetrate and articulate the problems. There perhaps is need at present of a more patient ruminating discussion that will identify and arrange the materials for a later definition. I would like to offer one strand of such a discussion. Hopefully, it may throw some light on the cause of the confusion that delays definition.

Theories of the Arts

The discussion of technology is very old, and it is almost continuous with the Western intellectual tradition. I suspect there is a similar continuous discussion in the Oriental tradition. Technology is a Greek word. Unlike many apparently similar scientific terms in modern languages, it is not just stolen from the Greeks and recoined to fit a scientific novelty. It was a part of their discussion of the human arts. It meant the prescription of rules for the arts, and the context for it was a rich, subtle and technical discussion of all the arts.

Plato is famous for his theory of ideas. He should be equally if not more famous for his technology, his theory of the arts. He is fascinated throughout his dialogues with the origin of the sciences

---

† Lewis Mumford's paper, " Science as Technology," was also distributed as a background paper for this session of the Conference. It is printed in *Proceedings of the American Philosophical Society*, Vol. 105, No. 5 (October, 1961).

* Mr. Buchanan, formerly Dean of St. John's College is a Consultant to the Center for the Study of Democratic Institutions. His books include *Poetry and Mathematics* (New York, 1929), *Symbolic Distance* (London, 1931), and *Essay in Politics* (New York, 1953).

from the arts. The modern notions about technology are elaborations of parts of the ancient discussion torn loose from the ancient context and developed independently because of the novelties of modern industry. I would like to trace very briefly and diagrammatically this separation and development.

The Greek word for art was *techné*, and it signified the power or capacity, the habit or skill, and the intellectual virtue of a man to make a product or an artifact. This formula is a highly condensed and for us oversimplified conclusion of the Greek discussion which continues on through the Roman period in somewhat degraded form and finally reaches its most subtle elaboration in scholastic thought. It belongs to the tradition of rational and moral psychology that we have honored more by neglect than cultivation since the eighteenth century. It emphasizes three distinct things: man the agent-artist, the end product, and the ordering of means by rational rules. A man realizes his natural capacity by acquiring a second nature in habits which are ordered rationally to the ends in the things he makes. Art is an intellectual virtue whose function it is to deal with contingent and empirical things by reasoned opinions or rules.

The Greek discussion begins and develops in a context wider than this compact humanism. The preceding analytic formula applies clearly to what the ancients called the intellectual or liberal arts and to what we call the fine arts, but it also applies to the useful arts or crafts, those arts that make useful things. The habits and skills of the formula are involved in the selection and acquisition of natural materials, what we would call raw materials, and in transforming them into the product.

It would seem that the scientific distinction between matter and form had its origin in the analysis of the arts. Matter is that which is fitted to receive forms which exist first in the artist's mind. The artist's or artisan's act is essentially putting such a form on this malleable matter. The means by which this is done are first the hands, but soon the extension of hands in tools or elementary machines. The typical example of the artistic act is the imprinting of the seal on wax, then the fashioning of the statue out of marble by the chisel, and then the making of a chair according to a pattern. These archetypes are easily extended to agriculture, carpentry, cooking, and building, some with many tools, and an order of applications, and some subordinated to others as wood-working to flute-making to flute-playing. There is also the art of tool-making to serve the arts which use the tools.

The tool or the hand operates between the form in the artist's mind and the raw material, but form also demands the training of the human capacity in skills that are learned. Some of these skills seem to be learned by rules that can be taught, some only by repetitive practice, some by the maturation of instinct, some apparently by inspiration, some by close attention to the material and its fitness to the end product.

This matter of skills and learning was the mysterious subject-matter of great fascination and thought for the Greeks, and it led to one of their more familiar contributions to the tradition. They concluded that art imitates nature, that nature is the great teacher of men. This conclusion came at the end of a long period in which they believed wonderingly in the many legends in which the gods were said to have taught men the arts and still presided over the practice. All the wonder was finally precipitated in the doctrine of the four causes, first applied to the arts and then to nature. The causes of any end product were first in the matter which could be fashioned or formed; then in the form in the artist's mind which could be impressed on the matter; third in the hands, tools, skills, and energies of the agent-artist; and finally in the end itself, the product, which ruled over all the other causes in the actual making. These were the four causes, material, formal, efficient, and final.

The recognition that the artist was imitating nature almost forced a reversal of the insight. The four causes also operate in nature so that their discovery and formulation make science. Art or technology thus becomes the midwife of science. If you want to understand something, make a similar object or artifact; then impute that artistic process of making to nature. We are not far from this in our current use of models in science.

There is no doubt that the Greeks used the analogy of art to penetrate nature and its secrets. Travelers brought back technical lore from Egypt which they turned into geometry. This is apparently the origin of the Pythagorean development of number theory and geometry. The three, four, five triangle became the universal device for squaring the corners of buildings and for surveying lots of land property. It also led to the proof of the Pythagorean theorem in geometry.

This fragment of mathematics in its two aspects, applied and theoretical, precipitated a crisis in the Pythagorean society. The theorem proved too much—that any right triangle would have the sum of the squares of its legs equal to the square of the hypotenuse. In many right triangles this would mean that the hypotenuse was incommensurable with the legs. This would not have worried a builder, or an engineer. He could work with rough instruments and approximations. It would worry an incipient mathematician who had glimpsed the possibility of theoretical understanding. It is said that a member of the Pythagorean brotherhood who divulged the secret scandal about incommensurables was deliberately drowned at sea. The Pythagorean theorem had to be kept a professional secret until the problem of the diagonal of the square and the square root of two could be solved. Of course the problem was later solved, supposedly by Eudoxus who was a member of the Platonic Academy, and the solution appears in Euclid's *Elements* as highly sophisticated arithmetic and geometry. But the crisis in the Pythagorean society has been repeated many times in the history of technology and science. It is the archetype of all those strains that exist between the technologist and the scientist, in which professional secrets play such varied roles.

Organization of the Arts in the Past

The arts organize themselves into crafts and guilds of artisans and technicians. They pass on the skills to their apprentices, they improve the arts, and they tend to have trade secrets. They also tend to generate and maintain theories that add understanding to skill. The so-called Hippocratic writings can be read with greater insight and penetration if they are understood as either exoteric or esoteric attempts to come to terms with two aspects of medicine—the arts of diagnosis, prognosis, and therapy on the one hand, and the sciences of anatomy and physiology on the other. Sometimes the writer is persuading prospective patients of the competence of the physician. Sometimes he is trying to persuade his professional colleagues of the truth of his theories. Galen later struggles through with the help of Plato and Aristotle to the establishment of theoretical medicine and the self-recognition of the profession. Primitive as Galenic medicine may seem at present, and corrupt as it may have been at certain stages, it was the only medicine practiced for fifteen hundred years. It set the standards for its own profession and for the other professions of law, theology, and teaching up to our time, when it seems that any sense of profession except its economic aspects of monopoly is evanescent.

The Pythagorean society, as far as we know it, seems to be the pre-professional prototype of what professions came to be. Its chief theoretical holdings seem to have been mathematical at a time when mathematics almost alone led the pursuit of theoretical knowledge. The word mathematics originally meant learning and things learned. The society was a novel kind of cult which generated and transmitted learning. This function was chiefly performed by the esoteric part of the brotherhood. It taught a somewhat vulgarized version of its knowledge to the exoteric members of the society which seemed to have made up the citizenry of a city, Crotona. The vulgarized learning was ethical and political in nature. The society was responsible for what it decided to investigate and what it decided to teach. It added to its membership and transmitted its learning from one generation to another. It is quite clear that the Hippocratic oath for medicine formalizes an imitation and adaptation of the Pythagorean learning to a more specialized body of learning. In both cases there was a tendency to unify a body of knowledge and to respect theory as magisterial and architectonic for a self-governing community of scholars, teachers, and practitioners of an art or body of arts. The secrecy of the cult is a sign at once of the lack and the need for some formal institutional structure which the social environment of the time did not supply or recognize.

Connected with the development of certain arts into professions by the development of appropriate bodies of theoretical knowledge is a medieval distinction between the kinds of arts that was not emphasized explicitly by the Greeks. Certain arts which had reached a professional status were practiced on human beings, who also had artistic capacities. In these human subjects of the arts there were primary natural and secondary natural processes which if left to themselves might accomplish their ends, but if aided by the professional would accomplish their ends more easily and more fully. Medicine and teaching were the frequently discussed examples of such arts. They were called cooperative arts because they were understood to be cooperating with rational natures.

But the term cooperative suggests that there might be another kind of distinction among the arts, those that can be practiced by the individual without needing aid and those that cannot be practiced without the cooperation of other artists. Building or architecture is a borderline case since presumably single men have often built their own houses and barns. But there are building operations that are unlikely to be undertaken and completed without the collaboration of many artists, such as the building of temples like the Parthenon or the cathedrals, which in many cases occupied several generations of many men. The brotherhood of free masonry was a society with secrets and standards of skill that recognized this kind of organized or collective art as its responsibility. Similarly, the building of harbors, aqueducts, and roads call for the orderly organization of many men and many arts.

There have been many kinds of organization that have met the need for order in the divisions of labor. Typically the Romans allocated this organizing function to the army for their greater public works, as the Greeks and Egyptians had trained and managed slaves. Self-governing guilds have often passed through their technological periods on their way from religious cults to polities. We tend to forget this ubiquitousness of organization in the arts since Adam Smith established the science of economics on the thesis that the market both dictates the division of labor and gives a semblance of organization to it. We forget that he also was giving the first description of the organized factory. Although he warned against the organization of the arts by the corporation, he actually laid the ground for its modern predominance. The market now appears to be a rather long, lively, and fruitful interim of disorganization of the much longer continuum of highly organized technology.

Present Organization of the Arts

I know no competent discussion of the question that this series of organizations of the arts seems to pose. There is the often quoted maxim of Marx and Engels that the means of production determine social and even cultural forms. Neither they nor anybody else has worked out the dialectical or other details of such determination. The question I am posing is somewhat simpler. What are the forms of organization that the arts demand for themselves? The Egyptians seem to say a slave system; the Greeks at one stage say a polity; the Romans say an army; the Middle Ages and many other ages say guilds; the eighteenth and nineteenth centuries seem to say the market; we seem to be saying now that the corporation is the answer. These seem to be little more than historical correlations. They do not answer the question that is now inescapable. We are very far and rapidly moving farther away from the individual craftsman who needs only to pay attention to his own art. The present organization of the arts, what we call our technological system, has passed beyond the powers of any of the preceding forms of organization. How shall we bring it into order and effective service to the human community?

Bright-eyed observers tell us that the answer is already given and that we are more than half-way accepting it in practice. The human arts will be completely built into automatic machines. Human beings are in principle in the position of the Pharaohs, freed from labor. Technology and art which can no longer be turned over to slaves can be given to machines. Peter Drucker tells us that we unknowingly have trained ourselves to behave so much like machines that the substitutions of machines for men is easy. During the final stages of automation we shall have to increase our engineering skills and scientific knowledge in order to finish the job in style and keep the apparatus in condition, but our main business will be those activities that free men have traditionally called leisure. Whether this be good prediction or prescription or not, we need to know a little more about how and why the possibility of automation confronts us.

The so-called Industrial Revolution has had many dimensions and causes. On the technological level the substitution of machines for tools seems to have been the essential change. The revolution has been the progressive passage from " manufacture " to " machino-facture." This process can be understood as the extension and penetration of the principle of the division of labor into technics. As labor was broken down into elementary crafts and integrated by exchange in the market, so complex operations in a given craft were broken down and re-assembled—sometimes with mechanical operations substituted for manual operations, sometimes with the multiplication and integration of many more operations than the original craftsman could manage. Usually this organization of operations was connected with the new prime movers—steam and gas engines, motors and generators—to supply the greater demand for energy. The factory was the progressive institution that could push the analysis of the jobs and organize both men and machines into larger patterns of organized operations.

Two parallel transformations can be seen in this factory system. The concatenation of machines and the use of the new prime movers progressively removed the human agent-artist from the linkages between the machines. The products of the separate arts or crafts were no longer the ends of the operations but rather materials for stages in the overall production process. To be sure there was an integrated end-product, but the many intermediate ends became mere means.

The consequent or parallel development would be what Europeans call rationalization, the formulation of the rules that control the productive process. In the crafts a great deal could be left to unverbalized and unmeasured skills. After fine analysis of jobs their reintegration needs both elaborate verbal and mathematical expression, not merely to pass on the crafts from one generation to another as in the past, but now for the coordination and management of the going technical process. This amounts to an emphatic return to the original ancient meaning of *technologia*, the giving of rules to the arts. It also connects with the development of the new techniques in analytical mathematics or algebra.

The invention and establishment of algebra as the art of mathematical analysis blots out many of the distinctions that older mathematics had maintained. For instance, arithmetic and geometry are no longer distinct. So when the factory is rationalized, it is hard to maintain any distinction between men and machines. They both are values in equations of efficiency. This suggests two alternative possibilities which have worried us for a long time. Shall machines be taught to think, as in computers; or shall men become robots? Automation offers its solution of the dilemma. It will teach machines to think and also to do the work, so that emancipated man may occupy himself with the liberal arts, politics, the fine arts, and the divine arts . . . until such time as men wish to automate these arts as well and free themselves for still higher existence.

What of the Future?

We are here on the edge of something eerie and not a little puzzling to the pragmatic mind. Let's see if we can establish our position, as the navigator says, and maybe plot a course or two. The kind of abstraction that makes us see automation as an all-encompassing net is like the thinking that the Pythagoreans did when they first happened upon the tricks of measurement. The story goes that they did this with the monochord, a string that vibrated in a musical tone according to its length—the shorter the length, the higher the tone, and the lengths could be expressed in whole numbers or integers. The Pythagorean mind quickly generalized, thinking of many things that could be reduced to numbers, and quickly concluded in a kind of arithmetical astrology that all things are numbers or shadows of numbers. It is hard for even a modern pragmatic mind to deny what is after all the basis for the great successes of mathematical physics. The Pythagoreans identified this process of measurement with music, and in celebration of their discovery made poetry about the music of the spheres, not failing to continue their development of the science of mathematics even to our day.

Plato took the Pythagorean theme as commonplace, and went on to develop a theory of ideas which had the same trick of abstraction and hypostasis in it, but included along with numbers many other kinds of ideas. It is a childish kind of Platonist that turns the trick into metaphysics, as Plato says in the great confrontation of the young Socrates with the venerable Parmenides. But Plato recognized the moment in the long life of dialectic as important and even essential to the intellectual enterprise. The theory of ideas, reformulated as the Logos doctrine, has had as long a life as the Pythagorean doctrine. Its development has been somewhat more versatile, serving law as natural law, serving theology as a person of the Trinity, supplying common sense with its root in reason.

As I suggested earlier, Plato might with his skill in abstraction and hypostasis have " found " a system of the arts, a set of rules for the arts, that would have reflected as in a mirror the firmament of his ideas, the ideas of his theory of ideas. There is a suspicion in his allegory of the cave that there was a level of artificial objects which made a kind of logistic pattern midway between the shadows on the wall and the ideal stars in the heavenly firmament. If he had been faced with the panoply of artificial technical operations, processes and products among which we live, he surely would have been led to construct something like the technical phenomenon that we find in Jacques Ellul's *La Technique*.

There is a great difference between Anglo-American and continental European thought about technology. The German and French philosophical traditions are more hospitable to many-storeyed imagination and speculation. Whatever we may think of Hegel and Marx as artificers of ideologies, their speculative skill and boldness, and their recognition of levels of being and action are not to be ignored or condemned. So French thought has always had a clear strong line of analytical thought established and controlled by the Cartesian discovery or invention of algebra or analytic geometry. Descartes generalized his discovery and hypostatized it in his own style. He called it the Great Art, *Ars Magna*, and thought of it as the universal method for the intellectual enterprise. He saw algebra, or analytic mathematics, as the master architectonic art of all the arts.

The essential power of all these abstractions and hypostases resides in their objective universality. They give clarity and logical mobility to speculation or theory. This kind of thinking gave us the great hypothetical worlds of modern physics: the systems of the worlds of gravitation, heat, and electricity within which our more empirical investigations still explore. So the idea of technology or of the technical phenomenon of Ellul offers us the schema for a logistic of the arts, a genuine theory of technology.

Suppose we accept some such abstraction, hypostatization, and universalizing of technology. What shall we make of it intellectually and practically? There seem to be three possibilities with some variation in each of the three. We may accept the technical logistic as a system of determinism, a kind of artificial fate which we have brought upon ourselves or in which we have been trapped. A superficial reading of Ellul tempts one to this conclusion. But Ellul himself warns us that this is not his intention, unrelenting as his method may seem.

We may see it as a system that has developed piecemeal without our intention except with regard to its slowly developing parts. A key to this view seems to be hidden in Ellul's many comments that the system has reduced all things, including our ends and purposes, to means. In other language this means that we have developed an un-limited, autonomous, universal system of exploitation. Both the things in nature and in human nature come under the sweep of unrelenting exploitation. We have been pious in the later stages about exempting men from the exploitation; they must be conceived as ends in them-selves. But the only assurance that this is still respected is that we have kept free contracts and the democratic processes. The irony of this may be that we have supposed that men themselves will not knowingly submit to exploitation. There is much evidence to the contrary. We may have at least temporarily been enchanted to submit our bodies and souls to the contingent processes of self-reduction to means. This comes close to my understanding of the alarm that Ellul is sounding. He is trying to wake the prisoners in Plato's cave and incite them to throw off the chains of their empirical piecemeal thinking about themselves.

If this is a good guess, the wide-awake conclusion might be that we should accept the logistic clarities and necessities in the technical phe-nomenon and do a thorough job of searching out the articulations in it, of looking to the shape of the integrated system, with a view to remaking by disassembly and reassembly the most familiar and least understood phenomena of our time.

It may be recalled that this abstraction of technics from the arts, the rules from the actual makings, leaves the agent-artist and his ends out. For the sake of organization they are assimilated as merely means. Thus we are left with an apparent automaton, an almost integrated and auto-mated technical system. But it is merely a stage in development and dialectical understanding. If we are to deal with it competently, we must find some way of bringing back human artists and human ends into the powerful order that the technological system presents to our amazed and puzzled view. My suggestion is that we trace the human role that the system involves and detect where we have surrendered our judgments and our wills. If we can find these points of default, we may be able to recover our truly scientific understandings, our objective knowledge of our ends and the ends of nature, and our individual and common wills. This might give us back our reverence and love of nature as well as our shrewd ingenuities in exploiting it.

Nature, Science, and Techology

THE PLACE OF HUMANISM IN A TECHNOLOGICAL WORLD

WILLY HARTNER*

I have trained myself in maintaining a last residue of optimism in the changing situation of the last forty years, despite the fact that its only constant characteristic was its apparent hopelessness. I therefore do not answer the central problem of our Conference by saying that the impact of technology on our modern world has proved sufficiently disastrous to show us that there is no more hope. I dare claim that there still is hope.

It appears that for some strange reason the last chances to save modern civilization from definitive bankruptcy and annihilation have not yet been missed. This was certainly not due to lack of circumspection on the part of the leading men of our time. Ever since the end of World War I they have evidenced an indefatigable industry to stop any hole through which a fresh breeze carrying along a new idea might percolate into the necropolis of human culture. And the millions in their custody, shaken by an everlasting frantic anxiety about perishing in one danger or the other, bless any step whatever taken in order to prevent the cataclysm from occurring tomorrow. A few succeed in not succumbing to the mass hysteria. It is on them that I place my hope, which is the last of all hopes.

Am I exaggerating? I leave it to you to decide. At the present moment, while I am writing this, the papers disclose the following news: The President of the United States, after having consulted with the leading scientists and military and other experts, has decided, at least in principle, that the open-air atom tests will be resumed. Four such tests are probably to be made in the nearest future. The men he consulted in taking this decision are the leading scientific, military, and political figures of the United States. Is he aware that a great expert on atomic fission who has devoted twenty or more years of his life to develop the most efficient, dreadful and inhuman kind of a bomb, will not necessarily be a philosopher? Does he not know that, on the contrary, the general wisdom of the greatest specialist will in all probability be lower than that of the average citizen? Don't we all remember that only a very few of our specialists—Einstein, Max

* Willy Hartner is Professor of the History of Natural Sciences and Prorector of the University of Frankfurt-am-Main.

Born, more recently Otto Hahn, and a few others—have ever given a serious thought to the philosophical aspect of the Atomic Age? As for the generals, I have not yet met the one whose philosophy is not exhausted with the idea that the safety of a country depends on the quality and amount of its arms. About the year 80 A. D. the great scientist-engineer Hero of Alexandria claimed to have devised a type of super-catapult capable of throwing stones or burning torches over a distance of hundreds of feet, which would exclude the possibility of war for all times to come. Ever since, if not already 2000 years before, the politicians have praised the Heros of their day as the preservers of peace. But what has been a joke until recently (though each of the bad jokes cost thousands and later millions of lives and cultural values) is getting serious by now. And time is getting precious.

Experts with whom I had a chance to discuss the newest phase of events tell me that the problem at present is not a new kind of atom bomb, nor any particular unknown effect produced by them, but the anti-missile missile, the possession of which will safeguard peace or, in case this should prove an error, at least survival. I abstained from asking when the anti-anti-missile missile will be due, and why the resumption of atomic tests is under discussion if they don't constitute the real problem.

Am I exaggerating? Ex-President Truman, when asked by British journalists some years ago, proudly said that in case he had to decide once more he would order the atom bombs to be thrown again on Hiroshima and Nagasaki. It's a safe feeling to know that whatever one has done is right. It's worse for a poor chap like the one who carried out the order. He was suddenly overcome by what old-fashioned people call remorse, though of course he had done the world's most normal thing, namely, to obey orders. Seeing no other way out of his difficulties he started doing abnormal things, got into conflict with the law, and was eventually declared insane. It is merely consistent with the situation prevailing in all camps today that his letters, which bear no witness whatever to moral insanity, have become a tool in the hands of Communist propagandists. Hence any man attempting to evaluate them (and their author) objectively risks classification as a Communist or fellow-traveler himself.

What about President de Gaulle, who thinks that the glory of France depends on the possession and independent use of the miracle bomb? What about the defense minister of Western Germany, who on visiting the White House pronounced similar ambitions on behalf of his mutilated country, only recently defeated and solemnly declared disarmed for all time to come after the greatest moral breakdown of German culture and then, within less than a decade, rearmed anew at the victors' most urgent request? Recent reports about tens of thousands of young people in Russia looking for a new way of life, for freedom from the bondage of political indoctrinations, do not seem to have impressed any of our Western politicians. How can we make them understand that it's neither the anti-missile missile nor the astronaut Glenn that can encourage those youngsters to pursue their aim—to regain personal freedom—which involves a tremendous personal danger, but in fact is the sole aim that justifies the highest sacrifice?

We have watched the complete failure of Western expansionism and proselytism. Whatever is touched by our hands is doomed to wither. Should we not admit as a fact, eventually, that all the great civilizations have perished after having contacted the West? It is a cheap excuse to say that they were rotten before. For even if this were true, with our taking over the power—be it in large parts of the Far East, in India, or in Africa—we have simultaneously taken over the responsibility, and no means can possibly be found to explain this away. Now we see Africa in flames. We are watching the total extirpation of the world's oldest living civilization and its substitution by the dullest of doctrines grown on the tree of European philosophy. We have just seen the leader of modern India, admired for unknown reasons by many, walk in the steps of fascist or communist aggressors. Yet our belief in our own mission, in our righteousness, and in the progressiveness of our culture remains unshaken.

The non-European peoples have good historical reasons to hate us, and they do indeed hate us with all their heart, although the original reasons for this hatred have fallen into oblivion. At the same time their highest objective is to imitate our way of life, to adopt our technical civilization with all its useful as well as its most useless products, and to eradicate what is left of the values that once formed the basis of their life. And we, intoxicated by the idea that whatever Western genius has invented is good for everyone, go on exporting indiscriminately all our goods: beads, liquors, machines, gadgets, literary products from the Divine Comedy down to the comic strips, democracy with all its political theories including socialism and communism, Christianity, and the belief in progress. Apart from archaeologists, ethnologists, and a few romantic collectors of exotic art, not many are aware that those so-called primitive cultures, the last remnants of which we collect carefully in our museums, have had their own intrinsic values. Fewer still perceive that any attempt to replace them by the standards of our own civilization must create chaotic confusion, which leads eventually to a radical negation of the values of human life altogether. By transplanting our democratic ideals and institutions (which function badly enough in our own countries) on civilizations in which individualism and personal spiritual independence are completely unknown concepts, we make them an easy prey to communism, whose interpretation of freedom and democracy is the most cynical perversion of great ideas. Africa, India, Indonesia, South and Central America are all threatened in the same way, thanks to the import of European and American immature ideas. They act like the germs of the most dangerous contagious disease, and, due to a strange automatism observable on many occasions, they will in the long run conquer and destroy our constantly weakening Western civilization too.

I am not defending cannibalism (though a closer study of this phenomenon reveals a certain cleanliness of thought which is alien to our modern civilization) nor do I advocate a utopian return to the primitive life. On the contrary, being aware of the immense beneficial possibilities of modern science and technology, I only venture to recommend that we stop the breathtaking realization of all the utopian dreams of our boyhood, to make the juvenile pioneers of science on both sides of the Iron Curtain understand that there are moral limits to scientific curiosity and that science and technology as the handmaidens of politics are not more worthy of praise than philosophy was as the handmaid of theology in bygone days. We should understand, finally, that our belief that the progress of humanity will result automatically from the progress of science is the most dangerous of all superstitions. All evidence being against it, it is incompatible with our modern inductive way of thought, and we should therefore abjure it definitively. As I cannot expect you to be content with this apodictic statement alone, may I be allowed to illustrate it.

In the course of the last 350 years, Western man's main concern, in consequence of an apparent intrinsic automatism, has been totally reversed. At the outset of our modern era, our ancestors became intoxicated by Francis Bacon's and other great men's captivating prophecy that man would be able not only to explore all the secrets of nature, but also to dominate nature, to make her the slave of the scientist. Each step taken to attain the utopian objective promised to break one more of the links by which man had been enslaved to a dogmatic world-view and chained to his own prejudices and superstitions. For three centuries the scientists tried to find the kernel of the fruit they were searching, and each new discovery seemed to confirm that man, finally, was on the right way—for never before in human history had there been progress comparable with the one now lying open to everybody's eye. Only during the last half-century did scientists gradually start recognizing on one hand, that the object of their investigation, nature, was not a fruit with a kernel, but rather an onion (Peer Gynt's onion!) with a thousand layers; on the other, that " progress" was a most delusive notion, indefinable in scientific or philosophic terms.

This new discovery was not bound to stop their industry, and this could indeed not be expected. What was amazing, however, was that only a very few of them became aware at the same late time that their practical philosophy based on that tricky notion of progress was a new kind, and at the same time the greatest of all superstitions. For what entitles man to assume dogmatically that the artificial progress of scientific knowledge and technological methods automatically involves the progress of humanity altogether? What does progress of humanity mean, by the way? Is it identical with better material conditions of life, social security, literacy, a better sociological doctrine, and a stricter social order? Or should there be some more to it which cannot be said in one single term? I believe we agree that the latter is true, and it will be worthwhile to analyze it. But before doing so, let us come back to our starting point.

Man's central problem today no longer can be to realize the utopia, but on the contrary to prevent it from becoming a definitive reality. For that, if we are to escape physical destruction would mean the end of humanity, the end of human civilization, and the beginning of a new way of life modeled after the communities of ants and termites. Not all of us seem to be aware that what Paul Valéry, about the end of World War I, visioned as the new type of a human-animal community —"*la grande fourmilière*," the great ant heap—has meantime been realized not only in communist and fascist societies, but to a large extent also in our Western, so-called "free" societies. Smaller still is the number of those who are able to understand and willing to admit that any measure taken exclusively for the purpose of defending materially our "free" society effaces by necessity the difference still existing between our own society and that of the East, and precipitates the process of enslavement.

We cannot indeed render our potential enemy greater service than by fighting the cold war on the place he prescribes to us. All our energy, during the first years after World War II, was concentrated on proving our material superiority. We waste it now on competing with him in devising superbombs capable of blowing more human beings to smaller pieces than was the superbomb of last year. Truly a noble task worthy of a civilization which still claims to be the world's greatest.

We still cherish the bad habit of boasting about the great men of the past, from Plato down to Hugo de Groot, Kant, Goethe, and Einstein. But what does their greatness mean to us if we do not try to live up to it, to the best of our faculties? We still pretend that our civilization is based on the principles of Christian ethics, above all Christian love, but it never occurs to us that the Christian commandment to love one's enemy could be made the governing principle of our communities. I cannot but deplore the youngster who on one hand is told to love his neighbor, even if he be his enemy, and on the other to be proud that his country possesses the world's most destructive arms. How is it possible to believe that this endemic schizophrenia, created by ourselves, should not affect our children and destroy their personalities, just as our own personalities have been poisoned and destroyed by the schizophrenic teachings of our elders, and theirs in turn way back through dozens of generations?

Is the term "endemic schizophrenia" appropriate to characterize our situation? I am afraid it is, and venture to adduce some proofs to my unpleasant assertion here: I am just old enough to remember in all details the time immediately before and during World War I, and not yet old enough to see the characteristic events of that period in a less unpleasant light than they deserve. I know nothing about American conditions at that time, but I do know something about the general situation prevailing among the average educated men in Europe. In spite of the growing and artificially inflated nationalism, there still existed a rather strong feeling of a European solidarity, a certain aware-ness of common roots definable by the traditional religions and human-istic values common to and respected by all concerned. There sub-sisted at the same time the dilettantic belief, inherited from the pioneers of science in the nineteenth century, in the benign, civilizing effect of science and technology, a kind of technological humanism that would automatically vouchsafe mankind's development towards a higher and purer stage of civilization. International friendships and an increasing racial tolerance, above all the normal educated man's aversion to anti-Semitism were typical symptoms of the time. Remember the noble fury that arose all over the civilized world in connection with the Dreyfus affair.

I am not speaking of the politicians, whose attitude was entirely different, but I dare claim that their aims and dreams were not shared by the majority of those whose fate depended on the decisions taken by them.

The outbreak of the war caused a change as radical and appalling as it could be. The Christian God, until then allegedly a god common to all, suddenly revealed himself as a multitude of national deities, and it was those different Huitzilopochtlis and Tezcatlipocas, each of them the deadly enemy of the other, who thenceforth were mobilized as the protectors of their various peoples and nations and to whom the priests and the laymen willingly sacrificed the millions. The creatures shaped in the image of their perverted gods proved worthy of them. A former personal friend beyond the trenches and barbed wire fences now was bound to be, and really *was* the despised enemy whose annihi-lation was a patriotic cause.

Not even the noblest spirits in the hostile camps, until then ardent defenders of the humanistic ideal, were immune to the contagion. I invite those who have forgotten Thomas Mann's panegyrics on the war as the " steel-bath " of German youth (" indeed, we had forgotten what beautiful and splendid a thing war can be ") to re-read them in the diary of one of the very few great, consistent, and independent humanists and anti-nationalists, Romain Rolland's *Journal des années de guerre 1914-18*. This book, published only ten years ago, long after the death of its author, deserves with all its 2000 pages greater attention than it hitherto has had. Whoever reads it carefully will agree that hardly ever before has there been a large-scale treachery of the humanistic ideal comparable to this.

World War I could have sufficed to prove that the traditional distinction between victors and defeated no longer made sense. For how can material gains or losses—reparations to the presumptive benefit of the victor, destined to "punish" the defeated—make up, on one hand, for the losses of human lives and values and, on the other, for imposing the task of peaceful reconstruction on a weakened and mainly disillusioned generation?

Indeed there still were men on both sides who had learned from their tragic experiences and recognized the futility of the idols mankind had worshipped. But their efforts were frustrated either by the gangs of patriotic murderers who, in Germany, branded every attempt at reconciliation with the former enemy as treason, or by the age-old hatred of the victors, in whose eyes only the dead German was a good German.

It was in those years of the most pitiful confusion that the young Austrian Count Coudenhove-Kalergi started his campaign for a better understanding based on the common humanistic tradition of all peoples of Europe. Thanks to his indefatigable efforts, some of the greatest statesmen—Stresemann, Briand, finally Churchill—became adherents of the new idea; by 1928, the new movement had gained considerable influence and become a dreaded adversary in the eyes of the defenders of the old concept that only the "balance of power" (i. e., the superiority of arms at the disposal of *my* nation) is capable of maintaining peace. Owing to the premature death of Stresemann, followed shortly by that of his generous partner, Briand, the attempt to find a new solution to the world's oldest problem was frustrated, and the movement, supported by the best and most constructive spirits of Europe, practically died away. No great effort on the part of its opponents was necessary to redress the old situation.

By the beginning of the thirties, communism in Russia had become sufficiently consolidated, and its propaganda abroad a sufficiently obvious threat, to make the Western politicians start looking out for efficient and cheap protection against the evil. It was not due to the fear of succumbing to intolerable spiritual slavery, but rather due to the threat of material loss and subjugation that immediate steps were deemed necessary. (If European political history is to be reduced to the simplest formula, we might say that it is a continuous series of immediate steps taken without premeditation according to the merit of the emergency). It cannot possibly astonish us that the strongest man available was regarded as the best man. It is far from my mind to exonerate one single German citizen of his treacherous passing over into the ranks of the previously despised and ridiculed leader of the Nazi Party; but it is for the sake of an impartial evaluation of the historic facts that I point out also the miserable role of the fence-sitting

European nations which carefully avoided taking efficient measures to do away with the evil while there still was time (by breaking off diplomatic relations after the first boycott of Jews in April, 1933, or at the latest after Goering's official announcement in the summer of the same year that the " enemies of the people " henceforth should be sent without trials to the newly established concentration camps). At that time Hitler's aggressivity was not yet directed against the Western democracies, which fact seemed sufficient to tolerate him and even to welcome his existence as a bulwark against a potential aggression of communism. Even the last chance to do away with him and to settle this most sinister matter in a peaceful way was missed when, on March 7, 1936, Hitler's phony remilitarization of the Rhineland with the aid of a couple of battalions—a flagrant violation of the Rapallo Treaty—was not answered by an efficient action on the part of the signatories of the named treaty.

I may be saved the trouble of completing this brief survey of fatal errors, for each one of us still has the tragic evolution fresh in his memory to do it on his own. It was not, I repeat, in order to reduce or minimize the enormous guilt of my compatriots—including my own guilt in those cases in which, owing to fear or lack of circumspection, I may have failed to do the utmost to counteract the evil. The question of guilt is not of interest in this context; the only thing I feel urged to say about it here is that however great the guilt of others may be, it does not make my own less grave, and in no case can the concept of moral guilt be applied to groups. It makes sense solely when applied to the individual.

Of the most recent evolution, only a few facts seem of such vital importance that it would be a serious omission not to mention them: In August, 1939, Hitler and Stalin signed their non-aggression treaty which enabled them to wipe out the Polish state, which turned over large parts of Eastern Europe to Russian Communism, and which gave Hitler a free hand to wage his imperialistic war against the Western democracies, as well as against the very idea of democracy. It was one of the great crookeries, worthy of two consciously inhuman dictatorships. Owing to Hitler's treachery against his own accomplice, however, the Western democracies, to their own great surprise, suddenly found themselves fighting side by side with Communist Russia, until then the bugbear of the free world. Instead of taking this change of the situation as a necessary evil and trying to keep aloof from emotional implications, all but a few of the statesmen of the West deemed it a necessity to revise their former opinion of their new ally—be it only in order to enhance the morale of their armies—until they finally succumbed to their own propaganda and accepted as a fact that Soviet Russia had become a democracy. The fatal effect of this deplorable inconsistency is too well known to be discussed here.

World War II, fought to defeat an inhuman adversary, brought an inhuman ally to the zenith of his power. World War II was ended by a crime which at the time was considered a necessity. It seemed an evil omen that the powers residing in the interior of the atom were unchained for the first time to serve not the benefit of human culture, but its destruction. And the events characterizing the last fifteen years confirmed the evil expectations provoked by the sinister outset.

It is pretty late to ponder possible means to remedy a merciless situation. I have a sincere admiration for the consistency of our leading men today who, even after this last gigantic failure, go on believing in the balance (= superiority) of power. My admiration, to be sure, is limited to the consistency, not to anything else.

May I ask what protection against an aggressor better weapons can mean today? After the Russians have tested a 50- or 100-megaton bomb, will the 200-megaton bomb to be constructed by the West " guarantee peace? " May I ask, moreover, in the case of an atomic war, what pleasure or satisfaction the man will have who, after having shot down his neighbor who failed to build a shelter and tried to enter his, emerges from his foxhole in due time after the attack to find a devastation that is ten or a hundred times as horrible as that of Hiroshima and Nagasaki? Do we all suffer from a progressive destruction of our grey brain substance, or is it just due to our technical gadgets that we all have stopped thinking and that even our imaginative power has been reduced to perfect imbecility?

It seems obvious that any society which concentrates all its forces on material defense alone and neglects the human aspects of life must deteriorate and become more and more similar to the authoritarian adversary. My question, then, is what we finally will be to defend.

To him who believes in arms and retaliation, I venture to say as a kind of consolation that even the stock of several thousand old-fashioned atom bombs up to the explosive capacity of only 30 megatons will probably suffice to strike back efficiently several times before we are completely wiped out. To the others, who still think there are human values worth living for, may I suggest they try to get rid of the hysteria and emulate Titian, who at the age of not far from a hundred thought of creating a new style of painting. We always speak about the necessity of defending our freedom, but only few of us seem aware that freedom is not something given to us and protected by others, but a spiritual ideal susceptible of development that forms an integral and decisive part of our personality. In a higher sense, the concept of freedom is inseparable from that of personal responsibility, and personal responsibility implies a conscious and conscientious willingness to contribute one's share to our democratic community; it implies also a constructive criticism whenever we observe that measures taken in the name of our community are incompatible with the ideal of humanism. As concerns this highest thinkable ideal, I am aware that it is difficult to define it in unambiguous words.

For practical purposes, however, I believe it will suffice in most cases to identify it with the principle not to allow any personal or group interest or ideal—be it national, religious, racial—to prevail over interests or ideals of a higher order, i. e., those of humanity.

Does it not seem a tempting, a really noble, purpose, to walk in the steps of the centenarian Titian and devise, in the very last minute, a new way of life?

We willingly have allowed the Russians to impose on us an arms race which gradually has become the greatest luxury in history. Why should not we in turn impose on them, here and now, a peaceful race to better social and sanitary conditions, medical research, and all that is capable of improving efficiently the material standard of life? This would be a great service to humanity, and it would be in line with one of the two main aspects of humanism. As concerns the other, I could describe it in no better way than by quoting a word of Bergson which I had the pleasure of getting acquainted with only recently: " Le corps de l'humanité démesurement aggrandi par la technique attend un supplément d'âme."

Nature, Science, and Technology
COMMENTARY

RICHARD L. MEIER *

The papers for this session contain three major themes. Hartner's paper discusses the endemic schizophrenia that exists in society, Buchanan is concerned with exploitation, and Lewis Mumford † emphasizes the organization of science. Rather than analyze these themes in detail I would like to indicate some of the relationships hitherto not brought up between nature, humanistic studies, and the sciences.

The sites of the classical origins of our culture are now homes for technology. Last August I visited Athens and discovered that there, as in Los Angeles, the uninhabitable peaks are the most valuable real estate because the distribution of mass culture depends on the installation of electronic equipment on these peaks. On Mt. Pelion, where the centaurs gambolled, machines commune with the satellites. On Olympus and Hymettus, the places once used for worship are occupied by electronic military installations that guide ships or look for missiles. The classical meanings attached to these locales have been overridden by technological demands.

While the lands of antiquity have been changed to suit science, the humanities have become sterile. This sterility can be illustrated by comparing the number of images that exist in the humanities with those in science and applied science. " Image " here means a conception or phenomenon that can be communicated and that is generally or publicly held. For example, a chemical compound with specific properties that has been produced more than once and identified by more than one investigator would be such an image. A species that more than one investigator had identified and classified would be a single image in the public domain. LSD would be more than one image, because it is not only a chemical compound but there are a series of images attached to it as a psychological material.

Using the " key word " method, a system for searching out the content of scientific work, it is possible to determine and compare the output of images of various fields since the same methods of indexing are used in law, medicine, chemistry, psychology, geophysics, and so on. A count of these annual outputs shows that images in the scientific and technological areas are growing at ten to fourteen per cent per year, psychology perhaps five to seven per cent, law at one and a half per cent—and law is growing faster than the humanities. The number of images within the humanities already amounts to less than ten per cent of the total images available to man, which encompass the total concepts and phenomena of contemporary culture. The humanities seem to have cut themselves off from the modern lines of creativity in general cultural activity. Perhaps

---

* Richard L. Meier is a professor in the School of Natural Resources at the University of Michigan. His books include *Modern Science and the Human Fertility Problem* (New York, 1959) and *Science and Economic Development* (Cambridge, 1956).
† See footnote, p. 535.

170

we are coming to a time when the humanities will be but a minor part of human endeavor. Far richer will be the debris left behind the progress of technology and science. Numberless scientific advances already wait for the historian of science and the historian of technology to find, analyze, and explain them. Such a diminution of the humanities in the face of the terrible human problems science has brought forth would be serious indeed.

But science may not continue its headlong acceleration. As Ritchie Calder pointed out, there are plateaus in the growth of science and technology. Rigid organization or lack of intellectual resources slow the advance of new knowledge in science. A dearth of recruits may bring about the next leveling off. Only between five and ten per cent of high school students are capable of carrying science forward. Many bright young people challenged by ideas are not oriented to science. As the scientific frontiers have expanded and become interlocking and interdependent, the number of trained minds needed to advance scientific knowledge has become ever greater. The baby boom of the 1940's provided us with a supply of talent that may last through the next five or ten years. But by 1970 or 1975 the raw material for continued growth of the body of scientific personnel will run short.

When the scientific boom levels off there is hope that a new branch of the humanities will take the lead and expand with the same exponential rapidity science experienced. Scientific manpower will be insufficient, and science may be de-emphasized as an intellectual pursuit, but the humanities may have better talent for its modern development that has ever before been available. An exciting generation of young people is growing up in this country. They have a serious concern about the kind of world we are making for ourselves, a great aptitude for organizing and bringing ideas to fruition, and an ideology of service.

The intensity of student concern over ways of applying new knowledge to the construction of a civilization was vividly evidenced at a seminar I recently visited at the University of Michigan. It was run by Marston Bates, the well-known ecologist and zoologist. Something like sixteen major fields were represented among the twenty-five seminar participants, ranging from art, English literature, and journalism to business administration, engineering, and physics. The group had chosen to investigate utopias. They were particularly interested in the ways of life that new kinds of science and new kinds of political organization open up.

Ethical questions, rather than materialistic, scientific questions engrossed these students. They discussed exploitation as a significant concept in understanding the problems of the newly developing countries. There two levels of culture exist—the international, technological level and the local, traditional level. Techniques are introduced to newly developing countries through a small, modern contingent within the society. The traditional culture does not understand the modern contingent and thinks it can be exploited, since the modern group offers payments—prices for raw material and services—at unheard of levels. Thus the traditional society exploits the modern at the same time the modern is exploiting the traditional. Since both tend to profit, this mutual exploitation is worthwhile. The modern grows and produces more goods which makes the traditional more prosperous and introduces change into an otherwise static culture. The main difficulty is an ethical one. The modern interests have superior weapons—they possess the power of technology. Is it possible to prevent the premature destruction of the traditional culture and to maintain the balance of beneficial exploitation?

The seminar focussed on the human implications of an experiment done with rats by the Mental Health Research Institute. These rats had electrodes inserted into the pleasure centers of the brain. They could press a pedal in their " Skinner box " and give themselves a jolt of pleasure which lasted a couple of seconds. They could then scurry to the other side of the box, re-set the pedal by turning a wheel, rush back and give themselves another jolt of pleasure. Connecting this experiment to immediate human concerns is not far-fetched. Electrodes have been experimentally inserted into human brains. Neurologists of several countries felt that some kind of experimentation should be done with humans in view of the discoveries made about brain functions in experiments on monkeys and other anthropoids. They sought a unique situation such as would prevent imitative experiments, and found it in the consequences of the influenza epidemic of 1921 which had caused malfunction or degeneration of the brain in severe cases. These patients, still hospitalized, were very close to being dead. They had minds frozen inside their bodies and had no control of any kind. They could not feed themselves and had been unable to smile for years. Electrodes were introduced into their brains, and in a matter of days the individuals could smile. Later they could eat in a normal fashion and even drink a glass of water. The studies made of these responses show that our knowledge of the human brain is already sufficient to utilize the same techniques on people that were used on the rats. The electrodes destroyed brain tissue, but there has been a breakthrough in the last three years. Natural compounds can be delivered through micro-pipettes to the pleasure centers, and there is no apparent loss of brain activity.

The ethics of applying this kind of scientific knowledge seriously worried these students. They suggested that " pursuit of happiness " was one of the basic Jeffersonian assumptions on which the American political system was built, and the capture of that state of being seemed close at hand. Why should the future have asylums or prisons? Why not put prisoners in a " Skinner box "?

There are even broader implications. The rats never get satiated with their self-induced happiness or pleasure. Within a matter of five, ten, or fifteen seconds, depending on which pleasure center is being affected, there is a need or willingness to press the bar again. Thus it is possible to get a very accurate measure of the economic utility of a rat for pressing a bar. The economic and technical utility of a man for a given object cannot be precisely determined. Studies in quantitative social science at the University of Chicago, Harvard, and Stanford ran into difficulty because of this uncertainty in measurement. Why couldn't this uncertainty be overcome by a manipulation of human brain centers?

The students suggested that though we may have inhibitions about regulating our society with electronic happiness, there are other cultures that would not. But must this knowledge of the function of the brain be used to regulate or manipulate people? Perhaps it can be used to make a great variety of utopias available at low cost to the newly developing countries. It may open unbelievable vistas in art. If art uses the senses to channel the impact of images to the pleasure centers, perhaps stimuli could be calculated to achieve the pleasure of consumption of artistic images. Recently a whole new area of music was illuminated through the computerization of some aspects of composing. Enjoyment of music seems to be a process resembling the reception of impressions in the rats' brains. Hypotheses of musical enjoyment have been formed, and a series of experiments are waiting to be carried out in the area of composition.

Within music alone it is possible to visualize the opening of virtually infinite realms for the production of new and exciting images. Science may have cleared the way for unimagined progress in the humanities. The room for invention in the arts is far greater than in science. All the senses are available for exploration of new styles of impressions, for the development of new images. What is more, pursuit of non-scientific images may reduce chances of conflict. It isn't necessary to deal in stone, steel, and energy in humanistic pursuits. War-generating collisions between antagonistic images may become less likely if the variety of images grows and the increase occurs in humanistic areas.

There is cause for hope in the concern of the generation reaching maturity today with the serious issues of science and society. As important as their interest is their ability to act on their concerns. They have a capacity to build, organize, and bring new ideas to issue tenfold greater than the university students of 25 years ago. This may be a function of an approach to organization that shows up in science. At one time scientists and students, particularly in Europe, sat at the feet of the masters. Now scientists congregate around machines—cyclotrons and reactors are the foci. A cooperative kind of professional association with machines as principal participants is facilitated, and techniques of collaboration have become polished. Students today show a remarkable ability to collaborate and make things happen in spite of the overwhelming complications of the problems they take up. For example, about three and a half years ago students at the University of Michigan wanted some way to get new graduates overseas to look at the problems of the underdeveloped countries first hand. The students felt the faculty was too slow taking up the issue. They set up their own organization, called Americans Committed to World Responsibility, and started movements on other campuses to introduce the issue into the 1960 election. At Ann Arbor, the Democratic candidate gave the speech in which he made the basic commitment to the Peace Corps.

Last year another student group decided that the institutional structure for handling decision-making at the international level was inadequate. They felt information and knowledge was available that should be introduced into the decision-making process. A university seemed to them the most desirable kind of institution, so they created the project "United Nations University." This idea, which began only six months ago, has been a bigger juggernaut than the Peace Corps project. Already students have started proselyting on other campuses and are setting up an international working party for this summer. Next summer they are organizing an international conference to plan the establishment of the university. Faculty members of the University of Michigan who saw the thing start thought it was just another student idea, destined to have a short life. They had not fully realized the organizational capability of these young people.

These students do not have a standard faith. They do not follow Marxism, or any of the simple-minded beliefs of the twenties and thirties. Many of them have abandoned their Protestant or Catholic backgrounds. If they have an ideology it is service. They believe they must take responsibility for this world and meet its problems. They bring new ideas and a different approach to organization to bear on the serious modern questions. If we can last long enough, this generation with its humanistic orientation and technological expertise may meet the challenges we all face. This is the principal note of optimism I can find in what is otherwise, as indicated by the papers, a gloom-laden outlook.

Nature, Science, and Technology

A REPORT OF THE DISCUSSION

WARREN E. PREECE

Morning Session

Mr. Tyler presided. In comment on the background papers and the two opening statements, Mr. Huxley complained that, despite the title assigned for the current session, "not much of nature" had been talked about. Noting that nature may be inanimate, animate, or human, he suggested that man must begin to consider technology in relation to his position on his planet and must decide whether he proposes to live in a symbiotic or a destructive relationship to nature. It is clear, he said, that the Golden Rule must somehow be made to apply to all of nature, rather than merely to other humans, and that if this is done "nature will treat us well," but if it is not done, man will be condemning himself to death. He warned that man is "in desperate danger" of letting such things as the population explosion reduce him to the status of a mere parasite on earth and said that we must stop exploiting nature lest misery or even greater disturbances result. Already, he noted, man-stimulated erosion has reduced vast areas of the world to a state of "soil infertility." Despite this, he said, man does have the resources to prevent further destruction of the planet and, in fact, to replace some of what he has already taken away from it.

In relation to the matter of human nature, and specifically in connection with Mr. Meier's remarks concerning the experiments with electrodes and rats, Mr. Huxley pointed out that when in the same experiment electrodes were placed exactly halfway between pleasure and pain centers the rats' reaction on pressing the activating bar was a blend of "intense orgasm" and something which appeared to be similar to "the pain of the rack." The rats, he noted, had to make "an awful decision" whether to push the bar or not, and the whole experiment seemed to suggest the "appalling possibilities" of a truly scientific dictatorship, a possibility which is "by no means a fantasy."

Mr. Huxley said he was, of course, interested in the possibilities of a new surge in the humanities as predicted by Mr. Meier, but he warned that such a development must involve a new educational program emphasizing a non-conceptual and non-verbal intellect, as opposed to the educational values so far preserved by all of our intellectual arts. We should, he said, attempt to develop a program of education capable of enhancing "the mind's being," an education which will "feed the mind" with pure perception "in benign passivity."

Mr. Huxley urged, also, that we consider the problem of science and technology in terms of all of its aspects and resist oversimplification. We must, he said, think in terms of multiple causation, because it is obvious that there can be no single cause or solution. Referring to his proposal that education be made non-conceptual, he suggested that the direct education of our perceptions can be "extremely therapeutic," that, for instance, Eastern teaching is almost entirely operative in this sense and that methods suggested by it have been helpful in

174

work with institutionalized neurotics, because "almost by definition" a neurotic is one who responds to a present challenge in terms which are irrelevant because they spring from either the past or a feared future. Thus, an education which emphasizes pure receptivity rather than, merely, the substitution of one conceptual-verbal teaching for another, Mr. Huxley said, would be most valuable in mitigating the effects of science and technology. Insisting that the truth is that "the simple facts of life make all people capable of enjoying life more," Mr. Huxley suggested that this is a major field in which the technologists' research into the workings of sense perceptions, as reviewed by Mr. Meier, might prove to be "immensely important."

Fr. Ong, in commenting on Mr. Meier's "new post-technology man," reminded the meeting that the meaning of "humanistic studies" has not been constant; that, for example, in the Middle Ages the term distinguished what was human from what was brutal and coarse, whereas today it seems to be used only to distinguish science and technology from everything else. It is hopeful, he said, that the United States, alone in all the world, has "liberal-general education" as a basic aim of its educational system and has, therefore, a "solid core of advanced literary study" which is new and more sizeable than that of the rest of the world "altogether and forever." He pointed out that, whereas there were only 29 Ph. D. degrees awarded in England in 1958, there were 211 listed in only one compilation of advanced study data for the United States in the same year. What is more, he said, the scholarship represented by these degrees "compared well" with the scholarship of the past.

Our work in the humanities would be better, Fr. Ong suggested, if those dedicated to the humanities (1) developed "longer perspectives"—better views of the past; (2) recognized that technology in the United States is strengthening the stronghold of the humanities; (3) realized that it is ill advised—and non-factual—to try to elevate the humanities by making fun of the technologies; and (4) were aware that the humanities can be no greater than man himself and must, therefore, be always in danger from man himself.

In further comment, Fr. Ong suggested that it may be important to note that technology is now permitting man to move out of "an age of sight" into "an age of sound." The alphabet which was central to the first age, he pointed out, was so hard to invent that there is a sense in which it can be said that "really only one" ever has been invented in all of time. The difficulty, he continued, rose from the nature of sound itself and the fact that spoken words can in reality be only "events in time" so that a spoken word cannot ever be totally present at any given instant. The function of the alphabet, he said, was, then, to reduce temporal sound to manageable space, and its invention stimulated the development of a "manuscript culture," a process which was accelerated by the subsequent invention of alphabetic typography which was so far away from the actuality of "saying anything" that type could be set by men who did not even understand the language in which they were working. This development, he pointed out, was obviously closely related in both its cause and effects to technology.

At the present time, Fr. Ong continued, we are moving into a new age, once more dominated by sound—sound in which the telephone, phonograph record, tapes, even television, which is "nothing more than a picture added to sound," all rely on the invisible electron. Other technological developments which relate to his notion, Fr. Ong suggested, include rapid transit systems which enhance the possibility of the face-to-face transfer of sound; sonar, which can transmit meaningful sound from beneath the surface of the sea; and the electronic telescope

and microscope which can " show us things, by sound, which our eye cannot see."
As a result of the new culture, he said, grammar " is going out," is " being
swallowed up " by linguistics which begin with the spoken word; in philosophy
the dialogue is replacing the dialectic and thinking is becoming no longer a private
venture. All of these things, he insisted, are revolutionizing the humanities in
ways related to Mr. Huxley's notion of a non-verbal, non-conceptual education.
The age of sound and its implications, he said, seem to emphasize the development
of " personalist philosophies " as countervailing forces to the depersonalizing
thrust of technology.

Mr. Kranzberg complained that if the humanities are as sterile as some people
have suggested, that sterility may well be the result of the quantitative approach
to them implicit in Fr. Ong's comments. He suggested further that most of
the present session had reflected a wrong understanding of the relationships
between nature and man and technology, and he insisted that, in the same
way that a lump of sugar in tea becomes useful to man only when he stirs it,
nature itself is useful to man " only when he works on it." The problem with
the background papers, he said, is that they do not clarify what it is that we
want to control when we control technology, and he suggested that it is important
to know whether controls should be directed to the organization, the man, or
the machine. In other general comment, Mr. Kranzberg pointed out that the
" Baconian idea " described by Mumford actually arose in " an age of scarcity "
and may, therefore, be irrelevant to modern technology which seeks maximum
production. What we have today, he said, is heavy production in the midst of
scarcity, and the question is: where should the productive resources go? He
noted in this connection that such people as Kenneth Galbraith have called for
some control of national productive resources for useful ends.

In commenting on Fr. Ong's remarks, Mr. Hartner said it is suggestive that
the alphabet was invented 3,000 years before the birth of Christ, in Egypt,
and that, " curiously," the Egyptians insisted on retaining their earlier non-
alphabetic symbols along with the new alphabet rather than abandoning all
tradition, but that when the Phoenicians " took over " the alphabet they wisely
ignored the symbols and appropriated only what was valuable and meaningful
to them. This sort of thing frequently happens, he said, and suggests, in a modern
context, that we cannot assume that indiscriminately sending all of our inventions
to Africa will help the Africans.

In more general remarks, Mr. Hartner said that although we seem today to
cherish the idea that we are revolutionary and open-minded, the fact is that
revolutions in general are really characterized " by very strict rules " in those
social areas which do not, in the opinion of the revolutionists, require revision.
It was a part of the greatness of Copernicus, he said, that he changed only what
was necessary, and it is a weakness of our own time that we tend to " throw
out everything " before we know whether or not it is any longer useful, forgetting that new ideas are not good merely because they are new and that there
is still some validity in many old ideas, such as the idea " that man should not
kill and that he who uses the sword must perish by it." He asked in this connection how Fr. Clark could justify his failure to condemn any increase of
defense technology.

Recalling that the terms " optimism " and " pessimism " had been used frequently
during the Conference, Mr. Hartner said he was more concerned that we distinguish between " optimism " and " illicit-optimism," that is, optimism which
is dangerous because it is not founded on realities. Illicit-optimism has charac-

terized the last 150 years of our civilization, he said, citing as an example the fact that "most people even today" insist on thinking that ways can somehow be found to feed an unlimited world population.

Mr. Hartner noted that Mumford's paper raises the question of the usefulness of scientific activity. Pointing out that in 1905 Poincaré said that mathematics is "good for nothing" and that "that was why he had studied it," he said that although he agreed with Poincaré that human activity need not always be directed to a specific end, he would insist that learning must always serve to perfect the human personality. This belief, he suggested, relates to earlier discussions of education and its reform. It is a tragedy, he said, that in recent years we have almost eliminated the humanities from education in order to increase the time given to training in technology, and that in so doing we have destroyed both the "intellectual consistency of science and technology" and our own traditions which "are 75 per cent of our life as humans." He warned that simply to reform education cannot reverse this trend and suggested that the new education must lay stress on the humanities, but in a "less playful way" than in the past so that people will not think "life is a game" in which "hard effort is to be eschewed."

His main point, Mr. Hartner said, was that, apart from the transmission of knowledge, education should imply the formation of the mind by offering to those being educated what may be useful to them, by showing them what they need to know and by stimulating them. We should not, he warned, insist on uniformity, but should stress the differences which exist among men as prerequisites to a democracy in which each man can feel responsible for his own decisions.

Fr. Clark said that the point he had attempted to make earlier in the Conference about the morality of defense technology was that it is not an adequate moral reading simply to make a blanket indictment against all who prepare for war; that although he would agree that the basic ideal should be to do away with war, a blanket condemnation of defense activity in the practical world of complex life is simply "not helpful." To caution a nation against danger, he said, is not necessarily bad, and we should seriously question any overly simple judgments which might be made in this area. The fact is, he concluded, that we cannot pass directly from the Sermon on the Mount to judgments about specific actions without the mediation of reason.

In going back to his earlier remarks, and in commenting specifically on the relationship of old and new ideas, Fr. Ong pointed out that in the development of the chain which he sees running from speech to the alphabet to electronics, man did not at each new stage automatically abandon all of the values of the previous stage, but that the older values were modified and became less dominant. It is interesting, he said, that even the symbols with which we think change with the media we employ, so that each medium develops its own notions, and words such as "grid" and "mosaic" replace the familiar words of earlier stages. Mr. Tyler suggested that the goal of the engineer is to perfect each new system that emerges. Fr. Ong agreed but pointed out that "this is one of the things" which first served to move the engineer away from the humanities.

Mr. Huxley complained that the group had still "not talked about nature." Mr. Tyler noted, however, that science is, of course, involved in improving nature and that this raises the question of defining which level or perception of nature we are to be concerned with.

Mr. Gorman suggested that in his last remarks Mr. Kranzberg had voiced a new metaphor for the relation of man to nature through science; that we have gone from the idea of conquering or mastering nature to the idea of possessing it as property. To the contrary, however, he pointed out, such people as Chardin suggest that if "the science and technology thing" is done well it enables nature to fulfill itself. He argued that it is important to distinguish an "ordering of nature" from the inanimate through the animate to the human and suggested that while it would appear that there are limits to what man can properly do to human nature and may be limits to what he might do to animate nature, the current view would seem to be that the nature of inanimate nature is such as, in fact, to require the intervention of man on it in order to make evident the power manifest in it. This means, he said, that science and technology have something to do with inanimate nature which may be good for nature as well as good for man.

In concluding the morning session, Mr. Tyler noted his surprise that no one had "picked up" Mumford's condemnation of the "over-production" of scientific knowledge. One of the basic functions of science, he suggested, is in fact to order—and thus enhance the possibility of compressing—knowledge.

Technology in Focus—The Emerging Nations

TECHNOLOGY IN FOCUS

RITCHIE CALDER*

Science and technology could, without a further remit, solve all the material problems of the world today. It is not a question of "Whether" but "How," and the "How" is not a matter of knowledge but of intention.

The story of man's survival and, indeed, evolution has been one of his ability to master his environment. The one creature which was naked to the elements without fur, feather, or carapace, managed to migrate from the tropics into the temperate zone and into the Arctic. He contrived to clothe himself, build himself shelter, and master fire to provide menial heat. The most defenseless of creatures, without fang or claw, he protected himself against his natural enemies by the fire he had mastered, by the clubs he contrived to extend his forearm and give weight to his fist, by the spears he could throw from safe range, or by the stockades he could build, or by the lake-dwellings which set water between him and his predators.

From being a beast of prey, a hunter, he domesticated animals and drove his herds, seeking pastures which would feed them so that they could feed him. From a food gatherer, he became a food grower. He noticed that edible seeds could themselves produce seeds and that they would grow more plentifully if he scratched the ground and better still when the ground was well watered. So he became a tiller of the alluvial lands of the river valleys. He found that he could be the victim of floods or the manager of the flood waters, so he developed the system of irrigation. But, while the individual could till, by irrigation, the land in the vicinity of rivers, if the area of cultivation was to be extended, it could only be by master canals, public utilities. So the individual became a hostage to water management, vested in pharoahs or kings.

The settled tiller could produce surpluses in excess of his, or his dependents', needs for sustenance. He could barter food for better skills. He could make his own implements or domestic utensils, but there were others who could make them better, so they became the

* Ritchie Calder, C. B. E., M. A., is Professor of International Relations at the University of Edinburgh. He has served the United Nations extensively as adviser to several agencies and member of Missions to Asia and the Arctic. His latest book is *After the Seventh Day* (Simon & Schuster, Inc., 1961).

179

artisans maintained by the productivity of the tiller. His knowledge was mixed up with the unknown, and he needed intercessors, who could intercede with or appease the gods. Thus a priesthood emerged and his family altar became the temple or the ziggurat. But a priesthood has a continuity beyond the span, or experience, of a man. The tiller might observe the configuration of the stars, or the lengthening shadows which divided the day, and the passage of the seasons; or the woman, from her own biological rhythm, would understand the living cycle. They would know when to plant or to harvest or when to expect calves, or lambs or kids. The priests, however, had a longer sweep. Their observations could extend beyond a generation or even the centuries. Thus we find the priests of Chaldea turned astronomers, giving a length to the year only 26 minutes 26 seconds longer than that determined by modern precision instruments. We find that they discovered the *saros*, the 18 years and 11½ days, intervening between the eclipses of the sun. The priestly ledger clerks of the Nile, a river on the rise and fall of which the whole livelihood of the valley settlers depended, had the Nilometer, a simple gauge. With the records derived from that they could predict not only the seasonal but the cyclical changes. From such natural observations they could assert supernatural powers. The Chaldean priests could predict to the moment when the sun would be blotted out and the watergaugers of the temple were obviously the confidants of Isis and Osiris. Thus from awe of science, as well as innate piety, the tillers endowed the temples with the fruits of their toil.

This had further consequences because the tithebarns of the temples became the warehouses of surplus products, which could be traded beyond the limits of the community in exchange for alien products or crafts to enhance the temples. Ledger-keeping needed ciphers, the clay jars of ancient packaging needed seals, and trade needed credit tokens. In this we have the beginning of the scholarly clerks, of men of commerce, and of financiers.

With the growth of the priestly hierarchy, the emergence of the priest-king was inevitable. Either by his learning or by his inheritance of temple lands an individual was bound at some stage to exercise authority over his fellows. He would reinforce that authority by identifying himself with a god and become the living embodiment of a deity to which the citizens already acknowledged allegiance. And as the cities grew and their external trade increased, the hostility which a nomadic people felt towards the tillers, whose settlements in the river valleys intruded upon their summer pastures, turned to envy and to a predatory urge. The cities and the accessible wealth which they represented were likely to be raided by marauders, and they, worshiping alien gods, would not be deterred by the supernatural sanctions of a priest-king. So the cities had to have walls and soldiers to man them, and the priest-kings became, or gave way to, warrior-kings.

Defense became aggression, and any pretext was sufficient for aggrandizement by conquest. There was another encouragement towards wars of conquest: the need for slaves. The peasant and the husbanded soil were now supporting a social superstructure as massive as the ziggurats which had been built over the modest shrines and peasant altars—the craftsmen, the priesthood, the tax-collectors, the dynastic households, the tradesmen, the money-changers, and the soldiers. The produce of the soil had to be increased to satisfy the stomachs and the avarice of those who no longer worked the land. The pious tithe-payer of the primitive temple, paying his dues for the land the gods had made and the crops which they gave him, had now become a serf of a feudal system, but the prisoner of war could, in turn, become his slave.

Among the public works for which the slaves were most needed was the construction of water channels. Once, however, irrigation systems were constructed then, as now, competition for water rights led to violent conflicts. (We have only to remind ourselves that the word " rivalry " comes from the Latin *rivus*, a stream, to realize that the struggle for water has always been a cause for feuding.) It called for an overlord who would not only make himself responsible for the building of the master-channels but could command the labor force to maintain them, the laws to regulate them and the soldiers to protect them. The story of ancient Mesopotamia is that of quarrels over competing canal systems. The systematic ruin of an irrigation system was the method of punishing a defeated enemy and the dead cities of the desert are those which died of thirst through a water blockade, or in some instances, those which died through the malaria which came with collapse of neglected canal systems into marshes.

Conversely, ancient systems of water management and soil conservation are reminders, more significant than pyramids or ziggurats which remain as gravestones of lost civilizations, of survival skills of thousands of years ago. It would be difficult to suggest or devise today systems more ingenious or rational than those of the past: the exploitation of the gravitational flow between the Tigris and Euphrates; the flash-flooding of the delta fields of the Nile; contour farming and terracing in middle east China and Peru; Persian *wanaats* or horizontal wells; Nabatean desert farming which from 100 millimeters of rain could produce crops in the Biblical wilderness; plant drainage of Sumer and Aral civilizations which without engineering enabled farmers to cope with salt aggregations beyond modern tolerance. We can provide bulldozers, mechanical shovels, gelignite, steel, and concrete but we can scarcely improve on their principles.

Mastering his environment, man created his own problems. Contagion and infections of crowded cities are not present in small wandering groups of pastoral peoples. Urban hazards included polluted waters, community sewage, and proximity diseases, such as leprosy, or insect-borne diseases such as typhus, bubonic plague and malaria, and the miasmic diseases of a fetid atmosphere. But we can find a recognition of all these. Nergal, the god of disease of the Babylonians, and Beelzebub, chief god of the Assyro-Phoenicians, had as their symbol the fly, a recognition of insect-borne disease; and Rhazes, the lute player of Baghdad, anticipated Pasteur by a thousand years when, ordered by the caliph to build a hospital, he hung pieces of meat around the city, and where the meat putrefied least he sited the hospital. In Mohenjo-Daro, in the Indus civilization of 5000 years ago, there was an impressive system of drains, and around the remains of water booths, where drinking water was sold, have been found spoil heaps of broken cups, far in excess of the casualties of the most careless dishwashers and strongly suggestive of sanitary laws which compelled the breaking of those rough cups; if someone bought a drink of water, the cup was thrown away, like the paper cups of today.

In the arts of industry, the ancients have also a great deal to teach. For example, the ancient Hindus were the supreme metal workers. They produced steel, which was imported into the West, to make the Damascene swords, the Toledo blades, and possibly the Excalibur of King Arthur, and which remained a craft secret until Réaumur discovered the metallurgical chemistry of steel in the mid-nineteenth century. And the metallurgists are still trying to discover the secret of the Delhi Pillar and the girders of the temples of Konarak (exposed to the salt winds from the sea) which are made of iron which, throughout the centuries, has remained rustless. And we must admire the combination of craft skills and medical knowledge which, at least 2000 years ago, produced the 121 surgical instruments of the *Susruta*—scalpels, lancets, saws, scissors, needles, hooks, probes, obstetric forceps, catherers, syringes, bougies, and so forth.

We should recall that the ancient Chinese anticipated the spinnerets of the rayon and nylon industries by employing the natural spinnerets of the silk worm; they anticipated block printing, rockets, and the mechanical timepiece, as well as so much else. And that Hero of Alexandria, in 140 A.D., forestalled Savery, Newcomen, James Watt, Parsons, and Whittle by inventing a steam engine which combined jet propulsion. This was a sphere into which steam was fed, to escape through right-angled jets forcing the sphere to spin. He also had a system by which hot air expanded and drove water out of a container into a bucket which, in descending with the weight of water, turned a spindle. By this, when fires were lit upon an altar, the doors of a shrine were mysteriously opened disclosing the god. But Hero's ingenuity remained no more than such conjuring tricks because his was the age of slavery when muscle power was abundant and mechanical power unnecessary; Hero's ideas were " uneconomic."

If excuse is necessary for this strip-cartoon approach to " Technology in Focus," it is that invariably we look at technology in fine focus, a close-up in function and immediacy; but, if we are examining the

effects, good or bad, on contemporary circumstance, it can only be
by resolution of modern detail out of the panorama of history. Otherwise we may be only magnifying our own mistakes. After all, the
ancients achieved their enduring results by trial and error over centuries. Just as mistaken as the conservatism of "We tried it once and
it didn't work" is the forgetting that "They tried it once and it did
work." Experience is a good substitute for experiment. For example,
the modern Israelis, when they are attempting desert recovery, start
not in the laboratory but in the field; their archaeologists and plant
palaeontologists go to find out how, by techniques that have been
forgotten, the ancient Israelites and the Nabateans and the Byzantines
contrived to feed themselves out of what might seem a hopeless,
inhospitable desert.

There is the further excuse that, in the arrogance of modern achievement, we tend to regard "Point Four" and other forms of technical
assistance to underdeveloped and developing countries as a charitable
endowment, an act of generosity by the highly-advanced countries
to the "backward" countries, forgetting that many of those countries had advanced civilization and what we would now call "technology" when the ancestors of the Industrial Revolution were running
around painted in woad. If we take into account the heritage of
science and technology from which our present achievements, and
perhaps excesses, evolved, we may be disposed to think of technical
assistance as a kind of reverse lend-lease. Moreover it is important
to the self-esteem of countries conscious of their own traditions that
they should not regard themselves as technological beggars.

To ignore the traditional is to assume a complacency which is
dangerous. The United States discovered this when the U.S.S.R. put
the first Sputnik into orbit. In the context of the International Geophysical Year, in which the U.S.A. and the U.S.S.R. were both scheduled
to put up satellites, it was taken for granted that the Americans would
be first. When the bleeps of Sputnik were heard they caused a con-
sternation which the *Times* of London estimated cost the U. S.
economy $13 billion. American technology had been forestalled. That
itself was not traumatic; it had already been conceded that the Russians
were no longer moujiks who tore the innards out of tractors copied
from America and that they had pretty competent engineers. What
was shattering was that they put it into an orbit which, at that moment,
America was not going to attempt. This was science and not just
technology, which would not have been surprising if it had not been
forgotten that the Russians, long before the revolution, had a tradition
of pre-eminent mathematicians, astronomers, astrophysicists, and ballistic scientists.

But in a wider context, the past has salutary reminders for the
present. A succession of civilizations, empires, and cultures have flourished and foundered, but those were localized civilizations and when

they became effete—reached, if you like, the limits of a dynamic technology and became the victims, not the masters, of their environment—others less improvident or more dynamic took over. Today, as a consequence of our technological advances, ours is a global civilization. It is an earth round which a man-made piece of hardware can circle sixteen times a day; on which a broadcast voice can be heard faster 13,000 miles away than it can be heard at the back of the room in which it is speaking—because of course, radio waves travel at 186,000 miles per second, and sound waves amble along at 700 miles an hour—in which the fallout of an H-bomb, exploded in mid-Pacific, on Christmas Island or in the Arctic, can return from the stratosphere, be distributed by the jet-stream, and be deposited in rain throughout the world; on which three billion people today and a certain four billion twenty years from now will have to contrive to live and work together.

We may talk about "Our Way of Life" as distinguishing us from the political or cultural values of others, but in terms of the material civilization or the problem of survival the whole world is interdependent and no longer bounded by the Tigris and the Euphrates or the valley of the Nile.

For one thing, man is now technologically capable of vetoing the continued evolution of his species. He can exercise that veto by the nuclear destruction of the race and the radioactive poisoning of his total environment. Or he can, by neglecting the development of food production and material resources, produce starvation. His ingenuity and capacity are such that he may reach out for the other planets, but his species as such must survive on the surface of this earth, subsist from the nine inches of top soil which feeds, shelters, and clothes him or from the seas, which cover seven-tenths of this small planet and from which he emerged all those hundreds of millions of years ago.

Even if we are thinking of maintaining or extending the standards of living of countries which are highly advanced, it will be found that no unit, except the globe itself, will be self-sufficient. The Paley Report (U. S. President's Material Policy Commission, 1952) estimated that if the United States maintains full employment and continues to expand her manufacturing capacity, she will have to import 50 per cent of her raw materials from abroad by the year 1975. The European economy is even more dependent. Britain already has to import half its food and most of the raw materials of its factories.

The United States, which in fifty years has taken more minerals out of the crust of the States than has been taken out of the whole earth in the whole previous history of all mankind, will become dependent on countries which we now call "underdeveloped" and to which President Truman made his Point Four promise: "We must embark on a bold new program for making the benefits of our scientific advances and technical progress available for the improvement and growth of underdeveloped areas."

Apart from the merits of good intention and the political considerations involved, the development of countries on which the advanced nations are going to depend for material resources is enlightened and intelligent self-interest. Point Four said: "It must be a world-wide effort for the achievement of peace, plenty and freedom." The Paley Report expressed it: "The over-all objective of a national materials policy for the United States should be to insure an adequate and dependable flow of materials at the lowest cost consistent with national security and the welfare of friendly nations." But it also said that "the habit of regarding diversified economic growth for the underdeveloped countries as an alternative to materials development is erroneous." It pointed out that "development should involve a balanced growth of agriculture, manufacturing, and other industries directed towards maximizing the real income and improving the standard of living." In other words, it is not enough to quarry the wealth of another country. Something ought to be done to fill up the morass of poverty. With the emergence of new nations and the bargaining of the conflicting ideologies, there is not much option. Even the military know that you cannot build secure bases in countries of disaffected poverty. But a reappraisal of bilateral aid in the 1950's will probably show that it was a mistake to confuse military aid with economic aid. Apart from introducing scepticism and, politically, encouraging neutralism, it must introduce technological inconsistency. Proper technical aid ought always to involve " counterparts "—the nationals who, with training, ought to be left competent to carry on and reproduce the demonstration programs when the outside help has gone. But the essence of military technology is to get things done—on a pretty lavish engineering scale—as quickly as possible. It is usually a " crash " program, which can be most efficiently done by massive (and alien) equipment and by army engineers, who can drill unskilled local labor but will not want to waste their time on anything but a minimal training program.

Once in Thailand, I was driving with a Thai forester over an excellent road through the northern teak forests. I congratulated him. " Oh," he said, " this is an American road. They built it." I remarked that it was very thoughtful of them to give the Thais a road on which to haul their teak. " This is not our road," he said, " it is the strategical road to the Mekong, and Laos." Never mind, I said, the road would still be there when the emergency was over. His comment was revealing: " They built it. They taught no one how it was built. They taught no one how to maintain it. To us, building a road meant mechanical shovels, bulldozers, concrete mixers—all things we have not got."

The essence of technical cooperation, or mutual aid, on the other hand, is to allow people to grow up with changes, learn as they go, and to be discriminating about the modern methods they want to adopt—not just to go into what Professor P. M. S. Blackett has called the "supermarket of science" and pick things off the shelves; things they never knew they wanted and things which, in terms of their way of life, they may not need. Genuine mutual aid must never be the huckstering of gadgets or glib methods.

Another lesson of the 1950's and indeed of today is the ignoring of the statement in the Paley Report which called for a dependable flow of materials at the lowest cost *consistent with national security and with the welfare of friendly nations.* That means a fair price for the products of the underdeveloped, or developing countries. As the late Dag Hammarskjold, as Secretary General of the United Nations, pointed out: " A fall of only five per cent in the average of their export prices is approximately equivalent to the entire flow of capital which they recive not only from the International Bank loans but from all other public and private and government loans."

The fluctuations in their price-return on their exports have been 45 to 55 per cent greater than in the industrialized countries. The net loss in any recent year in the primary producer countries has been of the order of $1.5 billion—an amount which offsets the financial assistance they have received from all sources. At the same time, in the 100 countries and territories which need development, the net increase in population was as high as 2.2 to 2.4 per cent, as compared with 0.7 to 1.7 in the industrialized countries. At the same time, with all the incentives as well as their natural urge toward development, those countries had incurred the service on huge debts assumed at financial rates of interest and for normal periods of repayment. They had been told what to do and were borrowing to do it. According to the studies of the World Bank, during the years 1956-1958 external medium and long-term debt nearly doubled in the low income countries of Asia, the Middle East, and Africa and increased by 40 per cent in Latin America. In both groups of countries it had reached $5 billion by the end of 1958 and it has increased since. They were selling cheap and buying dear.

When Prime Minister Mr. Harold Macmillan claimed that the British people had "never had it so good," it was because largely, as a country dependent on primary products from those countries, Britain had had the advantage of the decline in prices.

This is like trying to fill a bath with the plug out. A level could be maintained if the faucets were turned well on but if the inflow is less than the outflow, the level drops or drains away. And, in spite of all the zeroes behind the dollar signs of mutual aid, the inflow, in relation to the real needs, has been a trickle.

The advantages have been to the already highly developed countries. As George Orwell said in *Animal Farm*: " All animals are equal but some animals are more equal than others." So, it seems, " All aid is mutual but some aid is more mutual than other."

In the years which have intervened since Truman's "bold new program," the gulf between the prosperous countries and the impoverished ones has not narrowed; it has widened. The rich countries are richer and the poor countries are poorer.

As near as can be estimated, during the 1950's about $2 billion was spent on pre-investment activities such as technical assistance, fellowships, surveys and so on, and about $28 billion in investment—$30 billion in all, for all countries, developed, developing, and underdeveloped. The average *per capita* income of the 100 underdeveloped. territories rose from $90 to $100 in the ten years. Their annual income grew at the rate of three per cent and their population increased at the rate of two per cent. This is Sisyphean.

*   *   *   *   *

This would seem to be the realistic background against which to consider the technological order and the impingement of science and technology on world affairs. We could, of course, start at the other end, with high development, and consider—as though we needed to be reminded!—the political convulsions due to nuclear energy and space research. Those, like the $110 billion a year which the world spends on armaments, represent an enormous diversion of human ingenuity, human effort, and human wealth from the historic purpose of man's survival and the justification of his evolution—the control of his material environment. This is not the occasion to discuss the political circumstances which have induced this competition of military skills but it is obvious that, if we are trying to get technology into focus, this is a distortion.

On the chicken-wire fencing of Stagg Field, at the University of Chicago, there is a plaque which reads:

> On December 2, 1942, man achieved here the
> first self-sustaining chain reaction and thereby
> initiated the controlled release of atomic energy.

For the small group of scientists around Fermi in the squash court that winter's afternoon, the Atomic Age began as impatient clickings and a reasurring hum. Few, if any, thought that the reactor would explode; the drama and suspense for them was whether it would work. The prodigious energy of the atom, a thousand times greater than chemical energy, had been harmlessly tamed. If the story had been told as casually as the circumstances themselves and if the atomic engine had been presented to the world as something as innocuous and as easily controlled as the internal combustion engine, the emotional problems would not have arisen. Instead, the world's imagination was stunned by the cataclysmic violence of the bombs on Hiroshima and Nagasaki. Military secrecy had compelled the supression of the story of the squash court and the testing of the bomb at Alamogordo, in New Mexico, on July 16, 1945, and the world's first introduction to atomic energy was the death and destruction it could cause in one awful moment.

We know now that the safebreakers broke open the lock of the atom before the locksmiths knew how it worked, and multimillions are being spent on cyclotrons, synchrotrons, and all the other "-trons" and other kinds of accelerators to discover how the wards of the lock fit together.

When the UN International Conference on the Peaceful Uses of Atomic Energy met in Geneva in August 1955, there was a second dawn less lurid than the man-made "sunrise" over the New Mexican desert. In that roseate moment, it seemed that atomic energy could, in terms of harnessed power, offer to the power-hungry underdeveloped countries their short-cut to the second Industrial Revolution. By 1958, at the second Conference, it was obvious that that was hope deferred and that the promise of reactors of the type and size commensurate to their needs—using enriched fuels—were not to be forthcoming in any time which would redress the power balance sheet between those who had industrial power and those who desperately needed it. The prospect of H-energy, fusion energy—putting the H-bomb into overalls and putting it to work—was even more remote. There were all kinds of reasons, but leaving out the possibility of "sneaking" fissile fuels and turning them into bombs, and the lack of skilled personnel (who could have been supplied internationally anyway) to run the power plants, the argument could be summed up as: You need power to run your industries, but you have not the industries to absorb the power; and, since you have not got industries, you cannot afford power to give you the industries you have not got.

Space research, now escalating not only to the planets but in the budgets, began, so far as the world was aware, as an ambitious but innocent contribution to the I. G. Y. But, in the temper of our times, Sputnik (it might have been the U. S. satellite) became a potential mine-in-orbit and its rocket a potential intercontinental ballistic missile. A televising satellite, capable of photographing the back of the moon or relaying information about our weather from outside becomes a means of espionage. A capsule capable of carrying a man into orbit becomes a potential war-head.

Man's adventure beyond the confines of his planet thus became the competition between contending defense departments. It could be argued that the defense departments are also the trucking companies carrying scientific research instruments into space to acquire scientific knowledge—man and his electronic senses reaching out for the stars. As a by-product of military urgencies, and the corresponding budgets, they could find out more about our terrestrial climate; about the nature of radio communications, with the possibilities of global television; about cosmic dust which might tell us about the prebiotic elements and "jump" many of the questions about DNA (deoxyribonucleic acid) and the secrets of life. It can be argued, and demonstrated, that the same urgencies, and unlimited means, can produce "quantum leaps" in the advancing of electronics, of the use of solar batteries for the direct conversion of the sun's rays into electricity, and in the development of computers.

It will seem grudging and unimaginative, if one raises philosophic doubts. There could be none if science and technology were ends in themselves, but, if we are here considering their relevance to the problems of mankind, doubts may be expressed even if they are rejected. Will, for instance, commensurable attention be given to the "secret of life" when we have got it? Or are we going to confront it as ill-prepared as we were for the discovery of the "secret of matter"? Where are those "quantum leaps" in electronics going to land us? Solar batteries? Maybe. They have already, on the space account, been made more efficient, and research and technology have shown how they might eventually be made cheap enough to meet terrestrial need for solar power.

And computers? At the Computer Conference, organized by UNESCO in Paris two years ago, we had 2,000 delegates representing 100,000 scientists, technologists, and technicians, in an industry which had barely existed 12 years before. We were told then that there were already $2.5 billion worth of orders "on the books" for 1965. They discussed calculating machines; translation machines; machines which could be "programed" to make machines; pattern-identification machines with Pavlovian reactions; machines into which could be built the experience which previous machines had "acquired" as electronic-apprentices; machines, which would make "value judgments," or at least which produced judgments not predicated by the programers, and Professor Edward Teller said that "now we had machines which could make value judgments, he could produce the mathematical model for machine emotions." We heard about giant-midget memories, or midget-giant memories, which by cryogenics, could predictably store "all the knowledge of all the libraries of all the world" in a casket no bigger than a cigar box. (They admitted that they could "put it in, but did not yet know how to get it out.") Only one muted voice in all the deliberations of all those computer people was raised to ask whether they had ever got or could ever get together to consider the social implications of all this.

There are scientific implications as well. For the last 20 years nuclear physics has been able to command the big money and the big battalions of scientists; then it was the turn, with transistors, masers, and computers, of the solid state physicists; now it is the turn of the space engineers; presently it will be the cult of DNA. Nothing derogatory is intended toward those who are engaged in any of these projects, but all of them represent an imbalance in the ledger of problems of human survival and of human well being.

For instance, it is possible to clear the earth of malaria at a cost of about $50 million spread over ten years. That probably is less than one space sortie or a bigger and better synchrotron. But if we do not eradicate malaria in a measurable period, the consequences may be dire. This is an example of what we can see in the sands of time and the story of the lost civilizations—when man interferes with nature, he must go on interfering, otherwise nature revolts. With DDT and insecticides it became possible to control malaria, which afflicted 300 million people and caused three million deaths a year, throughout the world. By killing off the adult mosquitoes, the transfer of malaria from the blood of a sick person to that of a healthy person could be prevented. Whole areas where malaria had been endemic were dealt with in this way. Then insects developed DDT resistance. This was not Mithradatic—taking small doses of poisons to resist lethal doses— the insects had not just " acquired the habit." This was in fact evolution before our eyes. A tiny minority of mosquitoes have a genetic resistance to chemical insecticides. They survived and without even the competition of their kin, they multiply and will presently replenish the earth with mosquitoes. It is possible to " buy time " by switching insecticides and, possibly, finding new ones, but the genetic resistance reasserts itself. There is, however, a complementary way of getting rid of malaria. There are prophylactic and therapeutic drugs which can purge the parasites from the blood of human beings. If by insecticide control the extent of malaria can be restricted to public health or clinical proportions, individual cases can be treated. If there is no malarial blood to be transferred, the resurgence of the mosquitoes will not be a menace. This means eradication, as proposed by the World Health Organization. Without it, malaria may come back in epidemic proportions without the brakes which exist in chronic, or endemic, malaria. The response of governments has not been commensurate to the threat nor to their allocations for the incidentals of a defense program.

Next to the threat of nuclear destruction of the human race or, at the least, of civilized living, the biggest threat is the rising tide of population. It has taken *homo sapiens* two hundred thousand years to reach the present figure of three billion; it will take less than 40 years to double it. The figure by 1980 will be, inescapably, four billion—it may be more, but, short of a man-made cataclysm, it cannot be less. This is not due to the fact that women have suddenly become more fecund or that couples are having more children than they had in the past. It is because science and technology have introduced death control (more lives have been saved by antibiotics in the past two decades than have, in the aggregate, been lost in all the wars of all history). Fewer mothers and babies are dying at birth; fewer infants are dying. They are surviving the diseases of childhood, to marry and to multiply. The span of life has been increased. It is not the birth rate which has risen but the survival rate. The result is that the world population is increasing at the rate of 120,000 extra mouths to feed every day.

Already, more than half the existing population is inadequately fed. Actual starvation afflicts millions, but, apart from walking corpses, vastly many more do not get enough food for well-being. If they are sick and hungry, they have not the energy to produce food or the means, or perception, to improve their methods. Today, even the global figures for food calories are, for the first time since the war, not matching the population increase. In any event, the global figures have been misleading for years because they have included the rising standards, and yields, and farm price-support surpluses of the advanced countries, particularly in North America. The measure is not the global *per capita* but the local *per stomach*.

To the present shortages have to be added the needs of that extra one billion mouths before 1980. The answer, except in famines or acute emergencies, cannot be to disburse as an act of charity, the surpluses of the United States or Canada. The present accumulation of grain would be enough to provide the full calorie needs of the Indian subcontinent for one year or give an extra 200 calories a day for three years to the peoples of Asia.

The only effective answer, however, is to increase the capacity of those peoples to feed themselves. If, for instance, an effective hybrid of the *Japonica* rice of the high latitudes and the *Indica* rice of tropical Asia could be established, it would, theoretically, be possible to double the yields from the existing acreages of Southeast Asia. If the impoverished peasant of India, with an average income of less than $100 a year and unable to afford artificial fertilizers even if they were available, were to use his cowdung as manure instead of as cooking fuel, he could nourish his sickly earth. An effective, cheap, and acceptable solar cooker could increase crop yields. If in those areas where the population density is mainly riverine, the floods which drown or smother the lands could be controlled, multipurpose dams could help to irrigate the thirsty uplands and spread the population on yielding soil. With malaria control jungle regions could be recovered for cultivation. In Africa, the tsetse fly prevents man and his domesticated animals from using nearly four million squares miles of what might be productive land. But here one enters the caveat, on which intelligent Africans themselves insist. Before the "protecting" tsetse is banished the Africans must learn better how to husband this land which the insect has preserved from the ravages of shifting cultivation and overgrazing.

As a global contribution there are deserts, hot and cold, to be regenerated. The population is sparse and will increase slowly and any yields will be surplus to their needs. This, of course, is complicated by politics and economics. Throughout North Africa and the Middle East there are few indications that others are prepared to convert their deserts as intensively and as effectively as the Israelis have done the Biblical wilderness, and there is little encouragement for the Canadians with their embarrassing surpluses to extend, as might be feasible, their crop-growing northwards.

Seven-tenths of the globe is covered by oceans. As far as the plants and creatures of the seas are concerned, we are still at the cave man stage; we hunt our sea food. By and large we neglect the fish of the deep oceans and concentrate on those of the continental shelves. For thousands of years fish have been cultivated in inland fisheries, in the fishponds and the rice terraces in the East and in the carp ponds of the mediaeval monasteries, but, apart from oyster beds and some attempts to increase the growth and yield of inshore fish, practically nothing has been done to husband or herd the sea-creatures. It is estimated that the nutrient material produced annually by the sea amounts to 100,000 million tons, of which only 30 million tons the world over are recovered as edible fish. This contrasts with 1,000 million tons of vegetable produce and 100 million tons of animal produce from the land surface. Only about two per cent of the fish food available in the seas is eaten by the food fish. The invertebrates, like starfish, eat about four times as much nutrient as do a quantity of edible fish of the same total weight.

Sir Alister Hardy (British Association for the Advancement of Science, 1960) pointed out that the potential fish catches from any fishing ground could be increased many times by merely getting rid of the pests. This could be done by the submarine raking of the fishing banks, and the starfish would be useful as poultry food. In the discussions of the use of artificial fertilizers to increase the fish pastures and hence the fish crops, he pointed out that the bottom of the sea was itself a vast compost heap and that all that was needed was mechanical methods of stirring the nutrients up and getting them into the food fish layers.

The idea of sea ranching—The Riders of the Purple Kelp—and of range managing the sea bottom is no more fantastic than the idea of reaching out to the planets. Developing the sea pastures will be much more rewarding than exploring H. G. Wells' Moon Pastures. Sea farming is entirely within the range of feasibility. There are the already proven devices, like the fish hatcheries. The infantile mortality in the fish population is very high. The British Fisheries Research Laboratory at Lowestoft has shown that by rearing young plaice in tanks until they are past the stage of greatest mortality risk and then liberating them in the North Sea, the catches substantially increased. Such projects, however, would have to be done on an international basis, for the reason that no one nation, or national fishing industry, would put up the capital for this kind of stocking of fishing grounds which are free for all.

There have been schemes for fish farming in arms of the sea. The trouble is that one cannot clip the fins of fish, as one might clip the wings of poultry to keep them from migrating, and the problem is how to keep them within the confines. In experiments in a Scottish sea loch, the results of fertilizing the inlet to intensify the growth of fish food and consequently of fish were encouraging. It was found that the inlet was colder in winter than the open sea and the fish migrated. One proposal to overcome this was that one of the atomic energy electricity generating stations should be sited on such a loch and that the waste heat be used to warm the water. Just as it is practical to put a single wire around a field with a harmless electric charge to teach the animals not to stray, it should be possible to " fence " a sea-inlet by passing an electric charge through the water—an invisible gate—to discourage the fish from leaving.

Just as the introduction of the scythe and the hoe into Afghanistan in the 1950's for winter fodder saved the flocks and the only dollar earning trade (in karakul pelts), so comparatively simple diffusion of technological experience may produce extensive benefits. " For the sake of a nail the shoe was lost; for the sake of a shoe, the horse was lost; for the sake of a horse, the kingdom was lost." Or, to mechanize the metaphor, a missing piston ring or the absence of the ability to make one may be holding up an industry.

There is a tendency for those in advanced countries looking at the problems of underdeveloped countries, and for those in those countries who are looking for prestige, to think of spectacular projects. Multi-purpose dams and giant steel plants may be necessary for Walt W. Rostow's " take-off " into self-stabilizing prosperity, but in the pre-investment stage (before investment flows by gravitation), there are a host of technological problems to which the answers are not spec-tacular—just pile-driving into a morass of poverty.

Just as the Panama Canal could not be built (and $200 million had been lost in the ill-fated de Lesseps attempt) until Gorgas cleared the isthmus of yellow fever, so countries have to be cleared of diseases. Medical technology and the chemical and pharmaceutical industries can provide the answer. Hungry people represent a heavy labor turnover, so people have to be better fed as a precondition of industrial development. Sick and hungry people are ignorant because lassitude blunts perception and the capacity to learn to help themselves. But, given better health and food, they need teachers, not only to provide literates but to create the climate in which new knowledge is acceptable.

It is not difficult to decide what they *need*, but it is necessary to **find out what they *want* ("felt need"), because only through that can** they be taught what they need. And there is a dangerous tendency, in the huckstering of " mutual aid," to make them want things they never knew they needed and to feel deprived when they find they cannot afford them.

By way of illustration: At the World Power Congress in Belgrade, the advanced countries paraded for the edification of the delegates of underdeveloped countries, the wonders of 500 megawatt atomic power stations and multipurpose dams costing hundreds of millions. A Malayan was asked " What are you shopping for? " His reply was " A little bouyant generator which would float up and down in our streams, just enought to give light to read in our villages. Then we could read and learn about all those wonderful things they are talking about here." His next wish was for a cinema projector which could be used to teach better methods of cultivation and crop preparation and preservation. Then he wanted a road to the next village and to the nearest market town, because then they could market the surpluses which they would thus learn to produce. Then, with the village earnings, they might be able to afford a diesel generator and have local industries. " Then," he said, " we will come and buy all those wonderful things we will read and hear about."

Basically, it all comes back to the land. In underdeveloped countries with rising populations, the land is too congested for proper cultivation and improved methods. It is sub-subsistence farming, with under-employment on the land. The little that is not enough, from the plots which are not big enough, can be got in the few man-hours of scraping the soil, planting, and harvesting. The units must be made bigger. Systems of land tenure come in but so does the fractionating of patrimonial land among the members of a family. With bigger units, better methods of farming can be introduced, but that means that a large proportion of those on the land must, beneficially, leave it. If it is just displacement (like the dispossession from the common lands at the time of the enclosures in Britain), the landless will drift into the industrial conurbations. Instead there should be local industries to absorb them and still keep them available, at least in a transition stage, for seasonal labor on the land. This means small factories and industrial units far removed in size and geography from the massive, high-capital power sources. It also means making the most of local materials and developing local craft skills, with whatever help in terms of money, equipment, or experience they can get from outside.

Sometimes it is difficult to reconcile the three—local materials, craft skills, and outside help. For example, in India there is the problem of the sacred cow. A cow cannot be killed. It must be allowed to die. The farming community, however impoverished, is of a higher caste than the Untouchables, and by definition a skinner is an Untouchable. So a peasant will not readily become a practitioner in leather. But, as experience has shown, the expert brought in from some other country, however highly qualified, will have been accustomed to handling

" live " hides, from freshly killed animals, and may be baffled by the chemistry of " dead leather."

As Professor P. M. S. Blackett warned the leaders at the Rehovoth Conference in *Science and the New Nations* (Basic Books), there are risks in going shopping in the "supermarket of science." They ought to compile a cautious shopping list, embodying a rational choice of priorities, otherwise they might " come home with plenty of sweet-meats but no bread and butter."

More than embarking upon ambitious programs of advanced re-search, they need people who are capable of understanding and select-ing " know-how." And that " know-how " cannot just be " ordered off the shelf " because what is valid to the needs and experience of advanced countries may not be suitable to their circumstances.

Again the sacred cow: In the Ganges Delta 300 tube wells were sunk and pumps brought in from abroad. But the fresh water was left unused, and the people preferred their slimy ponds— because they had found that the pumps contained leather valves and they would not drink water that came through the hide of the cow. This was not the mistake of a sacrilegious outsider but of Hindu water engineers who had flicked through a mail-order catalogue.

Perhaps this contribution, which has been cautionary rather than constructive, can be best rounded off by recalling the United Nations International Conference on Science and New Sources of Energy held in Rome in August 1961. In a triennial progression—1955, 1958, 1961— this might have been the occasion of the Third International Confer-ence on the Peaceful Uses of Atomic Energy. The sixteen volumes of the first conference which became the thirty-six volumes of the second might have become the eighty volumes of the third. But it would, for the underdeveloped countries, have followed the law of diminishing returns. There would have been plenty of new detailed knowledge but no dividend. At the first conference they had been bewitched by the new magic—the reactors which were going to be their short-cut to the second Industrial Revolution. At the second conference, they had been told that they were not ready for this new benefaction of ad-vanced science. At the third conference (judging from the papers at the Rehovoth Conference) they would have been told that they would be " burning their own rocks," in breeder reactors—forty years from now.

The United Nations promoted instead " New Sources of Energy." Ironically, they were the oldest sources of all—the sun, the wind, and geothermal energy, heat from the crust of the earth. Atomic energy was dethroned. There were no nuclear physicists present.

It was a do-it-yourself conference. It was about solar stoves, re-frigerators, solar ponds (with prospects of generating electricity from them at unit cost less than from the atom), windmills, which they could contrive themselves, and, with some surprising disclosures, the possibilities of finding geothermal energy and of "custom tailoring" it to their own needs. This was the first time, in any international science conference, that geothermal energy had been seriously considered.

As a generalization it may be said that a large number of under-developed countries, geologically deprived of fossil fuels, have been compensated by the existence of geothermal energy. This had been thought of previously only as the obvious "showings"—the geysers, the bubbling mudpools, and the hot gases escaping from rock clefts. It has shown however that the geothermal structures, usually, but not always, associated with volcanic formations, could yield "economic" power. Tapped sources could produce hot steam or hot gases at as much as twenty times the temperatures of the open sources. This energy has the advantage that it could be tapped to meet local require-ments and provide power units with which industries could grow up.

Perhaps the sacred cow might remain the cautionary symbol for vaunting technology: Methane, from cow dung, with the residue returned to the soil as useful fertilizer, may be more useful in the short term than the civil atomic energy electricity generating stations on which the Indian government is embarking.

Technology in Focus—The Emerging Nations

TECHNOLOGY IN EMERGING COUNTRIES

ARTHUR GOLDSCHMIDT *

For more than a decade we have been engaged in the most comprehensive effort in history to transfer technology. It has been largely a voluntary and peaceful effort to improve economic and social conditions in less-developed lands through the application of science and the introduction of modern techniques. It has been undertaken by governments, international organizations, private philanthropic and business groups for a variety of motives. It has involved nationals of almost all of the nations of the world and most of the sciences, professions, and occupations. It has operated at all levels of government and society and has utilized a variety of methods. It has been characterized generally by open discussion, debate, negotiation, appraisal, and review. Although far from a planned and coordinated program, its major components of international and bilateral aid have been predicated upon a greater degree of planning and coordination than any comparable international undertaking in history, with the possible exception of some military campaigns. This deliberate effort to improve the economic and social conditions in the less-developed countries of the world evidences a significant step in the history of human relations.

There have been enormous successes. Few countries or areas have not benefited in some measure by some aspect of this peculiar phenomenon of our century. But these programs have not been large in terms of the need for them. They have been widespread and varied rather than sustained or comprehensive. The impression of their size results rather from the amount of discussion and debate involved in their financing and administration, from the mass of popular and scientific literature that has been produced on the general subject, and perhaps, from the number of ancillary workers engaged in some of the programs in locations where their presence is startingly obvious and discomforting. But if the programs have not been as large as the gaps in living levels and technology might warrant, they have been an adequate and ubiquitous sample that would provide ample means for studying the potentialities and difficulties in transferring technology.

* Arthur Goldschmidt is Director for Special Fund Activities, Department of Economic and Social Affairs, The United Nations. The views expressed in this paper are personal and not necessarily those of the United Nations.

197

It is not surprising, therefore, that a considerable body of case studies, analyses, and theory on the subject has been developed. What has been missing is a comprehensive synthesis of this experience and adequate research on, and evaluation of, the techniques of transferring technology.

Toward a Science of Transferring Technology

Concurrently with this broad experience, the social scientists, particularly economists, have been laying some of the scientific groundwork in the field by analyzing the processes of development and formulating techniques for their measurement and appraisal. The economists, unlike the other social scientists, have been involved in the aid program both as practitioners and administrators. They have thus begun to establish the reciprocal relationships between those concerned with theory and those engaged in practice essential to both the scientists and the practitioners. But even the economists have too often had a transient advisory role, rather than a concern with operational work of a continuing nature.

The behavioral sciences, in general, have been further removed from the programs. For the most part, their work has not been closely linked to operations. Some social scientists have, of course, been engaged in these programs. Specialized social science institutions and faculties have followed the work of practitioners. Symposia and conferences have brought scientists, administrators, and field workers together. But the programs have largely employed experts chosen primarily for their competence in such professional fields as agronomy, finance, engineering, health, or housing. Methods have been pragmatic. In their separate world, the behavioral scientists have been studying cultural patterns, motivation, semantics, incentives, and similar aspects of their carefully classified disciplines related to the problem of inducing change.

While those who framed the aid programs recognized some of the difficulties of applying technology in less-developed countries, the ease with which most technological innovations have moved through developed countries has, perhaps, taken some of the edge off concern with the problems of the process of transferring technology. In any case, the symbiotic relationship between science and technology that has effected advances in other fields has yet to be firmly established between the behavioral sciences and those engaged in inducing development and introducing technology. This symbiosis, increasingly characterized in other fields by programs of research and development, has been missing because the aid programs have not been adequately buttressed by such built-in and purposeful research. In part, this has been due to the fact that funds available have generally been too inadequate for obvious program needs. Perhaps, too, the social sciences have been slow in developing techniques and technologies. The language of the behavioral sciences presents a semantic problem to the practitioner relying upon " common sense." The evidence presented by the social sciences on the difficulties of change has generally been too gloomy for the administrator of programs based upon optimistic assumptions that illiteracy, disease, hunger, and insecurity can be mitigated in a variety of economic and social situations. In any case, the social sciences have never been brought systematically into the major aid programs to assist in studying the process of transferring technology.

The relationship of the social sciences to the aid programs may be entering a new phase. The Foreign Assistance Act of 1961 introduced the concept of research and development for the first time in the aid program of the United States through Title V, calling for " Development Research." This modest beginning is intended to bring the " formidable talents of the American research community," as a Senate Committee characterized it, to bear on the problems of the underdeveloped countries and on the techniques of helping them.

This same trend has been evident for some time in the focusing of the research work of the secretariats of the United Nations agencies on the problems of the developing countries. The current increased emphasis on planning and programing in the United Nations technical cooperation activities and in the Alliance for Progress indicate a further concern for research. This planning is something more than the usual demand, generally predicated upon a scarcity of resources or a reluctance to provide them, for coordination and priority determination. Behind this planning approach is the recognition that research in the field of development is needed. Inherent in its execution is the possibility of a more systematic development of the theory and the techniques of technological transfer. Research is one of the primary purposes, for instance, of the Latin American Institute for Economic and Social Planning, being established under the aegis of the Economic Commission for Latin America in cooperation with the Inter-American Development Bank and the Organization of American States and largely financed by the United Nations Special Fund. This Institute for training officials and providing governments with teams of planning experts is also required to undertake research into the process of economic and social planning itself. The General Assembly of the United Nations has called for the establishment of similar institutes in other regions, particularly in Africa. These research centers should provide an important meeting ground for scientific and practical workers in the field of development, both from within the regions they serve and from outside.

Again, the need for developing the science of transferring technology is recognized in the Resolution of the General Assembly calling for a United Nations Conference on the Application of Science and Technology for the Benefit of the Less-Developed Areas to be convened in the Spring of 1963. This Conference will not only explore wide areas of existing technology capable of transfer and fields of research "directed toward producing new scientific and technological advances of special utility to less-developed areas" but will also "explore the problems of transfer and adaptation."

While these initiatives are intended primarily to accelerate the use of science and technology in solving the problems of the emerging nations, they recognize that the problems of transferring technology also require research and development. They set the stage for moving beyond the study of the less-developed areas and of the phenomenon of development to the study of the processes of inducing development. Science will be brought to bear on the emerging "technology" of transferring technology to the emerging nations. Some observations may be helpful for putting into perspective some of the elements of the complex problems to be found in this new work in research and development.

Emerging Countries Differ

No comprehensive review of the experience of these past dozen years of economic and technical assistance nor any broad synthesis of that experience has yet been attempted. But the accumulation of studies, evaluations, reports, and reviews reveal wide variations in the accomplishments of these programs and in the time and effort invested in their achievement. Some places are generally easier to work in than others. Some fields of technology are more easily transferable. Some practices show greater results. But such generalizations must be replaced by specific studies of the various tasks to be performed and the environments in which they must take place.

Such terms as "emerging," "under-developed," "have-not," "low-income," "poor," and similar attempts at classification lose their convenience when dealing with specific problems respecting these areas, such as those relating to the transfer of technology. These generalized terms for the less-developed countries have little utility as a basis for thinking or acting about them as a group. Indeed, for each problem to be considered, the specific countries included in these general categories may differ. India, Guatemala, Mali, Thailand, and the Sudan have little in common except the fact that their levels of living are all below those of the more industrialized nations and the circumstance that they all straddle the fifteenth parallel. But they differ in climate, agricultural practices, levels of education, population-land ratios, and in their requirements for technical assistance and the likely pattern of their economic growth. These and other less-developed countries, numbering about one hundred in all and containing well over half the world's population, differ in culture, history, and degree of development. They present jointly a spectrum rather than a single classification. They would not always fall in the same order along scales of economic, social, or technological achievement and not always be separated out from the " developed " countries. The continuum from " poorest " to " richest " is not a growth curve; the use of the term " stages " in relation to economic growth has tended to confuse the layman into thinking that Guatemala or Brazil are simply less-developed versions of France or the United States into which time and effort will transform them. The differences between the emerging countries affect the techniques for transferring technology to them.

Internal Differences

There are also vast internal differences within the emerging nations that affect the transfer of technology. These internal gaps are generally greater than the gaps between countries. The most immediately noticeable is the difference between the capitals or major industrial cities and the countryside they command. The larger urban centers of the under-developed countries are more nearly like similar cities elsewhere in the world, including the developed ones. There is less difference between the apparent state of technology in the centers of Mexico City, Lima, Manila, and Bangkok than between any of these and the villages within fifty miles of them. Indeed, the technological gap can be more precisely located between the urban and rural areas in the less-developed world than between the have and have-not nations. The corona of slums that generally separates the cities of the less-developed areas from their surrounding countryside is a measure of the pressure to close that gap.

In those countries where agriculture is largely characterized by subsistence farming and a barter economy, this location of the technological gap takes on even greater validity. No similar gap between urban and agricultural worker exists in the more developed world, where the recent revolution in agricultural technology has increased the productivity of farmers. Although this has created serious problems that have not always been fully resolved, there is far less difference between the technological state of industry and agriculture and in the resultant levels of living in the developed world than between these in the emerging nations. An index of development might be calibrated by measuring the technological gap between countryside and city in the countries of the world.

The internal differences in technology in the less-developed countries are not confined to the gap between city and countryside. The technological developments in some agricultural fields may show considerable progress, generally in large-scale, one-crop developments often associated with corporate or other types of central management (rubber, bananas) or with development schemes (the Gezira in the Sudan). The dual economies of the less-developed countries are not the only evidence of their dual technologies. The problems of the emerging industrialist are usually exacerbated by the differences in the technological levels within industry in the developing countries. "There are two Argentinas, one developed and one not developed," said an engineer concerned with applied research in that country. He was referring not to the urban-rural differences but to the technological gap between the larger foreign corporations and the smaller indigenous industrialists, with no laboratories or standards control techniques.

Just as the tourist finds the airport management, the hotel or office building, and other superficial aspects of cities of the less-developed world showing little difference from those of the developed world, there are many industrial enterprises that operate at obviously the same technological levels as their counterparts in developed countries. Countries at the lower end of any scale of income, literacy, or any other index of development have power plants, bottling works, breweries, and textile mills that can hardly be distinguished from those in Europe or North America.

Most of these modern plants are in fields of capital-intensive production. Many have replaced, or are replacing, earlier forms of manufacture in which labor played a greater role. These plants inevitably take over the available market. Nostalgia for the hand loom or desire to maintain jobs by intermediate technologies does not reverse or diminish the trend to mechanize those textile plants producing for mass consumption in the local market economy. In Iran, for instance, cheap cotton textiles made in modern mills have, in a few years, preempted the market formerly shared with hand looms and imports. In addition to operations involving the construction of new plants, technological change is affecting existing industries through greater use of presses and other machine tools in the manufacture of furniture, building materials, clothing, and other consumer goods. Such modernization generally replaces labor-intensive operations. Many of these operations, however, still compete for the market with labor-intensive competitors on the one hand or mass produced imports on the other.

In the field of large-scale public works—roads, water and power systems, airports, and housing—the state of technology often appears familiar to the visitor from developed countries because some of the methods used are much the same. As these projects are usually in the public sector, the question of choosing the level of technology presents a most difficult problem to the planners and policy makers of the emerging countries. Unemployed and underemployed workers and shortages of foreign exchange are measured against the pressure for early completion of the needed facility. The technological gap is often spectacularly revealed when the choice between labor-intensive and capital-intensive methods is resolved by compromises that bring both methods together. Even in countries whose unemployment is not a measure of the pressure of population on resources, there is a tendency to intensify labor on public-works projects. Conversely, countries with a serious excess of available manpower often utilize capital-intensive technologies, in the interest of speed and economy.

Another evidence of the internal gap in the emerging countries, differing in degree among these countries, is found between the state of science in universities and other institutions and the application of technology. Scientific activity, both in the physical and social sciences, tends to maintain the divorce from technology that characterized earlier periods of Western science. Scientists in less-developed countries often have closer connections with their counterparts in the rest of the world than with their own developing technologies. Academic social scientists, particularly the economists, generally maintain a close relationship with government and business in the developed countries. Such arrangements are rare in the emerging countries, and the gap between science and its application is even greater in the physical sciences. The reciprocal relationship between science and technology that has proved so useful to scientific development elsewhere does not exist in the less-developed world.

Finally, there is generally an internal cultural gap in the emerging countries: On the one hand, there is a small educated class, at home equally elsewhere in the world, from which innovations are expected even if not always forthcoming. On the other hand, there is the mass of uneducated, often illiterate, populations. Educational policy in the emerging countries has tended to maintain this gap with higher educational opportunities for the elite and general literacy for the masses. The technologically important middle is too often neglected. The cultural gap is especially difficult to close in the agricultural sector, where the problem of productivity is most immediate, particularly where agriculture is largely on a subsistence basis with consequent lack of incentives to change. The conditions of rural life that make for ignorance, prejudice, and resistance to change are also repugnant to those trained people whose presence is needed to break down that resistance. The cultural gap is a formidable barrier to intensive technological change because precisely those elements needed to effect the process of change are missing.

Technical assistance personnel find the transfer of existing technology easier in the advanced sectors of the dual economies of the under-developed world, since there is generally no cultural barrier to be breached, no question of resistance and receptivity, no problem of absorptive capacity. The internal gaps within the under-developed countries inhibit the spread of technological advances.

The differences within the developing countries tend to bring into better focus the differences among them. The most immediately observed characteristics of less-developed countries are the gaps we have mentioned, the disparities among geographical areas and between economic sectors, the wide differences in income and education. Progress in transferring technology is affected by the differences between the countries in the less-developed world and within the countries as well.

Resistance to Technological Change

The development of the emerging countries will not follow the pattern of the older industrial societies. The international resources of capital and technical assistance provide a new element in the process; more important is the availability of new technologies for accelerating growth. New methods permit these countries to leapfrog certain periods and programs that were necessary but costly in time and resources in the development of the industrial countries.

Unfortunately, there are considerable pressures to follow the historical patterns of step by step development rather than to embrace these new technologies. Not all of these pressures are internal. Where new technologies require heavy capital investment, there is often a tendency to recommend that the under-developed countries seek older solutions requiring less foreign exchange. But economic considerations have not been the only block to the fuller uses of modern technology by the emerging countries. The built-in conservatism of the professions often tends to tell the less-developed countries that " you must crawl before you can walk." Failure to accept the full consequences of the technological revolution is evidenced even in the domestic policies of the developed world. The revolutionary results of modern technology in agriculture that have multiplied production per man-hour and per acre have not yet been fully reflected in United States agricultural policy, which continues to assume that these results stem from largely fortuitous aberrations of a natural production cycle that must be normalized.

The bias for using less modern methods is frequently found among experts engaged in technical assistance work. It is occasionally a reaction to uneconomic " showy " undertakings often requested by the developing countries. The generally higher age level of the experts made available to the programs through early retirement policies may also be a factor. In any case, this bias has often been manifested in economic and technical assistance programs by an emphasis on agriculture, on handicrafts and small industry, and on outmoded technologies. This tendency to disregard the use of modern technology has encouraged the belief in the less-developed countries that their development is being thwarted because the industrialized countries still want to use them as sources of raw materials and as markets for industrial products.

At the other extreme has been the widespread sharing of atomic research facilities and materials which has engaged important resources of scientific and technical manpower and a considerable amount of limited funds in less-developed countries with little possibility for making important contributions to their immediate economic development.

The industrialist who undertakes the transfer of technology as a business matter tends less to go slow on the use of the most advanced technology. Where a large manufacturer branches out into the under-developed world, these undertakings will differ little from those at home. Considerations of the market will affect his operations more than questions of employment policy. In general, the major difference in his operations abroad will be the manner in which he meets the problem of supplies and maintenance. Without the support of the rounded technology of a developed economy, he must build into his own operations many of the things for which he would depend on the market at home; for example, maintenance and repair facilities.

The internal pressures against leapfrogging over intermediate stages in development are, perhaps, more difficult to resolve. Lack of capital and foreign exchange are naturally basic problems in the application of modern methods. But much of the opposition to change is embedded in the social and economic structure of the society. A class or group resists changes that will affect its relative position in that society. The witch doctor's objection to penicillin, the landowner's rejection of agricultural machinery, the merchant importer's opposition to indigenous industry have their counterparts in developed economies. But in the emerging countries these elements have greater relative significance.

A curious example of the attractions of outmoded technologies, even in economic sectors not characterized by private interests, is the persistent emphasis on railroads. While some railroads need to be built in specific instances, no developing country need invest its manpower and resources in railroad building on the scale that was required in Europe or North America. Railroads require heavy investment in steel, and although shortage of steel is a major concern of developing countries, railroad building and extension has been emphasized in many development plans. Railroads seem to represent not only glamor or political power to the developing countries but also to advisers from developed countries. This may be a reflection of the historical importance of railroad building in the economic development of the industrial countries. But in opening up new areas today, the substitution of newer and more flexible forms of transport will provide one of the great potentials for saving capital in the development process.

Large power developments and related transmission facilities similarly could leapfrog the need for costly local power plants. While such large-scale plants are being built throughout the less-developed world, a fully planned and integrated power supply is rarely available. The power supply position of most of the cities in the emerging countries is a primary limiting factor in the development of industry. The requirements of foreign capital inhibit large-scale power installations; but, more often than not, the individual industrialists' investments in diesel plants imported from abroad are an equal or greater drain on the countries' exchange requirements, without providing the same incentive for development.

Technologies to Telescope the Process of Development

Despite the resistance—economic, psychological, or sociological—to technological change, there are important examples of the ways that technology has telescoped the development process in the emerging countries. The most startling example is in the field of public health where the effects of technological improvements are measurable. Modern technology in the field of health has even been so effective that it has tended to exacerbate the solution of other development problems, such as employment and food supply, and to raise the question, appropriate to some of the less developed countries, of population control.

In the industrial field, the widespread use of alumnium, plastics, glass, and other new materials is evidence that newer technology can replace many of the methods followed in the development of the industrial countries. Perhaps the textile field has shown the most widespread disregard of the pressures against modernization. The hand loom has virtually disappeared as an important economic factor in the period since World War II, even where labor surplus or cultural pressures were brought to bear in its favor. Moreover, efforts at introducing intermediate technologies, such as improvements in the hand loom and small mechanized looms, have not halted the leapfrogging process. Textile mills based on the latest technology are characteristic landmarks in most under-developed countries today.

Modern agricultural techniques, including the use of hybrid seeds and fertilizers and the introduction of newer water-finding and irrigation methods, are also leapfrogging the period between these techniques and the use of the sharpened stick and the sickle. Although technical assistance experts have occasionally had local successes that have bemused readers of their reports by the introduction of the scythe, the iron-faced plow, a hand pump, or animal-actuated threshing devices, these charming examples of step-by-step development do not show the same impact on developing countries as the transfer of such modern technology as hybrid-corn programs or the erection of modern milk and packing plants or the development of the use of fertilizers.

The field of communications, so important for the development process, provides one of the most pervasive examples of the leapfrogging process. The advances in telecommunications not only provide a basis for avoiding waste of scarce resources but also open up possibilities of mass communication and resultant education. In this they provide the greatest impetus to hope for meeting the needs in education, one of the most persistent internal gaps in the emerging countries. The process of modern government itself is dependent upon this technology. Telecommunications are essential to the very viability of divided Pakistan or scattered Indonesia.

To speed up the development process in most of the under-developed world, there is an immediate need for data upon which development programs can be based. The lacunae in information about their resources must be filled if investments, domestic or foreign, are to be wisely made. These countries need maps, topographic surveys, river gauging, meteorological data, groundwater studies, geologic and soils information, forest evaluation, and other counts and appraisals of their resources. They need census data on their population, its distribution and activities. Fortunately, technology has taken some of its greatest strides precisely in the fields necessary to provide this pre-investment information. Modern techniques can supply in months data that has taken decades to accumulate in the developed countries.

Aerial mapping has replaced, with greater accuracy, older ground methods. Interpretation of aerial photographs for geologic, soils, and forest surveys can effectively replace many of the time-consuming ground methods of the past. Geophysical techniques, such as the airborne magnetometer and the scintillometer, provide means for pin-pointing areas of potential development, thereby conserving the time and effort of scarce technical personnel. Statistical sampling techniques make possible census information for under-developed countries with speed and accuracy undreamed of in the early periods of our own American quests for census data.

New Research and Development

These and other examples of technological developments that have telescoped the time required to meet the needs of the economic development process have been demonstrated by the technical assistance programs. The demonstrations of the successful transfer of such existing technologies are so compelling that there is ground for the view that, given the financial resources and capacity to apply them, existing technologies in the physical sciences would be adequate to the task of raising the levels of living throughout most of the world. Only the current plight of some of the larger less-developed countries with populations too large for their resources and this foreshadowing of the results of current population trends elsewhere makes it necessary to modify such an optimistic view of the present state of technology.

Further research and development in the physical sciences is attacking three critical areas of current shortages: energy, water, and protein supply. Additionally, work on the means of population control is being developed for the long-run population-resource balance on a world scale. Basic research and technological advances in these fields can be expected to yield early results. Similar work must also be continued in other resource and industrial fields in order to adapt existing technology to the conditions of the less-developed countries.

Work of this nature is being done in a number of countries, especially in health and agriculture. Some regional and national institutes to provide technological research for industry have also been established. But, in general, the centers for adapting technology have been inadequate to the task. This is partly a reflection of the fact that the technical assistance personnel assumed that most technology can be transferred with a minimum of adaptation. They were expected to share known ways of doing things with those who did not know them yet. Their purpose was to extend, geographically, the utilization of technical knowledge in fields related to economic and social development rather than to extend the boundaries of that knowledge. In general, they avoided research programs except in rare instances, and these exceptions called for applied research of a limited nature.

The concept of research and development, moreover, must be extended to include the fields of the social scientists. Much of the work of adaptation of technology is less in its own modification than in adjusting the people and their institutions to its introduction. The primary problem in aiding the development of the emerging countries is that of providing the means and improving the methods of transferring technology. Although the technologies for speeding up development have already amply demonstrated their capabilities, their application is yet far from general. The gap must be bridged by the social sciences. An evolving technology for introducing technical change must be concerned in countering the pressures tending to limit the introduction of new technologies and in developing the institutions required for their introduction and adaptation.

The Institutional Base

The transfer of technology requires experts of a high order who are not only competent in their field but also are capable of teaching others. The adaptation of technology often requires technicians of even greater versatility. At the very least, it requires greater competence than merely practicing a known technique. At most, it requires the scientific skills and facilities to do research and development work in circumstances where the expert must also be an administrator. The use of hybrid corn in a new area is not accomplished by a sympathetic technician with a packet, or even a carload, of seed. The effectiveness of photogeology requires more than good air photography and an itinerant geologist. Statistical sampling techniques are not transferred by a statistician from abroad, even if he carries a computer in his baggage. These and most important technologies necessary to the developing countries require laboratories, experiment stations, organizations, institutions. And these must be equipped with people with the requisite training, experience, and interest.

The major point on which success or failure in technical assistance has hinged has been the existence or strength of the necessary institutions in the country being assisted, or the ability of the program to create them. Neither skill in the selection of experts nor funds to implement their recommendations can overcome the lack of local institutions for carrying out an assistance program. The ability of the less-developed areas to provide the necessary institutional base for transferring technology varies from country to country and from field to field.

The aid programs have recognized the need to build and strengthen local institutions. Many experts in health, agriculture, education, or other subject fields have spent most of their efforts in making more effective the ministries and offices to which they were assigned or to building up new services, such as agricultural research stations, public health departments, and geological survey organizations. These institution-building activities have escaped the criticism generally heard of those experts whose reports and advice, however valid, dropped into an institutional void.

Recognizing that the reports of *ad hoc* survey or planning missions have generally been of greater use to students abroad than to the country for which they were undertaken, wiser administrators of aid programs have made it their business to change the terms of reference of such missions so that they will build planning institutions rather than simply present a plan. Experience has turned programs away from supplying data or works. Too much costly air photography has been wasted where no local institutions for its maintenance and use existed or were created. Costly geological studies repeated each other because of a failure to maintain systematic files of hard-won data. Costly new strains of seed and stock were squandered because their introduction was unaccompanied by the necessary institutional instrumentalities for adapting and maintaining them. OPEX, the United Nations program for providing operational and executive personnel to the developing countries, is a practical response to the need for strengthening the institutions of these governments.

The under-developed world is littered with demonstrations that have not demonstrated. The effects of many large-scale assistance efforts have been dissipated because there was no means of fixing their innovations in the local economy. Experience is multiplied only if there is an institution to effect the multiplication. Roads, irrigation systems and other works have been built for the less-developed countries, but their usefulness has been limited by the failure to arrange for the institutions necessary to their maintenance.

These requirements for an institutional framework for the introduction of technology are even of greater importance where the adaptation of the technology to the conditions of the local scene is required. Here, in the long run, the symbiosis of science and technology will be required to provide the " take-off " of an indigenous technological order and the self-sustaining growth of technology.

Institutional Development

Although it has long been recognized that the introduction of technology in the emerging countries must be accompanied by the introduction of the institutions required for its adaptation and use, little systematic work has been done on the problem of how to create institutions or to stimulate their growth. The Research and Development concept needs to be applied to this key problem in the aid programs. The advance of resource and industrial technology and particularly its adaptation to new environments will require a joint effort of the physical and social sciences. The need for more knowledge of the techniques of transferring technology will involve the social sciences in many ways. Among the problems for which the social scientists' contribution is required, none is more crucial than the need to discover ways to develop institutions for introducing change.

The programs of the past provide some experience in this field. The United States aid program began at an early stage to transfer the principle of the land-grant college as the key to agricultural extension services, an institutional complex that had effectively served American agricultural development. Much of this work was contracted to universities on the assumption that the land-grant colleges were the most likely instrumentalities for creating counterparts in their own image in the less-developed world. Similar contracts for creating other training and research organizations in other fields, such as faculties of public administration and teacher-training schools, have been a major feature of the United States program. Many of these projects have been successful in spite of administrative difficulties and the invalidity of the two basic assumptions upon which they were predicated: that such institutions can be transplanted with little modification into the emerging countries; and that the personnel required by such existing institutions at home would also have the competence to build a similar institution abroad under differing circumstances.

Efforts in the institution-building field by the United States program go back to the " *servicios* " that characterized the work of the Institute of Interamerican Affairs, the pioneer assistance program in Latin America that preceded Point Four. The " *servicio* " was a joint enterprise of the United States and the country assisted, being established for the purpose of improving agriculture, health, or education. It was financed by contributions from both, with a specific and agreed program of work and staffed with experts from the United States and professionally trained local counterparts. The important early successes of the " *servicio* " in introducing new techniques and developing new services have tended to blind partisans of this approach to some of its defects. Primarily the *"servicios"* were kept outside of the normal government structure to avoid the uncertainties of politics—and the host government's contributions were financed outside of its normal budget and guaranteed by intergovernmental agreements to assure continuity and stability. These factors, and better pay and perquisites, tended to draw many of the better professionals away from other governmental offices with a consequent weakening of important government agencies. Moreover, as an extra-budgetary item, the *"servicio"* tended to command a greater share of the financial resources of the government than subsequent policy makers might find desirable. The *"servicio,"* which was intended to be a step in the development of an indigenous institution, locally financed and operated, often remained an alien thing not fully integrated into the government's family of services.

One would expect that the propensity for organization in the United States would have created a technology for institution building. The recent publication of an *Encyclopedia of Associations*, claiming to be a "reference guide to America's 11,000 national associations," is evidence of a knack for institutionalization. But the adaptation of this aptitude or technology for the purposes of the developing countries has not been uniformly successful. Perhaps there has been too much emphasis on the transfer of United States institutions and not enough on their adaptation.

Other countries have also lagged in devising techniques of institution-building. Even the former colonial areas are generally deficient in local institutions essential to their development. An exception may be the creation by the United Kingdom of the Indian Civil Service, which provided the basis for important institutional developments in the Government of India. Elsewhere, the British emphasized training people rather than developing institutions. The effort to build the services of government necessary to their development has been a major preoccupation of Burma, Ceylon, and other former colonies. Where geological and other resource services important to the process of development were created, they were often based upon the professional resources and the interests of the metropolitan powers rather than upon the needs of the local economy. In the newer emerging countries, efforts to develop indigenous services have generally come too late. But, if institutions are inadequate in the former colonies, the problem is even greater in those countries that had no institutional tutelage. From the standpoint of services necessary to economic development, such countries as Iran and Ethiopia have been an institutional wasteland.

The emerging countries of Africa south of the Sahara are generally inadequately endowed with institutions necessary for their development. This is one of the primary difficulties in making an impact with technical assistance on that continent. Governmental organizations, formerly staffed from abroad, have not been Africanized fast enough to take up the reins dropped by expatriates who are leaving. Education policies have not produced the required African professions to fill the jobs being vacated. Higher education of the young has not only been meager, but it has also been unrelated to development needs; it has traditionally emphasized the fields of law or medicine with, perhaps in the past few years, some economics. The people required for development programs—agronomists, hydrologists, geologists, engineers, statisticians, and chemists—are rare in these emerging countries. Moreover, where these are available, there are none of the middle-echelon technologies—the laboratory workers, surveyors, cartographers, and other aides of the professions—who come from the high schools and trade schools in developed countries. Thus, while most of these new nations may be able to get a quorum of legislators with some training in that field, few can staff the technical services required for their national development programs. Experience in the Congo highlighted the crucial importance of the availability of "human capital," as Harbison calls it, not only for effective utilization of physical capital in the development process but also for the maintenance of a viable government. The current emphasis on training to provide the infrastructure of skills essential to increasing productivity must be matched, however, by an effort to develop the institutions necessary to utilize trained manpower. The unemployed intellectual is a growing problem in emerging countries. He is, often, a product of the wrong training. He may be unemployed because the government or the economy of his country has not the resources or the institutions required for his effective employment.

While the French established a number of local services in Africa and trained a considerable number of middle-level technologists, their effectiveness has been seriously impaired by the small size of the independent units into which these territories have split. The divisions of Africa, stemming from long-standing tribal and cultural patterns or from recent colonial administration, have made it more difficult to develop viable indigenous institutions. A checkerboard of cultures, languages, and administrations with little opportunity for joint consideration of common interests or problems has not made easy the creation of regional associations that reinforce local institutions. The Consultative Committee on Technical Assistance in Africa South of the Sahara sought to bring African leaders in science and technology together on their development problems. Regional projects of the United Nations family of Specialized Agencies worked to the same end. But these efforts have as yet resulted in few organized regional activities of a continuing nature of the kind found in other regions of the world, such as Latin America. Fortunately there is a growing interest among African leaders in the development of regional institutions.

The recipient governments themselves are not always aware of their need for institution building. Moreover, when governments have asked for help in creating local institutions, they too have failed to reckon with the problem of adaptation. The impulse behind the request from the Turkish Government for assistance in establishing the Middle East Technical University was the desire of a group of government officials and businessmen who had been trained in engineering colleges in the United States to transplant these institutions to Ankara. They wanted it to provide the same kind of education they had received abroad, including the use of the English language in all courses. The opposition from the leaders of higher education in the country to this revolutionary move and the inability of Turkish secondary education to provide the ecological framework for such an institution have made the process of adaptation long and difficult.

The lure of physical plant as a substitute, symbol, or starting point for institution building has often appealed to both recipients and donors of technical assistance. Laboratories have an especial appeal, but it is easier to equip a laboratory than to recruit people who can make it useful. Community centers, clinics, schools, orphanages, agricultural stations have also been built without providing a basis for their use, maintenance, and development. In the industrial field, arrangements for training local operators and developing local management are generally included in the construction or equipment contracts. The arrangement for the Russian-financed steel plant in India, for instance, involved its operation by Russian experts in each job until an Indian counterpart could be trained to take over. But neither the Russian nor other bilateral assistance has always followed such careful planning in other fields or other places.

Research and Development in the Social Sciences

Research and development in the social sciences for improving the techniques of inducing technological change cannot be confined to the institution-building field. Economists must still improve and adapt techniques of planning and of financing economic development. Building up local savings mechanisms, liberalizing external financing, and improving the terms of trade of these raw-material supplying countries are still the crucial problems in inducing development. Delays in solving them are the principal cause of delays in development.

Educational practices require adaptation. The development of short cuts to training is basic to accelerating the development process throughout the under-developed world. Inter-disciplinary approaches between social scientists and communications technology should be brought to bear upon this important problem. Problems of recruitment and conditioning of experts for the technical assistance programs have never been given enough attention. Leaders and entrepreneurs in the developing societies must be identified.

Most of these areas for research and development call for the attention of the behavioral sciences. These sciences and their less-developed technologies must begin to accompany the economists who have begun work in the field of inducing development. Experience has demonstrated Wiesner's charge that the behavioral sciences have been "timid" in asking support for their scientific activities. But more important, the behavioral sciences have not been brought to bear sufficiently on the specific problems of the transfer of technology. Problems involved in the recruitment and conditioning of people engaged in overseas assignments, problems of motivation and incentives in different societies, problems of semantics and attitudes and related sociological and psychological issues have engaged the scholars as well as the practitioners. But, for the most part, the social scientist has not had the close relationship to the technician in this field that would provide a feedback of experience data for the further development of the science.

One of the principal areas of social scientists' concern must necessarily be in the field of institution building. We must know more about the birth, growth, health, and decay of institutions. We must know more about their interrelationships, their effect on one another, and how they may be affected from outside. As institutions are the primary instrument for transferring technology by accepting and adapting it, and by applying and perpetuating it, institution building and strengthening are key skills to be sought. The identification of personnel with these skills becomes an important area of study itself. The methods of developing these aptitudes must also be studied.

These studies are unlikely to yield simple answers that are universally applicable. Not only are we engaged in different cultural and economic circumstances, but there is great variety in the institutions required for the purposes of development and transfer of technology. We are not merely seeking to identify the charismatic leaders of movements; the institution to be built or strengthened may not call for such political aptitudes but rather for administrative ability and for a measure of organization orientation. Nor is the quest for the possible institution builder simply for the person who makes the decisions for a village, an industry, or a ministry. These leaders may well be the nay-sayers concerned with the maintenance of a particular institutional *status quo*.

Incipient innovators are required in many " private " and " public " areas of activity. Tata in India or Di Tella in Argentina, Ford, Jane Addams or Mark Hopkins in the United States, have developed private institutions in both the immediate organizations they founded and in the larger sense of founding a process. Innovators in government are equally varied: John Wesley Powell's role in the United States Geological Survey; Macedo-Suares' leadership in the Brazilian steel works; Lilienthal in his TVA period; Navarre of the Institut Français de Petrole; Gallatin; Monnet. These " bureaucratic " empire builders of governmental institutions and programs must also provide historical models for the innovators and entrepreneurs needed in the emerging nations.

The study of institutions will be more than the study of the attitudes, aptitudes, and incentives of the people who give them leadership. Economic considerations and patterns of custom and culture will be of major importance in measuring the viability, indeed the possibility, of institutional development. The aid programs are not the sole source of material for reviewing these questions. Experts, merchants, immigrants, and other foreigners have had diverse roles for many years in relation to indigenous institutions. Such outsiders as the Pharsees, Jews, Lebanese, and overseas Chinese have had important impacts on the development of local institutions, especially in the private sector of developing countries. But the aid programs provide the possibility of combining research and practice on a broad basis that would be difficult to duplicate elsewhere.

Institution building, moreover, may require the destruction or weakening of other institutions. Such ground-clearing operations are also a fruitful area for study. Why do the bulldozing tactics of Kemal Ataturk or MacArthur appear to have been more effective in preparing the ground for institutional changes than the similar methods of Reza Shah? What is the relationship of Mexico's current phenomenal development of the 25 years of institution wrecking that followed the fall of Porfirio Diaz?

The variety of the institutions required is itself formidable. Both governmental and non-governmental institutions are necessary to the economic and social development of the less-developed countries. The specific institutional requirements may vary from country to country and circumstance to circumstance, but the resultant complex will be much the same. Education, credit, transport and communications, health and welfare, production and trade, as well as law enforcement and taxation, call for organized offices, bureaus, firms, and associations. The planning of institutions becomes especially important where there is a scarcity of personnel to man them. Any effort to accelerate the process of development calls for the establishment of priorities and other planning techniques to assure the most effective use of resources. But the creation of planning agencies assumes the availability of institutions for providing data, on the one hand, and the institutions for carrying out the plans, on the other.

The place of institutional forms in the rapid and unique industrial development of Japan or in the maintenance of Denmark's relatively high levels of living on her relatively low resource base deserve the attention of those concerned with technological changes. Such broad questions have been under review by social scientists. But of more immediate concern to the aid programs for the under-developed countries is the possible role of the outsider in institutional development. For these programs are an institutional embodiment of the outsider.

The aid programs provide, in this field as elsewhere in the study of institutional development, the most recent basis for sharpening up the questions as well as the constant flow of fresh data in which the answers may be sought. To be sure, the aid programs cannot stand still for these examinations. Nor would a static inspection be likely to reveal ready answers. The social scientists must formulate methods of studying the programs while they are in motion. To this end, they must seek the cooperation of the successful practitioners, even though these practitioners may not always be their most helpful allies. Not only are the practitioners busy and preoccupied, but they themselves may not know the reasons for their success or even be aware of the methods they have used to bring it about. The social scientists must recognize that most of their offerings of guiding information and interpretation are still too tentative and lacking in immediacy to be of great help to the practitioner. On the other hand, a close relationship between the scientists and the practitioners is essential to progress in this field.

The study of the institution-building process requires an interdisciplinary approach. The required reciprocity between the scientist and the practitioner, although difficult to achieve, is essential to the task of creating a science and technology in the field of transferring technology. The research and development concept, itself an institutional approach, has shown such success in other fields of human endeavour that its introduction into the field of development of the emerging nations is a welcome initiative at the beginning of this Decade of Development.

Technology in Focus—The Emerging Nations

LONG-TERM PROSPECTS AND PROBLEMS

ROBERT THEOBALD *

Unfortunately, mankind has not yet accepted, or even understood, the responsibility increasing knowledge and technical capacity has forced upon it. Gaston Berger, President of the *Encyclopédie Française*, describes our situation well:

> The day before yesterday we followed unconsciously what was called Nature; yesterday we tried conscientiously to conform to "nature" but today, our power having grown considerably, it behooves us sometimes to protect nature and sometimes to arrange it in ways which seem favorable. We have somehow become responsible for evolution . . . a reality is to be constructed and not events awaited.[1]

This paper offers some speculations on our responsibilities, with particular emphasis on the problems and prospects of the developing countries. It deals first with the changes science and technology can be expected to bring about in the developing countries and the social systems that will become possible, and indeed necessary, if these countries are to achieve a "human" society within the framework of a productive technological mechanism. It then considers the essential differences between the process that took place when technology was introduced into the countries now developed and that occurring today in the countries trying to develop. The final section examines some institutional arrangements that might make it possible to determine how to safeguard a human society under changing conditions and how to develop and transfer the technological base essential for a nation in today's world.

The Effect of Technological Development on Society

It would probably be generally agreed that science and technology, and their creature economic growth, have had two particularly important economic effects. First, they have allowed a rapid increase in

---

* Robert Theobald is an economist and management consultant who has written two books on the responsibilities of the advanced nations to the developing countries: *The Rich and the Poor* and *The Challenge of Abundance* (New York, 1960, 1961).

the amount of energy available to each individual in the rich countries as compared to the poor nations of the world. Second, they have led to a continuing change in the distribution of the labor force during the process of development.

The relationship of technology and available levels of energy has been fairly well understood. For obvious reasons, there is normally a very high correlation between energy levels per head and income per head. It is clear that present levels of production in the industrialized countries could only have been achieved on the basis of a major increase in the amount of power available to workers. Table 1 shows the extent of the present energy gap between the industrialized and the non-industrialized countries of the world.

Almost everyone, whatever his views about desirable forms of society in coming years, would find the development of energy resources both favorable and necessary. It would seem that the availability of power to relieve man from back-breaking work—in the literal sense of the phrase—must be considered progress. This does not mean that the process of introducing this power may not be severely disruptive.

TABLE 1

ENERGY CONSUMPTION IN KILOGRAMS OF COAL EQUIVALENT
PER CAPITA, 1959 [2]

Selected Countries

United States	7,834	Japan	965
Canada	5,606	Cuba	770
United Kingdom	4,594	Taiwan	498
Czechoslovakia	4,590	Greece	400
Belgium	3,853	Iraq	336
Australia	3,684	British Honduras	200
Germany	3,266	Nicaragua	180
Poland	2,955	Tunisia	163
Russia	2,942	Paraguay	71
Venezuela	2,512	Liberia	49
Union of South Africa	2,469	Haiti	43
Austria	1,959	Nigeria	42
New Zealand	1,886	Gambia	41
Finland	1,404	Laos	22
Israel	1,122	Afghanistan	20
Argentina	1,033	Ethiopia	8

The relationship of technology, economic growth, and occupational distribution has been obscured by incorrect economic theories about the process of changing from the distribution of labor common in a poor country to that now prevalent in the rich. In effect, it is usually argued that changes in the countries now developing must necessarily follow the historical pattern of the nineteenth and early twentieth centuries.

Economists have developed a theory about the shifts in occupational distribution which necessarily take place during the process of economic growth. F. Dovring expresses it in these terms:

> It has become almost axiomatic nowadays that a highly developed economy should have only a small proportion of its population engaged in agriculture. The relatively low demand elasticity of most foodstuffs and the advantages of specialization are now common knowledge, to the extent that it is regarded as self-evident that expanding secondary (manufacturing) and tertiary (services) sectors of the economy are a condition for economic progress. The facts seem to underscore this, since practically all the economically less developed countries are predominantly agricultural and all of the most highly developed ones have only a small sector of their population engaged in agriculture or depending on it for their livelihood.[3]

In effect, Dovring is arguing that the countries now developing will follow the same pattern of change in occupational distribution as occurred in the rich countries during the nineteenth and the early part of the twentieth century. The question is whether this is a sound view in the light of the rising tide of automation.

While experience in the countries now developed *cannot* provide us with a blueprint for the future, it does contain much of the information available to determine future trends. It reveals that during the development process there has been a steady decline in the proportion of the population living in rural areas and an increase in the number living in towns. A continuing increase in the number of people employed in manufacturing and mining took place until recent years. At a later stage in the industrialization process, the transfer of people ceased to be primarily from agriculture to industry, and the service areas became the growth sectors in terms of employment. The extent of the recent shift of growth in employment into services is demonstrated by Table 2.

The development process has apparently resulted in an extreme contrast between the percentage of persons engaged in various types of work in the rich and the poor countries. However, it is important to recognize that statistical conventions are partly responsible for the " evidence." Statisticians claim that it would be too complicated to classify an individual by the proportion of time spent in various types of work. Usually he is counted in the sector of the economy where he spends most of his working time. This works fairly well in the developed countries where most people do only one job. It is not satisfactory in rural areas, for many agriculturalists do not work full time at farming. Another cause of incomparability is the fact that women in the rural areas of the poor countries do much work without

TABLE 2

EMPLOYMENT IN VARIOUS SECTORS OF THE AMERICAN ECONOMY [*]
(Figures in thousands)

| Production Sectors | | | | | Distribution & Service Sectors | | | | |
Mining	Contract Construction	Manufacturing	Transportation & Public Utilities	Year	Wholesale & Retail Trade	Finance, Insurance, & Real Estate	Service, Miscellaneous	Gov't	Total
916	1,294	10,780	3,013	1940	6,940	1,436	3,477	4,202	32,058
826	1,132	15,302	3,872	1945	7,522	1,428	4,011	5,944	40,037
889	2,333	14,967	3,977	1950	9,645	1,824	5,077	6,026	44,738
777	2,759	16,563	4,062	1955	10,846	2,219	5,916	6,914	50,056
665	2,795	16,369	3,921	1960	11,698	2,494	6,673	8,522	53,137

pay and are therefore not counted in the occupational statistics, while similar work often enters the economic complex in the industrialized countries.

The real difference between the pattern of occupational distribution in the rich and the poor countries today is certainly less than the crude figures would suggest. Better information must be available before we accept the thesis that major shifts in occupational distribution are necessarily correlated with economic growth. The necessity of re-examining this belief is particularly great because there no longer seems to be a need, or indeed a possibility, to build a large labor force in the manufacturing sector of advanced technological societies. This view is supported by the experience of the developed and the developing countries.

In the United States, for example, recent events suggest that employment possibilities are being limited. As a result there is some confusion about economic policy. The economic system is set up in a way that brings pressure on everybody to ensure maximum production. If the wages of workers rise and it becomes cheaper to employ machines, firms install more equipment to preserve their competitive position. Similarly, if it becomes possible to produce a new material more cheaply than an already existing one, market forces ensure that it will be introduced. This system is based on the belief that free markets are a completely satisfactory method of determining how to produce the largest amount of goods at the least cost and on the theory that those thrown out of work by " progress " will necessarily find new jobs which will, in general, pay better salaries.

However, while the *economic* system is structured to achieve maximum production at minimum cost, social aims have diverged increasingly from this goal. America *is* still trying to obtain the maximum possible increase in production but not because more production is considered of great immediate value in itself. The most common justification today for a rapid rate of growth is the need to ensure jobs for all. This may appear surprising, but if statements from business, government, and social commentators are examined, we find that they often call attention to the breakdown in the social system which could be expected if a rate of growth sufficient to provide employment for all is not achieved.

As early as 1958, August Heckscher could write about conditions in America:

> When production lagged (in 1957) no one at first seemed particularly worried by the unused capacity. It would not be entirely an exaggeration to say that a characteristic first reaction was a kind of relief in the relaxation of pressure, with the compulsion to absorb an inexhaustible stream of goods and materials being temporarily reduced.

Such a mood must seem paradoxical considering how generally it has been taken for granted that production is in itself good—that the more there is of it, the better and stronger a nation is. If people really believe this, why has there not been a wider outcry and a greater sense of dismay at the sight of a steel industry producing far below its potentiality? Why has there not been a more general concern at the thought of output falling below its top level? There has been dismay and concern, to be sure; but this has been due primarily to the unemployment accompanying the economic slowdown. The country feels, understandably, that it cannot tolerate the hardship to individual men and women which lack of a job entails. To alleviate this hardship no measures seem too strong. As an editorial in a national magazine puts it at this writing: "Unemployment is the chief reason for trying to end the recession." If it were simply a matter of faltering production, the recession, we may presume, could be allowed to run its course.[5]

In this situation, functions originally considered ancillary to the productive process—advertising, packaging, etc.—are coming to be considered as necessities because they will help to ensure a more rapid rate of economic growth, more jobs, and therefore adequate incomes for a larger number of people.

It is difficult to avoid the conclusion that if economic growth is *primarily* required in order to provide jobs and incomes for all, it would be better to try and tackle the income problems directly by changing the principles on which money is distributed. This would seem more satisfactory than an attempt to keep the economy growing at a fast enough rate to provide jobs—and therefore incomes—for all.

The greatest problem is not that of adapting *economic* systems, however, except insofar as these are reflections of deep beliefs. The real issues arise from the alterations in *social* systems that will be required to adapt our present attitudes to a new type of society where many people will be freed from the necessity of work. Both Russia and the West will have to face the social issues raised by abundance in the very near future, and both of them will find it very difficult to adjust. The possibility of abundance was created by a set of social values—a belief in hard work and abstinence and by man's desire to understand and control the universe. The very success of this ethic destroyed the value of abstinence and is now undermining the value and the possibility of present types of work.

It is generally accepted that economic development will require some changes in value systems. But values are not rapidly malleable; only a new generation is able to develop a radically different approach to life. As the developing countries *already possess* many of the values appropriate to a society of economic abundance, we must re-examine the thesis that these countries must embrace the values that made abundance possible in the advanced nations.

Events of the past ten to fifteen years have proved conclusively that the economic gap between the rich and the poor countries is so wide that our only hope of equalizing conditions throughout the world is to allow the poor countries to evolve from their present state to a system under which they will benefit from abundance, without requiring them to pass through the agonies of an industrial revolution. This thesis is usually rejected as visionary and/or dangerous. It is argued that it is impossible for a country, or even the world as a whole, to give what it does not yet possess. But ways can and must be found. Ways can be sought, because we have developed a totally new approach to problem solving which could be applied in the developing countries. The Stanford Research Institute expressed this idea in a report to the Senate:

> Someone has said that in recent times we have invented the art of systematic invention. Organized scientific research and development, which has become a great industry in the last few decades, is itself one of the most significant social inventions of the twentieth century. It is unlocking the secrets of nature and putting the knowledge to practical use at an unprecedented rate. Also we have invented the art of systematic innovation. . . .[6]

A new approach is also *necessary*. The developing nations cannot provide enough employment. India and Pakistan, for example, have claimed that various measures proposed in their five-year plans would decrease the amount of unemployment or at the very least absorb the new entries to the labor force. At the end of each plan period this result has not actually been achieved. Even the statements of intent become less optimistic in each successive period. The International Labor Organization has reported an increasing tendency toward unemployment and underemployment in many developing countries.

Teodoro Moscoso has explained this tendency on the basis of the experience of Puerto Rico, which is often considered an example of how successful industrial development on Western patterns can be:

> Where, in terms of economic objective, do we hope to find ourselves in fifteen years? Our basic economic objective is to reduce our still too high unemployment rate of 14 percent of the labour force to fractional proportions. Notwithstanding the great strides we have taken along the path of economic growth, a persistently high unemployment rate continues, and we are inclined to believe that every underdeveloped country is going to find itself in a similar predicament. For as industrialization advances and modernization gathers momentum in commerce, transportation and agriculture, labour-saving equipment will be forced upon those sectors

if they want to retain their workers and be able to pay them increasingly higher wages. Otherwise the pull of industry, always strong, will become increasingly so. Our experience has been that rationalization in other sectors far outpaces the creation of new industrial jobs and that at times, make-work programmes preferably of a social overhead type such as accelerated highway construction may have to be undertaken to take up the slack, until such time as industrial development catches up and supplies the needed jobs.[7]

The process of industrialization and modernization will not provide sufficient conventional jobs to allow every nuclear family to provide for itself. Government therefore has a responsibility which it can discharge in one of two ways. First, it can provide what Moscoso has called "make-work" jobs. Second, it can reconsider the principles on which it is going to distribute income and develop a system that would not necessarily tie rewards very closely to the "economic value" of the work performed.

Make-work programs generally use otherwise unemployed labor to carry out work which is necessary—such as building roads, schools, etc.—but which is not normally economically practicable. There is some question, however, about how much work of this type can be carried out economically, whether based on a paid, voluntary, or compulsory basis. It is, of course, true that unemployed labor is often a free economic resource. But is it possible that the effective mobilization of the available labor necessarily requires the use of an uneconomically large quantity of other scarce resources? For example, if a dam is to be built by hand labor, rather than by machine, is a real saving in the scarce factors of production—particularly that of management—actually achieved or not? How far can labor substitute for capital in industrial processes which require skill?

It should be clear that this question goes far beyond the usual economic problem of the choice between labor-intensive and capital-intensive methods of production. It deals with the *total* issue of how to deploy resources. There is already much evidence that capital is not really scarce in many of the developing countries. It is management skills and drive that are usually the acute bottleneck. Processes requiring much supervision may therefore be highly wasteful for the country even though the money cost appears to be relatively low. If this is true, many projects designed to employ additional labor have no economic justification.

We are in urgent need of a new philosophy to justify the distribution of income, in both the industrialized and the developing countries. It will be much easier to graft this new philosophy *directly* onto the present value systems of the poor countries than to first inculcate the present value system of the West where work is considered the determinant of income, and then to move back into a set of values in which leisure is once more an integral part of life. Many of the developing countries appreciate the value of leisure, and this appreciation should not be destroyed.

Available Technologies for the Developing Countries

What can science and technology do for the developing countries? There is no available catalogue of possibilities in this field, indeed, it seems fair to say that this question is only now starting to be discussed. The field is so vast that the process of examining it is, in itself, a major task.

What is the basic difference between the position of the countries now industrialized and those trying to develop themselves? The present position of the industrialized countries was determined by the *chronological* order in which new technological possibilities became available. Prospects for invention were determined to some extent by what had gone before. The developing countries, on the other hand, can choose between the wide range of technologies that have been developed over the whole period of the industrial revolution. By way of example, the range of choice in one particular area—that of electric power plants—is set out in Table 3.

It is helpful to examine the potential of science and technology by considering its impact in one particular field—transportation. The countries now developed passed through various stages of transportation possibilities, running from poor roads through the introduction of canals, railroads, automobiles and trucks, and airplanes. Each of these had to find its economic place within an already existing framework— although its potential was often affected by government action. In recent years new forms of transportation such as the monorail and the hovercraft have been developed, but none of these has appeared economical within the already existing transportation systems of the industrialized countries.

The situation in the developing countries is very different. Many have little money invested in existing forms of transportation. The economics of the installation of a complete transportation system will necessarily differ from those in a country where parts of a network already exist. Some obvious questions come to mind. Might not the hovercraft, which does not require a good road surface, be far cheaper as a method of transportation in the developing countries? Given the non-existence of railroads in many cases, can new methods of moving bulk cargoes—the main reason for expensive railroad building—be devised? What is the proper place of airplane transit in a country with few roads and where the climate is highly destructive? The list of questions is lengthy, and very little research has been carried out on them.

A similar set of problems exists in the city. What will be the most efficient way of moving people within a modern city—particularly one being designed from scratch? Will the automobile be the basis of city transport or will modifications be required, such as the battery-driven vehicle? Can some new form of rapid transport system be evolved?

TABLE 3

CATEGORIES OF ELECTRIC POWER PLANTS

Category Size Range	Individual Power Plant Watts-5 Kw	Village Power Plant 5 Kw-100 Kw	Area Power Plant 100 Kw-1000 Kw	Grid Sub- Station Power Plant 1000 Kw and up
Power Plant Type				
Batteries	X			
Muscle Power	X			
Solar Cells	D			
Thermoelectric	D			
Wind Turbine	X	X	D	
Hydroelectric	X	X	X	X
Fuel Cell			D	D
Biochemical Fuel Cell	D	D		
Gasoline Engine	X	X		
Diesel Engine	X	X	X	X
Stirling Engine		D	D	D
Gas Turbine			X	X
Closed Cycle Turbine		D	D	
Closed Cycle Engine		D		
Fuel Availability				
Solar Radiation	X	X		
Wind	X	X	X	
Water	X	X	X	X
Wood	X	X		
Agricultural Wastes	X	X	X	
Dung (gas)	X	X		
Crude Petroleum Products			X	
Refined Petroleum Products	X	X	X	X
Lignite/Peat		X	X	X
Coal			X	X

D—Major development required for practical economical equipment
X—Available

These questions are basically those of technical efficiency, cost, and aesthetics. But the scientific progress that has been achieved in other fields makes clear that the choice is much wider than one of economics and efficiency. The whole pattern of living of the countries now industrialized was determined by the chronological order in which technologies were developed. The reasoning behind cities and suburbs, the rural areas, and the small communities needs rethinking in terms of the best possible social pattern. The politician and the social scientist must help build good societies in the new environment that science and technology are creating.

An Institutional Framework

At present there is little willingness to look at the social issues raised by increasing knowledge. Most of the work in the social sciences is too fragmented to be relevant. Funds are seldom available for examination of the frontier issues, such as the organization of a peaceful world and the distribution of wealth in an economy of abundance, for these problems fit within no traditional discipline, and their consideration is deeply disruptive of present beliefs.

The problem we confront was well described by the Interim Committee on the Social Aspects of Science of the American Association for the Advancement of Science:

> We are now in the midst of a new and unprecedented scientific revolution which promises to bring about profound changes in the condition of human life. The forces and processes now coming under human control are beginning to match in size and intensity those of nature itself, and our total environment is now subject to human influence. In this situation it becomes imperative to determine that these new powers shall be used for the maximum human good, for, if the benefits to be derived from them are great, the possibility of harm is correspondingly serious.[8]

We may well ask if man is capable of planning the evolution of his own world. The present course of events leaves no doubt that we can expect a further process of dehumanization so long as we allow the effectiveness—rather than the appropriateness—of the machine to determine its use. The technological apparatus could soon cease to meet human ends, and men would live within a glittering mechanical apparatus, created *for* them but actually destroying their freedom.

Research is urgently required if we are to use the potential of science and technology as a force for good. To make it possible, we must provide an institutional framework that would bring together those scholars who can cope imaginatively with the complexities of our present situation. The kinds of institutions needed include:[9]

1. *The Institute of World Social and Political Organization.* An international body to examine the social, economic, and political systems which could be viable in a world where unlimited destructive powers exist, where there is no real shortage of resources, and where new techniques to meet problems can be developed through research and development. The Institute would aim to discuss the *real* questions in today's world: What methods can be found to allow peaceful settle-

ments of disputes between sovereign nations? What are the criteria on which wealth should be distributed both nationally and internationally? How can the freedom of the individual be preserved in a technological world? What are the real limits of learning at various levels of intelligence?

The Institute would operate on both a philosophical and a social science level. Its staff would try to develop the principles on which questions should be resolved. They would also attempt to translate these principles into concepts that could be used in the policy-making process, thus replacing the present terminology of the social sciences which is often irrelevant or positively misleading.

The Institute should be small, with limited costs. It is essential that it be endowed for an extended period, for if it is to play a major role, it is certain that it will become unpopular in many quarters. A conflict between its beliefs and the need for money should be avoided. It should be completely independent.

2. *The Institute for the Study of Technological Systems.* An international group working to determine suitable methods of organizing society's technological base from the human and economic standpoint. It would examine the available forms of technology with a view to deciding how they could be efficiently combined in various sets of conditions.

This would require the integration of knowledge of existing technologies in transportation, communication, water supply, energy production, etc., and the availability of experts in all these fields. It would also require a re-examination of the conventions under which the cost of various solutions are presently calculated—for the relative efficiency of various engineering approaches is very heavily affected by the cost of capital, labor, etc., which it is assumed will be charged during the life of the project. Finally, the needs of the human being for a good life must be more clearly known if it is to be possible to plan change in society effectively. Here a close relationship to The Institute on World Social and Political Organization would be especially helpful. Unlike the first organization, there seems to be no reason why this Institute should not receive steadily increasing support. Initial funds could come from foundations, from a consortium of governments, or from the United Nations family. Further grants would be obtainable as the need for, and success of, such an approach could be demonstrated.

3. *Agency for Contract Research and Development of Technological Systems.* It must be expected that the Institute for the Study of Technological Systems would identify serious gaps in available technologies. Methods of arranging for research and development must be provided. However, to require the Institute to undertake the administrative work involved would ensure that its original purpose would be lost. This responsibility should fall to the Agency. It could

fill a similar function, on request, for regional and national bodies described below.

Several techniques should be used in arranging for research. Some problems might be solved by Agency staff, particularly when most of the information is already available. A panel of experts on a voluntary or paid basis might be set up to work on some of the more limited problems. The existence of " Volunteers for International Technical Assistance " and similar groups would seem to prove the practicability of this approach. It might also be possible to work through the research units of national technical assistance organizations. Other problem areas could best be tackled by working with non-profit organizations and obtaining foundation financing.

For many contracts, particularly those involving the development of hardware, a somewhat unconventional competitive bid system should be used. It can be anticipated that a certain amount of new knowledge would emerge during the course of many contracts, much of which might be of commercial value and some of which could be expected to be patentable. Firms would therefore be asked to bid on two key factors: the percentage of cost of the research which they would meet from their own resources and the percentage of the value of the patent rights which they would require to have vested in their firm.

Each commercial company would obviously prefer to receive 100 per cent of the cost of the research and to have 100 per cent of the patent right assigned to the company. However, the competitive bidding process, particularly on an international basis, would force the company to bid on a basis less favorable to its interests if it wished to receive the contract. The organization should request bids from companies or research bodies it knows are capable of performing the work but should also invite bids from others subject to eventual determination of their qualifications.

It seems reasonable to expect that highly favorable bids may be received. The fact that a query has been put out to tender will usually confirm that there will be a market for the results. Such an implied guarantee could often be of the greatest importance. The profit potential of action in the developing countries, which is presently diffuse, would come into sharp focus.

The Agency could choose the type of offer best suited to its immediate needs. One aim would be to build up a backlog of patent rights fairly rapidly as the return on these patents would lessen the need for future financing. On the other hand, it is unlikely that sufficient funds will be available to finance all the research required—allowing companies to finance the research and to be compensated by the patent rights will therefore also be attractive. Whatever the choice, it will be possible to avoid the situation where research is financed by outside funds and the benefits of this research accrue in large part to a private company.

Funds for general support of the Agency might be made available through the United Nations Special Fund and also directly from governments. Some foundations might also be willing to contribute.

4. *The International Technology Information Center.* Information flows in the field of development work are not satisfactory. Increasing duplication of effort is taking place throughout the world. Attempts to keep up with the flow of new knowledge and literature on the basis of conventional techniques will not succeed. Computers must be used if problems in this area are to be solved.

The Technology Information Center would have an operational purpose. It should make it possible to check whether technologies required in a certain area had already been developed and to have available the names of those who had studied in each field and who could do further work. The system should not be primarily concerned with another basic area—that of allowing the interrelation and correlation of new knowledge in the sciences and social sciences, although this function is also necessary and might well require the creation of another information system.

It seems probable that part—and even a major proportion—of the cost of running the system could be met by charging search fees to commercial firms, governments, and other organizations. The remaining cost should be met by many of the other organizations proposed in this paper, which would require the Center's services for efficient operation. Initial financing might come from many sources. There would seem to be a genuine possibility of substantial financial support from a few of the computer companies around the world.

5. *Regional Technological Institutes.* These Institutes would be designed to carry out research on area-wide problems and would hold particular promise for the smaller and poorer countries of the world. They would often provide the only possible method by which some special problems could receive the attention they deserved. Close cooperation will be needed between Regional Institutes in different parts of the world to minimize the duplication of research. The United Nations Special Fund has already taken some steps toward setting up regional technological institutes and will probably take more. A policy of making foundation funds available to institutes in the developing countries in preference to those in the developed countries would, where appropriate, have the desirable result of attracting scientists to work in the developing countries.

6. *Centers for the Study of National Institutions.* These Centers would be designed to study the type of society that would be required and desirable within a country, given its historical background and the new possibilities being opened up by science and technology. Most

economists would hold that such Centers would be a complete waste of resources for the developing countries. This attitude, however, fails to take account of the fact that effective planning for economic and social change is impossible until it is known what the aims of the society are. Indeed, our most basic failure has been our apparent inability to help the developing countries look realistically at their own societies and determine what their goals can and should be. We have been content to export, either implicitly or explicitly, our own goals and values.

Some countries already have organizations answering more or less to this description. Others would have to create them. In the developing countries, it must be recognized that such Centers would be operating in extremely difficult conditions. Urgent action is required in all the developing countries and effective programs may only be possible by using charismatic leadership. The Centers would have to refrain from rabble-rousing and recognize that the elements required for a country-wide discussion program do not always exist. In many cases, their programs and publications would have to be designed primarily to help the leaders of the country to decide on their proper policies. Such national organizations would require endowments to ensure their independence. Sources of funds would include the foundations and private donors.

7. *National Operating Organizations.* In both the developing and the developed countries it may often be advisable to set up a special office within the government in the field of science and technology. Its personnel would be available on a loan basis to the various ministries to solve technological problems. It should also serve as the liaison between the national level organizations and the regional and international bodies which have been suggested.

Conclusion

The breadth of the effort suggested in this paper is so great and the challenge is presented in such wide terms that there must inevitably be a tendency to reject them on the grounds of "impracticability." I am not prepared to contest rejection on these grounds, for the approach is unrealizable without far more imagination than we have so far been willing—or is it able?—to employ. Failure to innovate on this scale means, however, that we will abdicate the course of events to "technological" and "economic" forces.

There is no precedent which would suggest that innovations of this magnitude can be carried out peacefully. In the past, when a social system ceased to function adequately, only violence was able to dislodge those groups benefitting from its illogic. Mankind, however, has never confronted a situation in which failure would mean the destruction of the whole world. For this reason, there is considerable and growing support, although it is still unorganized, for revolutionary changes which will create conditions in which human society can survive. We cannot be sure of success, but we can be sure that if we do not make the effort we will fail.

REFERENCES

[1] Quoted in C. F. Stover, *The Government of Science* (New York, 1962), p. 3.

[2] Drawn from the *Statistical Yearbook of the United Nations* (1960).

[3] F. Dovring, "The Share of Agriculture in a Growing Population," *Monthly Bulletin of Agricultural Economics and Statistics*, Vol. 8, Aug.-Sept. 1959, No. 89, p. 1211.

[4] Drawn from the *Statistical Abstract of the United States* (1961).

[5] Twentieth Century Fund, *Annual Report of the Twentieth Century Fund* (New York, 1958), p. 11.

[6] Stanford Research Institute, "Possible Nonmilitary Scientific Developments and their Potential Impact on Foreign Policy Problems of the United States," in *United States Foreign Policy*, A Compilation of Studies Nos. 1-8, U. S. Senate Committee on Foreign Relations (Washington, 1961), p. 108.

[7] Teodoro Moscoso, Address given at the Conference on Methods of Industrial Development, sponsored by the Organization for European Economic Cooperation.

[8] *Science*, Vol. 125 (1957), p. 143.

[9] It should be made very clear that there is no suggestion that this proposed list of institutions should be created without detailed study. Nor is this list intended to be exhaustive. The aim is to set out certain necessary tasks and to suggest in a preliminary way steps which would be taken to carry them out. Difficulties inherent in setting up international organizations of this type are explored and thought-provoking fictional solutions reached in Leo Szilard's short story, "The Voice of the Dolphins," in *The Voice of the Dolphins and Other Stories* (New York, 1961).

Technology in Focus—The Emerging Nations
COMMENTARY

CARL F. STOVER *

The benefits and risks of modern technology come to focus in the new nations. They undertake technological development because it offers the principal avenue to full membership in the world community and provides the means to a new material and spiritual life. At the same time, efforts to adapt their lands and cultures to its necessities raise critical problems. Whether technology proves to be a force for good or evil in the world depends very much on how it is used in these countries. What we learn from our experience there can be crucial to our understanding of technology everywhere.

But learning is not easy. Technology's impact on these nations is complex. Their situations are not simple. The process of transmitting technology is not unitary. Generalizations are difficult to make and often impossible to defend.

In the first place, technological development in the emerging nations is not an isolated phenomenon. It occurs in the context of other revolutionary changes to which it contributes and by which it is affected, but of which it is neither the sole author nor the only outcome. One of these is the revolution against colonialism and for the eighteenth century right to freedom from domination. Another is the revolution against lack of opportunity and for the twentieth century right to freedom from want, drudgery, and disease. A third, much less clear, is the emergence of an incipient world order, effectively described by Etienne Gilson in these terms:

> Whatever the judgment future history may make on our time, we, who are living it, at least cannot be hesitant about the profound sense of its efforts, of its miseries, and of its many convulsions, of which we are either the causes or the victims. The throes of the contemporary world are those of a birth. And what is being born with such great pain is a universal human society, a society which will be to the States of today what they became for the peoples, previously divided, from which they were composed, and what, still earlier, these peoples seemed to have been for families, clans, and tribes, which ended in an assured unity . . . .
> That which characterizes the events we witness, that which distinguishes them from all preceding events back to the origins of history is, as it is said, their global character, or, to say it perhaps more exactly, their planetary character. Local history no longer exists. There no longer exists a history exclusively national, a history with events interesting a particular people and it alone, in the sense that it alone would be the cause of that history and it alone would be undergoing its effects. The unity of the planet is already accomplished. For reasons economic, industrial, and, generally speaking, technical, reasons all linked to the practical applications of the sciences of nature, such a solidarity of fact is established between the peoples of the earth that their vicissitudes are integrated in a universal history in which

* Carl F. Stover is Director of Studies in Science and Technology at the Center for the Study of Democratic Institutions and Assistant to the Chairman of the Board of Editors of *Encyclopaedia Britannica*. He has been a Senior Staff Member at The Brookings Institution and a member of the Stanford University faculty.

they are particular moments. Whatever they may think themselves regarding it, these peoples are in fact parts of a Humanity, still something more natural than social, but something of which they must now become conscious, in order to will it instead of being only subject to it, in order to think it with a view to organizing it.*

Technology gives impetus to these world-wide developments. They give it direction. It is practically impossible to separate the different strands of influence and interaction.

Other barriers to understanding arise because the new nations are not uniform. Each presents unique problems. This novelty is particularly evident to those working in the field. They become deeply entangled in a particular society, where they encounter ecological problems of fantastic proportions. It proves burdensome and hazardous enough to analyze the situation of one country without trying to generalize about them all.

Still more difficulties are introduced by the fact that technology is not a simple, unitary thing. There are great variations in the hardware and the ideas that accompany it. Every bit of technology carries with it the fiber of the total culture from which it springs. Its transmission to another country requires that this fiber be woven into the cultural pattern of the new society.

Every experienced technical assistance worker knows that transplanting a technique involves a great deal more than the technique itself. If men are to use technology, they must be able to think and act properly in relation to it. They must know the ideas inherent in its operation and the processes for its use. Both are particular individual and group adaptations to the technique. These, in turn, are interwoven with the general matrix of social and cultural practices. In a good many cases, what begins as a simple introduction of a tool or a method turns out to require major social adjustments.

Industrialization requires the development of an entire technical system, including not only the factories and machines, but the economic, managerial and scientific practices that permit them to function. The physical technology must be accompanied by a social technology, and both require the development of those ideas and habits that will make them effective. Technology is interlaced with the total culture and society. To understand technology in the emerging nations we must understand the complexities of a total society. It is no wonder that the process is difficult to comprehend.

Yet if we turn this around, our awareness of all of this complexity may actually signify a great deal of understanding about what technology is. At least we are aware of its systematic role in society. *It is not neutral.* It is not without demands on those who would use it. It does contain ideas and judgments of values. This was well put by Melvin Kranzberg when he said that "technology is pragmatic; it asks only if the means effectively reach the ends." But that "only" is a rather large order, carrying significant implications for the society committed to technology's use.

Jacques Ellul's work has impressed me, not by the weight of his particular examples, but by the breadth of his view. He recognizes that technology is more than simple artifacts. It has a culture of its own. To use it, men must adapt to that culture. Since technology teaches its culture to those who use it, it does provide its own dynamic. Ellul does not invent a demon, he recognizes

---

* From *Les Metamorphoses de la cité de dieu.* Excerpt translated by William **Gorman.**

a complex fact—one that our experience in transmitting technology to non-technological societies should have taught us long ago.

About two years ago a man long concerned with technical assistance in public administration told me that he felt the main thing he had learned from almost fifteen years of work was that there is a cultural underpinning to Western administrative practice. I was a little sorry that it had taken that long, but when we went on to talk about what this meant, I found that he was still loathe to admit the full burdens of his insight. I think he was afraid to acknowledge the tremendous responsibility it imposed on him.

Earlier in the week we talked about the fact that along with tremendous power we have lately achieved greater self-knowledge. It no longer seems possible to proceed in the world doing simple, direct, and good things. We recognize that we have become responsible for evolution. We have the power to take hold of a society and transform it, being confident that the physical and social techniques to provide the means are there or can be invented. At the same time, we know this cannot be done without human pain and social disruption, which has always been a part of social and technological change. Yet it is hard to be aware of the fact that we are deliberately bringing about human suffering.

In a paper on "Freedom and Development—the Challenge," V. K. R. V. Rao, Director of the Institute of Economic Growth at the University of Delhi, responds to critics who complain that India's economic development programs are not bringing freedom, justice and equal opportunity to everyone immediately. He reminds us that all the advanced nations used people as means, in order to build technological societies. This is an uncomfortable fact, past and present. In order to fulfill humanitarian goals it may be necessary deliberately to make some groups and generations hostages to the fortunes of the future. Mindful of the fact that it is not good to lay hands idly on the human spirit, we are reluctant to admit that this may be involved in our acts. But it is, and nowhere more clearly than in the systems engineering of total societies where man becomes a means to the end of more perfect technical development.

We need to decide whether we want to transform the emerging nations into technological societies or into societies benefiting from technology. The technological revolutions in the United States, Western Europe, and the Soviet Union will fail in their full potential if they have to be repeated at the same human and social cost elsewhere. Our technology has reached the point where we can overcome this problem by building technological systems that exclude man rather than include him. This is what is going on in advanced technical societies. It is a great problem for those caught in a technological culture. To those who are not yet caught, it may be a great opportunity.

In the emerging nations, if we are wise enough, we may yet trick technology. To do so, we must stop trying to construct there the technology that advanced nations had 20 years ago and turn to developing the technology they will have 20 years hence. The rest of the world should not be made to relive our past but be given the opportunity to live our future—to build cultures that are largely free of the technological imperative.

If this is to occur, we are going to have to exercise judgments on technology and try to control it by the canons of reason. The bases for this must be found in the rediscovery of the ends of man and of nature. The major question that we have to decide in the advanced countries is whether we, having lived so long as instruments of technology, can now learn to step aside and let technology become our instrument.

Technology in Focus—The Emerging Nations

COMMENTARY

VU VAN THAI*

In a political discussion the expression "emerging nations" may be appropriate, but it is somewhat optimistic here. When talking about the technological order it would be more accurate to refer to these nations as "submerged." The main problem of the twentieth century for these countries is the fact that the separation between the under-developed and the developed world is becoming more marked. The gap will continue to grow as the technological order advances, unless we handle technology differently.

The rift is not new. It developed as part of the technological revolution. Countries undergoing technical transformation were compelled to seek out sources of raw materials and new markets. This led to colonialism, which was motivated not so much by a thirst for power as by economic necessity. The submerged countries became the producers of raw materials and purchasers of manufactured products. Such international specialization was a product of the Industrial Revolution, but the end of the colonial era did not halt it. The gap between the developed and the underdeveloped countries widened as international economics became more and more determined by technological progress.

The underdeveloped countries have been trapped in a vicious spiral in the world of free competition. As Gunnar Myrdal has suggested, technology impels economic and national integration, which in turn causes international disintegration. The disadvantages of international disintegration have given impetus to corrective measures—international assistance and cooperation on one side, international regional developments on the other. During the last ten years large-scale technical and financial assistance programs have been effected. But despite the growing recognition of the dangers of international economic disintegration for world stability, efforts promoted during the past decade have not been enough to reverse the trend. The rich countries have become richer at a faster rate, and the poor countries have remained stagnant.

Reviewing the past ten years, Paul Hoffman has clearly described this economic gap:

> The 1¼ billion people inhabiting our [underdeveloped] 100 countries received in 1957 a total income of around $120 billion, or about $100 per person.
> From 1950 to 1960 these countries did increase their total national income. The estimated annual rate of increase is 3 percent. But while this was going on, population in these same countries increased at an average rate of nearly 2 percent. . . . The average rate of [income] increase per capita per year was only 1 percent, and this figures out an increase of $1.00 per person per year, or a gain of only $10 per person in ten years.

* Vu Van Thai has been economist to the government of President Diem of Vietnam and a consultant to the United Nations Secretariat. He is now economic and financial adviser to the President of the Republic of Togo under the United Nations technical assistance program.

This is not enough either to make a very substantial difference in living standards or to supply the savings needed for increasing capital development.

We can better understand the significance of this low growth rate in the underdeveloped countries if we contrast it with the rates of growth prevailing in the industrialized countries. . . . Whereas the 1¼ billion people in the less developed countries gained only $10 per person in ten years, per capita income, in dollars of constant purchasing power, increased by $225 in the United States between 1950 and 1957, and by over $200 in the six countries in the European Economic Community.[1]

Besides the economic gap, the widening technological gap is a serious problem, perhaps more serious in the long run. Technology is progressing in industrialized countries at such a cumulative speed, spurred by the feedback between economic, scientific and technical advances, that it is questionable whether technology will long remain transferable. Technology is exploding so fast that the dialogue between the countries belonging to the "technical civilization" and the rest of the world may cease because of lack of a common language.

My United Nations colleague, Hans Singer, has analyzed the difficulties of countries attempting to undertake industrialization in the mid-twentieth century:

In their attempt to develop economically, underdeveloped countries have to make use of a technology that has been evolved, over a lengthy period of time, in countries that are much higher on the economic scale. This is most dramatically evident in the technical assistance programs, in which the transfer of technology from the more highly developed to the underdeveloped countries is explicitly organized. To say that the more developed countries have a practical monopoly of industrial and scientific research and of productive experience with modern technologies is true almost by definition.

Modern technology—which is equivalent to technology evolved by and for industrialized countries—is both deliberately and innately determined by the requirements and factor endowment of industrialized countries. In particular, it is shaped by the underlying assumption that capital is abundant, that labor is relatively scarce, and that wage rates are correspondingly high. This assumption of a relative abundance of capital has three major effects on the evolution of technology.

In the first place, it results in the rapid evolution of new and superior technologies and in a correspondingly rapid scrapping of capital goods embodying only slightly inferior older technologies. In the second place, technology is strongly directed toward labor-saving devices, and toward the substitution of capital for direct labor. And in the third place, which is perhaps the most important, the application of modern technology requires those levels of scientific training and understanding, and those levels of education, which have now percolated widely in industrial societies.[2]

Three related features of modern technology that make it unsuitable for the developing countries are gigantism, automation and complexity.

Units of production are becoming larger and larger in the push for higher productivity and efficiency. The European Common Market is likely to accelerate this drive toward gigantism. With the exception of a few large countries, such as India and China, the developing nations can no longer support the minimum optimum size of an industry, because of their limited market possibilities. Industrial capital, built for the giants, is not transferable.

Another technical development that interferes with transferability is automation. Automation's displacement of personnel is harmful to underdeveloped countries since manpower, as unskilled labor, is their one abundant resource and obtaining specialized workers and technicians one of their greatest difficulties. In addition, demand for high level technical cadres and suppression of the need for middle level specialists and unskilled labor causes a cultural schism more serious than the problem of unemployment. It increases the separation between the technical and non-technical sectors of the economy.

Furthermore, as technology progresses, techniques interlock into extremely complicated interdependent units. Since the component techniques are no longer available separately, developing countries have to accept "packages" of inter-related activities. They cannot acquire techniques one by one, progressively, but must try to absorb a whole technical complex at once. They are increasingly unable to find products that fit their needs in the "supermarket" of science and technology.

Education poses another transfer problem. Technological training in developed countries is ill-adapted to the needs of developing countries. An engineer or a technician who goes to a school in the United States or Europe and returns to his own environment is unable to apply his learning to the problems of his own people. He has mastered a specialized technique which cannot be used without the support of a wide variety of other techniques. He is uprooted, having learned a discipline that cannot be communicated to his compatriots. His country needs to have a technological environment created, and this requires wide experience. He would be more effective if he returned after a career in an industrialized nation, which is what his training has prepared him for.

The difficulties of technical transfer are only symptomatic of the real problem. Using derived technologies will never close, or even narrow, the technological gap. The answer does not lie in adapting modern techniques or in handing down outgrown methods and equipment. If the new nations are ever going to catch up, new techniques must be created especially for them. As Mr. Goldschmidt pointed out, we must have "technologies to invent technologies" precisely suited to the needs of these countries. The emerging nations cannot skip all the preliminary stages of industrialization, but if they must take the path followed by the pioneers of industrial development, equipped with obsolete or inappropriate devices, they will always lag behind. Unless a new approach is taken to this dilemma, the lead of the industrialized countries will be steadily lengthened by the onrush of technological evolution.

Closing the economic gap requires solutions as unique and specialized as does the problem of the technological gap. A new science of economic growth is necessary. It is impossible for the emerging nations to grow in the modern world using the economic methods of the past. Almost all the underdeveloped countries feel this. They speak of their *own* process of growth. Even those who follow Western or Marxist views wish to develop their special variety of capitalism or communism. But the means to achieve their own economic structure elude them. They perceive the negative aspects of the systems they have adopted, and speak strongly of the flaws they will eliminate. But when they try to use positive terms, they evidence an unsureness which shows that they have not found their way. They have no programs to fit their peculiar situations. They know what they want, but don't know how to get it.

To develop a new economic approach attitudes will have to be changed, in the developed countries as well as the underdeveloped nations. Conventional beliefs must be reviewed and re-evaluated. Two conventions that are now obsolete are nationalism and traditional economics. They were useful concepts that aided the transition from tribes to nations, and supported the technological revolution.

But this revolution has gone so far and is continuing to accelerate so fast that the conventional approach no longer serves. We must revise our basic economic notions, and it must be done quickly.

One serious conflict of attitude exists between the political powers and the technicians in the new nations. The politicians tend to approach the problem of economic development as a continuation of the struggle for independence. The technicians think in terms of efficiency, and feel that sustained growth depends on building up efficient industrial machinery. This clash between technological and political necessity is very clear in the recent history of Asia. All the military coups from Pakistan to Turkey to Korea have been partially rooted in the conflict between the technicians and the political forces.

Another potentially explosive problem has been caused by the pressure of rising expectations. The impact of technology on the underdeveloped countries has brought about a revolution of value. The promise of technology has been embraced by these cultures and traditional values have consequently declined. In the past, happiness was sought by these peoples by struggling with nature to decrease desire. Accepting technology has caused an increase in desire but none in possession. Expectations have risen, but fulfillment has not. Inevitably, the result is discontent.

The peoples of the underdeveloped countries want the fruits of technology without recognizing the cost, or being willing to pay it. Yet they must pay the price. They must make a synthesis between their own culture and the technological order. They must integrate technology and make it their own. The developed countries cannot carry their technological cross for them, but this does not mean the emerging nations must carry a cross of the same weight as those who undertook the revolution in the nineteenth century. Now the cross can be made of aluminum.

REFERENCES

[1] Hoffman, Paul G., *One Hundred Countries, One and One Quarter Billion People* (Committee for International Economic Growth, Washington, D. C., 1960), p. 21.

[2] Singer, Hans W., "Obstacles to Economic Development," *Social Research*, Vol. 20, No. 1 (1953), p. 24.

Technology in Focus—The Emerging Nations

A REPORT OF THE DISCUSSION

WARREN E. PREECE

Morning Session

Mr. Ashmore presided. In summarizing the opening statements, he recalled that Mr. Stover had noted that three concurrent revolutions are going on in the world—revolutions toward freedom, against want, and toward a world order; had suggested that technology must inevitably be interlaced with the society in which it exists; and had expressed hope that in the underdeveloped nations we might somehow "leap over" many of the problems of our own technological revolution. Continuing, he pointed out that Mr. Thai had spoken of the difficulties involved in such an experiment; had said he is optimistic that under the impact of technology East and West will somehow find a way of meeting; had urged that we need to develop a flexible approach to the problem outside of existing orthodoxies; had warned that we are failing to solve most of the problems of technology in relation to the underdeveloped nations; and had concluded that the methods of the past, alone and unadapted, cannot work and, further, that within the individual underdeveloped nations conservative political leaders and flexible technocrats alike must be made aware that the cost of meeting the desires created by rising expectations must somehow and some day be borne by the receiving country.

Mr. Goldschmidt said that although his thinking during the Conference had tended to move toward what he called "the Theobald-Stover position," Mr. Thai's remarks had served to bring him back to the reality of his own work. He suggested that our acute awareness of the affluence of our own society may be blinding us to the lack of affluence of many other areas. In this connection, he pointed out that those parts of the American past which should most enhance our relations with the underdeveloped nations sprang seminally from our Great Depression; that, for instance, it was in the Depression that the American theatre had its renaissance, that murals were painted on public buildings for the first time, that living music was taken to people outside of New York City, that national area guide books turned inward on our own American past, and that, indeed, the first electronic computer was constructed as a work relief project. Perhaps, he said, "we Americans need a built-in depression" along with our affluence. At any rate, he submitted, in assisting the underdeveloped nations, the fruits of our technology should be exported in such a way that "all these other good things" will be able to flower along with technology.

Continuing, Mr. Goldschmidt said that, through Mr. Thai's eyes, he could see the Theobald program as "a new imperialism" in which the advanced nations would export "these good things" to the underdeveloped nations without paying due regard to the necessity of keeping some of them at home too.

Though agreeing with Mr. Thai "that the cross must be borne" and that the processes of technology must be adapted to the conditions of the receiving country,

240

Mr. Goldschmidt said he is fearful that, since the "kind of flexible adaptation" required in adapting to any new system would appear to take place easier "in rich sectors" than in poor ones, the effort to export technology can only widen the existing technological gap. He pointed out that this related to Mr. Thai's discussion of the conflict between conservative and contemporary power sectors within new nations and warned that in many such nations there is a strong "looking back tendency" standing side by side with the desire "for the fruits of contemporary technology." The fact, he said, is that many power leaders simply will not spread the benefits of technology among all their people.

As an example of "the wrong way" to export technology, Mr. Calder pointed to what he called America's "Hollywood approach," that is, the promiscuous exportation of films, without any concern for whether or not the ideas expressed in them are relevant to the situation of the receiving nation. He said it is clear that we have not yet thought sufficiently about the problems of the culture to which we are exporting, nor about the problems which may arise whenever alien ideas are set down without preparation in a foreign culture, that we have not recognized, for instance, that though we talk and act as if democracy were a totally exportable commodity, the fact is that while the theory may be exportable, the practices dictated by the theory must be indigenous developments within the culture.

Continuing, Mr. Calder pointed out that parts of the Congo provide an interesting case history of the problem of the underdeveloped nations. "There is little doubt," he said, that Belgium did a unique job in its territory in the Congo "in terms of material things," but the problem was that the Belgians paternalistically decided simply to "do well for the natives" and, unfortunately, saw "doing well" in terms relevant to Western man and irrelevant to the Congolese. In practice, he continued, the Congo was run by an "amazing telecommunications system" set up between a few "like-minded people," and within the system a few talented nationals became first-class technicians but were never taught to become administrators. Thus, he noted, when Belgium withdrew, the resulting collapse freed the atavistic impulses of the people, and, strangely, these impulses fed themselves on an ancient desire for vengeance for the slave trade so that the reversion to type was almost immediate. Despite this, Mr. Calder said he believes that the Congo, if "given half a chance," will develop into one "of the very best lands of Africa"—in large part, ironically, because of the very things for which, he conceded, he had criticized Belgium.

Mr. Calder warned that a fourth revolution should be added to Mr. Stover's three, that is, a revolution in the advanced countries of rising expectations for the underdeveloped countries, expectations which are completely distorted. In order to bring about the "leap into the future" for which we hope, he said, we must understand these things better, we must "learn before we try to teach," and we must know what the recipient nations really want as well as we now know what "we think we know they need."

The hopeful and novel aspect of our time, Mr. Calder said, is that for the first time people everywhere "know" that something can be done to solve their problems and no longer simply assume that it is necessary to tolerate them. This, he insisted, is a new condition in the world. The danger of the situation, he warned, is that, since the "felt needs" of the people of the underdeveloped nations are known and progress toward the realization of them is slow, strongly nationalistic leaders have at hand a major device to exploit in taking over the country. The people of the underdeveloped nations, Mr. Calder submitted, do not "really want television tomorrow," but "they want food and better health and they want it now." Their needs, he continued, cannot be met on the level of a "too advanced technology." He said in conclusion that he agreed with Mr. Thai's belief that one of the great tragedies of the underdeveloped nations occurs when we of the advanced countries take their people out of their environment, train them in the sophistries of our technology, and then somehow expect that they will be able to go back to the villages where they are really needed but where there will be no base for the kind of work they have been trained to do. It is tragic, he said, when doctors trained in the West find it almost impossible to practice medicine in their own villages because they have been trained largely in the advanced "technology of medicine."

Mr. Theobald restated his belief that we must not continue to deal with the issue of the underdeveloped nation in the ways which we have been following but must somehow "leapfrog" to the development of a technology which will not subject those we would help to the negative aspects of our own experience. He pointed out that the advanced lands have in the last 15 years tried to handle the problem of the new nations on the basis of three theories which evolved more or less in the following order: (1) "send them capital," (2) develop the necessary local enterpreneurs, and (3) "educate everybody immediately." All of these methods, he insisted, were bound to fail, and a fourth approach, the wholesale transfer of trained manpower cadres as outlined in Professor Zvorikine's remarks about the development of Uzbek, is impossible when dealing with sovereign nations.

Insisting that much of what we of the advanced nations have been doing is little more than a new form of imperialism designed to tie the underdeveloped nation to the providing nation, Mr. Theobald said that a better answer would provide that the underdeveloped nations themselves "have got to be in on" the development of technology within their own countries. He warned, however, that much time will be required if technology is not simply to be dumped bodily on the new nations, and if the new nations themselves are to be encouraged to help work out the nature of a better technology tailored to their true needs. Further, he warned that because of the delicate balances between population segments within nations, time may serve to increase frustrations and jeopardize stability. "There may not be enough time," he said, unless we buy it with an immediate and temporary program to give these nations the food and material goods required to prevent internal chaos. Such a program, he emphasized again, must not be thought of as anything more than a "stop-gap" and should in no way blind us to the more complex problems inevitably involved in any attempt to modify cultural patterns over the longer run.

Conceding that the effort will be marked by troubles, riots, revolutions, and social unrest, he insisted that the fact is that no other plan is likely to be successful. In addition, he suggested, that in slowing down the present artificial development of an alien technology in the underdeveloped nations and participating with them in working out a technology of their own, that is, one capable of meeting their own best interests, the underdeveloped nations might reinform us as to how we might again become a human society. "Utopias," he said, "are not enough; humanity must remain."

Professor Zvorikine said that Russia's practice in regard to the underdeveloped nations does not involve "offering them our own solutions" as to what, where, and how they should create their own industry. These nations, he said, go to Russia with concrete propositions to which the Russian government responds, so that for example, in the implementation of a program India will design its own factory with the help of Russian specialists; the factory will be built by Indians under the guidance of Russian advisors, and Indian employees will be trained in advance in Russian factories so that they will be ready to operate their own plants when they are completed. He submitted that this approach solved the problems being discussed " not too badly " and insisted again that Russian practice is to refrain from mixing " our politics in the internal affairs of their country." He said the Russian solution has an advantage over others proposed at the Conference because it attempts to solve an individual question for an individual country rather than to " solve the whole problem of the underdeveloped nations " at one time.

In reference to Mr. Stover's remarks, Professor Zvorikine agreed that it is impossible to separate technique from culture or from the educational level of the worker. He pointed out that Russia's first automatic factory was at first unable to meet its expected norms because its planners had not taken into sufficient account the specific and special qualifications required of the workers. This problem, he said, is now handled by automated " model factories " in which workers are trained and from which they then return, along with the necessary equipment, to new factories as they are constructed. The answer obviously lies in the proper training of cadres, he said.

Professor Zvorikine said, finally, that it is unfortunate that most of the literature about the problem of the underdeveloped nation offers " interesting theories " but does not meet the urgent need for " practical data."

Mr. Calder commented that " it is interesting " that India's experience with the construction of steel plants involved factories built for them by West Germany, England, and Russia, and that after these plants had been in operation for some time, the West German plant was found to be 60 per cent below its quota, the English plant 40 per cent, and the Russian only 20 per cent. The Russians, he said, were the first to recognize the need for modifying the plant and its operation to meet local conditions; the English did this somewhat later, and the West Germans " haven't done it yet."

Noting that the uses of history had been questioned in earlier sessions of the Conference, Mr. Kranzberg pointed out that the background papers for this session seemed to indicate the practical value of history as " group recall " in the comparison of experience and in relating current problems to their other and earlier manifestations. History, he said, helps highlight the significant conditions to be met in dealing with a given problem, so that, for instance, history does hold out hope that we will be able to control, guide, and direct the development of technology in the underdeveloped nations because of a novel factor in the situation—for the first time the impetus is from the government rather than from " hit or miss " economic forces. Knowledge of the past, he said, enables us to be more sophisticated about our problems and suggests that in developing new technologies we can guard against leaving the people unprotected from their pitfalls. He noted, finally, that he was " happy " that the Conference had seemed to move away from " Ellul's hopelessness "; that " the optimists ' seemed ' to have taken over " so that we might now assume that man need not adapt himself to either the machine or the machine environment.

Mr. Hutchins noted here that while he is " all for optimism," he was alarmed by Mr. Calder's insistence that we have to understand the culture of the underdeveloped nations before we attempt to develop their technologies on the one hand, and the warning that we have only a brief period in which to act before it will be too late, on the other. " I can't be optimistic about that," he said. Mr. Theobald said he was pessimistic in that though he believes that there is a solution, he does not believe that we will prove able to use it.

Pointing out that he had suggested in earlier remarks that we might have as " few as three years " left in which to accomplish the required groundwork in the underdeveloped nations, Mr. Calder emphasized that he had not intended this to mean that a complete program must be developed within that time. All that he would hope to accomplish at the outset, he said, is acceptance of the fact that the people of the emerging nations " are different," so that when we go into their territories we will move " tentatively " and not delay the ultimate solution by the mistakes of precipitous action.

Mr. Wilkinson said it seemed to him that " the so-called optimism " at the Conference was a " one-man affair." He pointed out that when the Indian steel mills discussed earlier failed to achieve their quotas, the performance of the German mill was so alarming that a special commission was appointed to investigate the problem and, at the conclusion of its work, agreed on the importance of previously trained cadres and greater adaptation to local environmental conditions, but that when the report was presented, the Communist argument was that only Marxism " can build the proper structures."

Mr. White suggested that the Conference was overlooking many important non-technological elements which " are still viable " in the American culture. President Kennedy's recent exhortation to Latin American peoples to " raise guillotines on their public squares," he said, relates to the theory that democracy is not exportable, since the President realizes that the massive development efforts which he wants to encourage in Latin America will not be supported by the American taxpayer unless local democracy develops in those countries; that Americans will not pay the bill involved if the money is simply going to go to local oligarchs. He said he questioned whether American public opinion would support subsidization of the export of technology unless democracy—a non-technological factor—is a part of the export.

Mr. Meier noted that there are three " levels of sophistication " at which technology can be introduced into those nations in which it does not exist in a fully developed state:

(1) At the level of fundamental science, involving " high-level design." Although we are often " warned against this approach," he said, the fact is that most underdeveloped nations seem to feel that they must have some of it if they are going to maintain their dignity in the world, and many of them therefore campaign vigorously for the creation of " extremely advanced institutions " within their territory. One hopeful avenue for this type of development, he said, lies in the fact that many world-wide problems can best be studied on the spot and that this can justify creating laboratories in some of the underdeveloped nations where scientists from the advanced nations can work on an international basis.

(2) " The steel mill sort of thing," which, he suggested, involves transferring the technology and the " know-how " for its operation, and is satisfactory " if the demand is there."

(3) At the level of the small local industry primarily engaged in " reordering " the forms and uses of manufactured materials. This, he explained, involves such things as the importation from advanced nations of plastic to be reformed into new shapes by local industries on the basis of cultural wants. Pointing out that such a program involves the need for some consultation with advanced nations

but that as much as 90 per cent of the effort can be local, he suggested that "something over 50 per cent of the total effort" in underdeveloped nations might well be at this third level, some 10 to 15 per cent at the first, and the balance at the second.

In more general remarks, Mr. Hartner said that one of the problems which he has observed in West German programs to train men from underdeveloped nations is that the visitors frequently misunderstand the nature and spirit of "free education" and as a result "simply do not work"; but despite this, sooner or later, and because of external pressures, they are given licenses even though they have not met the requirements for them. These people, he said, almost inevitably fail in their work when they return to their homelands.

In commenting on Mr. White's remarks about the unwillingness of the American taxpayer to export technology to non-democratic nations, Mr. Theobald said that the important fact is that America has the necessary resources for the program he had proposed and that the problem is therefore one of finding ways of "getting them" assembled for distribution to the underdeveloped nations. He said further that he disagreed with Mr. Meier that we can only think of exporting technology in terms of the three historic levels of our own development. Limiting ourselves in this way, he argued, will result only in duplicating the Western system, including all of its bad results, in the developing lands. He insisted, for example, that the development of Western plastics has "practically killed" all native craft industries.

Afternoon Session:

Mr. Ashmore recalled that the morning meeting had ended with discussion of "the time available" in which to resolve the problem of technology and the emerging nations. He asked Mr. Thai for further comment on the importance of the fact that technology is likely to be a monopoly of specific power sectors within the underdeveloped nations. Secondly, he asked at what point an underdeveloped nation will become incapable of developing its own technology and will be forced to utilize a system derived from the experience of more advanced nations.

Pointing out that, in general, the notion of a derived technology implies that a country must somehow digest and then reestablish a fairly advanced technology, Mr. Thai said that the transfer of a too-advanced, push-button type technology to an underdeveloped nation will certainly result in the creation of "islands of technological control" within the country and thus widen power gaps already existing in them. It is imperative, he warned, to re-think a technology adapted to the underdeveloped nation and its peculiar needs, and if this is not done soon more and more of the people engaged in technology in the advanced nations will each year become less and less helpful in meeting the needs of the undeveloped nations. He pointed out, for example, that it would have been much easier to establish a textile factory in any given underdeveloped nation a few years ago than it will be to do so a few years hence because the advance of technology will mean that the receiving nation will have to take "the whole package or nothing at all."

Mr. Stover suggested that in a significant way the American people during their depression had an opportunity to be free of the economic necessities of life, to be free of the demand that they somehow keep the economic machine going, with the result that while they were repairing the machine, they were at the same time "able to look at other things." By the same token, he said, we may now again have the power to free a people of the necessities imposed by the technological system, in the underdeveloped nations we may be able to create a technological machine which will " keep the human being out of it." He said that while he would not want to impose an artificial technology divorced from their culture on the people of these nations, neither would he want them to have to be " totally integrated " with their technology, as we have had to be with ours. He suggested that the " institutions " discussed in Mr. Theobald's paper might help us find a " better road through the forest."

Mr. Theobald said that the argument behind his " so-called institutions " was that decisions as such are human; that we can impose our will on the computer but that to do so wisely we will require better methods of evaluating our actions. The institutions proposed in the paper, he said, are therefore seen as tentative approaches to the development of such " better methods," and while the institutions themselves may be debatable, their functions are necessary " as given factors."

Pointing out that the institutions apparently rest on the assumption that " everything material will be free," Mr. Tyler asked Mr. Theobald where the endowment necessary to maintain such a system will come from without a prior private enterprise system to provide it. Mr. Theobald said that this problem might be " real " during the transition period, but that later the distribution of material would be a government function. Mr. Tyler pointed out, however, that " it is just as hard " for the social engineer to deal with the government as it is with private enterprise. Mr. Theobald explained that in his system a person would " have the right to opt to work," for example, at the Center for the Study of Democratic Institutions if that is what he wanted to do, and at the same time the Center would have the right to opt for whatever it needed to keep its functions going, and that the exercise of these options would not require " dealing with the government " in the sense implied by Mr. Tyler. Mr. Tyler noted, then, that " someone is still going to have to make major decisions " about what is made, when it is made, how it is made, etc.

Mr. Ashmore said he had understood the Theobald plan to be only for the immediate future. Mr. Thai said that although the Theobald proposal " is satisfactory," the fact is that the problem still has to be " tackled from the grass roots," and in terms of the reality of the existence of nationalism and notions of economic profit. He warned that in developing any new plan we must recognize the existence of the present method of dealing with the problems through either technical aid or regional arrangements, and said that unless we stimulate existing favorable trends we will be merely engaging " in describing utopias."

Mr. Theobald said again that he had wanted consideration of his institutions to lead into a discussion of how the technological system is to be controlled. Mr. Tyler replied, however, that the fact is that we already control the system through existing institutions, that is, either through modifications of the free enterprise system or by socialism or communism. He said he believes we have two problems in this area: the acquisition of more knowledge and more thorough understanding of programs for action, and the negotiation of agreements necessary to support the intellectual institutions required by the first problem. He said that although he saw what had to be done, he still felt Mr. Theobald's institutions were unrealistic in not being built on a basis of accepted understanding and agreements held by the people. A viable institution, he said, simply cannot spring " full blown " from someone's head, but must evolve from the tradition.

Pointing out that (1) the Theobald paper states that an affluent society requires people able to use leisure time and (2) that the underdeveloped nations are "rich in people with leisure time," Mr. Goldschmidt said that Mr. Theobald's plan seems to be calling on the advanced nations to "produce like mad" so that the people of the underdeveloped nations can enjoy their leisure. If we are going to talk about the institutions of the underdeveloped nations in any practical sense, he continued, we ought to talk first about the problem of institution building in an underdeveloped nation. He said it is easy to create a new institution in the advanced world, that "all you need is an idea and a program and you can get the money for it quite easily"; that it is even relatively easy to create international institutions, but it is almost impossible to "get an institution going" at the local level in an underdeveloped nation. You cannot start things in Iran or Africa the way you can in America, he warned, since the requisite organizational "turn of the mind" simply does not exist there. He pointed out that technical assistance can work only when supported by the immortality of an organization, and that in many underdeveloped nations even government does not really have any organization.

Mr. Kranzberg noted that he had found Mr. Theobald's scheme "un-American in the best sense, un-English in a bad sense, and un-United Nations in a disastrous sense." He explained that the paper "is wise" in being "un-American enough" to think of the problem in terms of functional necessities rather than of manifestos, but is unwise in being "un-English enough" to miss the opportunity to utilize existing local institutions, and most unwise of all in being "un-United Nations enough" to fail to utilize existing international agencies.

Mr. Ashmore said it seemed to him that there had been substantial agreement about the lack of institutions inside the underdeveloped nations and the consequent necessity for developing indigenous ones, and that he had understood Mr. Theobald to be attempting merely to bridge this gap. Mr. Calder said that the alternative approaches suggested by Mr. Kranzberg are not unreconcilable. He pointed out, for example, that in 1946 UNESCO followed one approach when it took over an existing, and excellent, science organization that simply "needed to have its pump primed," and suggested that, since there is not now a similar organization in the humanities, that is, an organization which would relate itself to the necessity of determining "what this thing is all about," there is no reason why the United Nations could not follow the other approach and foster the creation of such an organization. This, he suggested, would redress the balance in an area which needs to be studied and in which tentative thrusts toward such an institutional arrangement are already present.

Mr. Wilkinson said he believed that "the gap needs much more definition as to its size and bridgability." Mr. Tyler said he had understood Mr. Thai to have defined the gap in terms of the relative and absolute difference between the per capita incomes of the advanced and underdeveloped nations. Mr. Wilkinson agreed, but pointed out that the Conference had gone on to use the word in other senses, as, for example, in Mr. Thai's discussion of the gap between technocrats and political leaders. Mr. Thai said he had intended to speak of the situation as a matter of conflict rather than of a gap; that he had used "gap" in terms of speed and acceleration and, again, as that which exists between the technological and non-technological sectors of any given underdeveloped nation. Mr. Wilkinson then commented that the gap between technological islands and the other sectors of a nation is widening "right now" in the United States where a scientific elite is developing. Since the number of technocrats is always relatively small, he said, it should be no harder to establish technology in Turkey than it was in the United States.

Mr. Goldschmidt pointed out that there is also a gap between the city and the countryside in underdeveloped nations and that a similar gap exists in some degree—but " nowhere as much "—in the United States. Mr. Wilkinson replied that his point had been only that the gap " between science and non-science " is growing rapidly and that non-science seems to be " on its way to becoming functionless." Mr. Tyler asked Mr. Wilkinson if he meant by this to suggest that the farmer, for example, has no function, and Mr. Thai commented that the big difference between the United States and the developing nations in this respect is that the son of an American farmer can become a part of the scientific elite if he desires but that in an underdeveloped nation he cannot.

In returning to the Theobald paper, Mr. Stover said he had taken Mr. Theobald's proposition to be that a major problem of our day is " a failure to understand " and that the institutions he has proposed are needed to spur understanding at the levels of theory, of discussion, and of implementation. In this sense, he pointed out, the Theobald " institutions " were similar to " a national and international Fabian society." In agreeing with Mr. Stover's analysis, Mr. Theobald said he could not understand why the Conference seemed to be unable to " link up " his program with its own earlier general agreements about the need for a human control of technology and the inadequacy of present institutions for achieving this control. Mr. Goldschmidt said that he did not like the word " control " as it was being used by Mr. Theobald, since Mr. Theobald's paper did not offer " control instruments " so much as it did means of study. Mr. Theobald replied that before instruments can be devised it is necessary to know what it is that we are planning for. We do not know this now, he said, and so we need institutions to get on with the planning.

Mr. Tyler asked how it would be possible to control the whole political and economic system of which technology, " after all, is only a part." He pointed out that methods of control are inevitably different in the United States from what they are in Russia, and said that the basic problem is really quite different from that of the mere " necessity to understand." It is one thing, he summarized, to learn about the consequences of technology, and it is another thing to determine wisely who should exercise control and how it should be done. Mr. Theobald agreed that the matter of who controls politics is important, and said that because of the relationship between political leaders and their advisers, the real question is: who advises the political leaders?

Mr. Goldschmidt said specifically that he had " no necessary problems " with Mr. Theobald's first two institutions, but that the others suffered insofar as they failed to stress the importance of stimulating already existing institutions. Some progress is, after all, being made even now, he said, and new indigenous institutions for guiding future planning are constantly emerging. These emerging institutions, he said, although they will operate functionally on a group basis, will, because of their organization, be oriented to the needs and aspirations of the separate countries represented in them, and, if they are successful, it will be because, being " country centered," they will be better able to adapt technology to the circumstances of given nations. Such institutions, he said, will be more helpful than those proposed by Mr. Theobald in " nursing along " the purely local basis required for an integrated technology.

Fr. Ong asked how these organizations would do their work, and Mr. Meier said that the agencies now emerging will strive (1) to secure people with knowledge relevant to the statistical problem of decision-making and (2) to win acceptance in the separate countries for any programs proposed. The work of the regional organization, he said, will be reinforced by parallel institutions within each of the member countries. Mr. Goldschmidt emphasized that the main point is that the effort will be indigenous.

Fr. Ong asked then if there was any likelihood that the Theobald institutions were even feasible in terms of the reality of the situation. Mr. Meier said that the major necessity of determining methods of " establishing test controls " through local institutions is totally lacking in Mr. Theobald's paper, and that no method of control can succeed without provision for it.

Mr. Real complained that although members of the Conference had spoken of such things as the " urgency " of a solution to the problem of the " acceleration of the system toward disaster," Mr. Meier was now proposing that an elaborately complex program involving test controls and feasibility studies should be set up. He insisted that there must be realistic limits on " how far we can go " and " how much time we can spend " in " this sort of scientific planning " and he suggested that the limits will have to fall between the extremes represented by the Theobald program on the one hand and Mr. Kranzberg's " status quoism " on the other. He said he is convinced that " gradualism " cannot work and that it is impossible " to square " expressions of urgency with proposals for an " easygoing evolution " based on either the corporation " or a grass roots demand."

Mr. Gorman suggested, however, that if the issue is to be only the matter of speed, then there is a logical requirement that Mr. Theobald demonstrate that his plan will be faster than any other. Mr. Tyler cautioned that despite the feeling of urgency, it is one thing to talk about an ideal world possible largely only in someone's mind and quite another to talk about what is feasible. If we are going to be concerned with the latter, he said, we must first recognize that there are, after all, only two existing models to work with—free enterprise or socialism. The necessary work of getting people to see the whole problem and to understand their roles in relation to it, he said, will take time, " whether we like it or not."

Pointing out that the question then would seem to involve determining what is desirable and what is feasible, Mr. Ashmore reminded the meeting that Mr. Thai had suggested that the " slower grass roots approach " is in reality unavoidable. If this is true, he said, then the number of plans open to us is limited to begin with.

Mr. Calder argued that the problem " isn't that simple because its exists on more than one level "; that, e. g., there are some kinds of things which can be done— " and well "—for an illiterate society by an outsider acting on an emergency basis, and the requirements for such an operation will be different from those of the " follow-through " program which should succeed the emergency. For the latter, he said, local support at the grass roots is clearly necessary. Restating the position, he said that in each of the underdeveloped nations there are " certain crying needs " which obviously can be met by outside agencies, but that once these have been taken care of the problem of building for the future must be approached in the knowledge that a long-range program can succeed only if it has the " built-in underpinnings " of local support. Mr. Thai noted parenthetically that in most underdeveloped nations the really urgent necessity is " to get us the digestible parts " of technology rather than the parts which " make us sick."

Mr. Gorman suggested that the structures of the three background papers for the present session lead "almost inevitably" to Mr. Theobald's paper and to the differences and difficulties surrounding it. He pointed out (1) that Mr. Calder had called for immediate minimal aid in meeting the urgent needs of the people on the one hand, and sensitivity to the nature of the receiving culture (to be gained from studying that culture) on the other; (2) that Mr. Goldschmidt would apparently like to transfer "the whole technology" as soon as possible, but recognizes that the technology involved in that transfer will require a serious study program; and (3) that Mr. Theobald wants us to undertake the job, not by transferring our technology as it now exists, but by transferring a technology which will have to be invented in such a way that it will not be disruptive to the receiving culture, and that he too has a study program requirement, a requirement made more elaborate than the others by the necessity of inventing the requisite technology.

Mr. Goldschmidt said he thought that Mr. Theobald's list of "practical institutions" had not been "sufficiently considered" and required expansion. The first two institutions, he said, were "rather philosophical" in their approach, whereas it would be better to have practical people working on the problem in a close relationship to those aware of the philosophical factors.

Pointing out that the questions involved are "tremendous," Professor Zvorikine said we must first establish for ourselves the nature of a desirable total industrial pattern and then help to direct that pattern as it evolves. This, he said, "is a very complicated and dynamic problem" because it is necessary at any given time to understand simultaneously the present character of a system and how new circumstances are affecting it. In the U.S.S.R., he pointed out, production is in the hands of a single force, a factor which allows for rational decision-making not only in regard to the present but also for long years ahead. He noted that Russia changed its planning system several years ago in order to set up a "more solid organization for planning" and that this in turn made possible a "twenty year plan" as contrasted with the earlier five year programs. "To compose a twenty year plan," he continued, required a "tremendous amount of work" by everyone involved, from local factories through national academies, and yet despite all of the work and despite the fact that Russia is convinced that its plan properly reflects all contemporary conditions, the fact is that since "things in science and technology change so rapidly" it is generally accepted that the plan must be continuously revised. "We in Russia," he said, are aware that it is really possible to solve any problem "only for the immediate present."

By way of explanation, Professor Zvorikine explained that despite what the current plan says about steel production, it is always possible that new uses for plastics can bring about a reduction in the uses of metal and "thus upset the production pattern." For this reason, he said, Russia does not try to set quotas on such things as metal production, "except on a provisional basis." He said the Communist government is aware that it has to "watch which changes the plan of life offers," for at any given moment planning requires the government "to know what each industry will give and what it will demand." Finally, he said that sufficient reserves must be maintained "so that an overproduction by one factory will not necessitate shortages at another."

How, Professor Zvorikine asked rhetorically, it is possible to transfer this system to other countries? He said that as a member of "the other side," he would not try to give the West "the secrets of Russia's success," but would offer a clue by pointing out that in Chile "actual feudalism still exists." How, he asked, can an underdeveloped nation do anything about technology, without agricultural reform? Pointing out that he has heard that Chile was told that the United States would pay 60 per cent of the cost of buying up land for land reform if the government would pay 40 per cent, but that the offer had been rejected, he asked: what can possibly be said about a country which hasn't even yet reformed its own agriculture? Certainly, he continued, it is impossible to develop any country in which it is necessary to get the consent of feudal landowners and private industry to any development plan. The government of each country involved will have to decide what it needs, he said, and only then can plans be established.

Mr. Tyler pointed out that each of the conferees had appeared to see the problem of guiding technology in a different shape; that Mr. Goldschmidt saw it as a local matter while Mr. Theobald wanted a technology " less in conflict with human values " but was aware that this could not be devised at a local level, since it involved the " whole matter of economic control." Mr. Theobald's international institutions, he said, would seem to have the functional values of an international university, and " the fact is " that other universities are already studying the kinds of problems he would want his institutions to study.

In concluding the session, Mr. Theobald said he agreed with Mr. Goldschmidt that he had not sufficiently spelled out the nature of the local institutions required by his program. Despite this, he insisted, the important fact about the institutions is that they are required by the situation and, at the same time, that the possibilities of their success are enhanced by the situation. He suggested that the advanced technologies of the West are what they are today because they developed on chronological time scales with the result that the system is composed of a " whole range of technological levels existing at one time." This fact, he continued, requires us to consider what is actually in existence and to start from that basis in dealing with the problem of our own technologies. Since the underdeveloped nations do not have technological systems in this sense, he said, we do not have to respond to their problems merely by dumping our technology on them, but, instead, can plan a rational system for them—if we have the institutions with which to plan.

Achieving a Perspective on the Technological Order

COMMENTARY

ALDOUS HUXLEY

I would like to talk about some aspects of technology's effects on human individuals and society which have interested me particularly. Mr. Hall touched upon the effect of the development of modern technological methods on the old arts and crafts. He compared the Chinese porcelain cup with the plastic cup of today and pointed out that a plastic cup can be produced only as a result of the most elaborate interlocking technology. A huge volume of applied science has gone into the making of these curiously repulsive objects. The question is: what have we gained and what have we lost?

The cost of plastic containers is smaller than the cost of baked clay and porcelain containers. The people carrying water jugs are no doubt happy to have a lighter jug. Certainly we have gained. But there is one disturbing difference between the technology of mass production and the technology of the empirical handicrafts. The handicraftsman produces complex effects with incredibly simple tools simply by skill of hand and mind, whereas modern technology uses immensely complicated tools which require little skill of hand or mind. The technological systems of production and organization are virtually foolproof. But if anything is foolproof it is also spontaneity-proof, inspiration-proof, and even skill-proof. Against the advantages of the plastic cup we must set the grave disadvantages to the people deprived of the opportunity of craft expression, of artistic expression. Probably you will agree that it is a question of the greatest happiness for the greatest number. The number of jug carriers is greater than the number of plastic cup makers. On a voting basis there is a net gain. But in this universe nothing is free. We pay in one way or another for our gains. We must consider how much we pay, and whether the price is worth it.

The relationship of technology to nature has deeply concerned me. It is, in fact, immensely important to everyone. We often act as if we were not animals and did not have to live in a symbiotic relationship with our surroundings. We behave as though we were not part of the total ecology, as though in some way we were privileged and could throw our weight around *ad libitum*. This, of course, is perfectly untrue. We are part of the natural order and must conform to the rules of that order. Ecology, the youthful science, is beginning to discover this. The term "ecology" was invented by Haeckel not more than 75 years ago, so recent is the concept of the interwoven nature of reality and our own close involvement in the pattern. A moral tenet emerges from this study of the relationship of parts within the natural world. We are getting away from the infernal doctrine of the Middle Ages that animals have no soul and therefore may be treated as things. Now it is perceived that even things should not be treated as things. Things should be treated as though they were parts of a living organism. Our natural world is like a vast living organism. Indeed, a great deal of it actually is living. For instance, we now know that a large percentage of soil is composed of living bacteria. Bits cannot be cut out of a living organism without endangering the organism as a whole. We should be intensely aware of this.

We must approach nature with a good deal less bumptiousness than we have in the past. Modesty and absence of arrogance are essential ethical correlates to the enormous powers we have achieved. We can't commit acts of overweening pride against inanimate nature or we will suffer disastrous consequences. This is the Greek idea of hubris. In *The Persians* of Aeschylus, Xerxes is guilty of hubris—not only because he has attacked the Greeks, but because he has done something outrageous to nature. To us his action seems harmless enough—he built a bridge across the Hellespont. But to Aeschylus this seemed an outrage. The realization that nature cannot be recklessly outraged exists in the minds of good applied scientists and good technologists. It deeply affects their thinking. But caution is not a property of the advertisers of technology—popular science magazine writers, for example, who keep talking about conquering nature. The people who profit by technology have been boastful and hubristic. They have had to pipe down when consequences they failed to anticipate have shown up. But these alarming surprises have not cured their hubristic illusion that nature can be dominated.

Man has always thrown his weight around and upset the natural order. Now, with the enormous resources of modern technology he can tilt the balance disastrously. Even when his powers were small he was remarkably successful. It is astonishing how rapidly human beings can destroy their surroundings even in primitive countries. What mankind has made of its environment is a depressing spectacle. In Lebanon, for example, the magnificent mountain terrain was once covered from one end to the other with cedars. Now perhaps 1200 trees are left. The land has been eroded down to the naked rock. Reforestation is no longer possible. Serious changes have come about in Africa where the desert is spreading, the savannahs getting drier. I remember the terrifying dust storms in Oklahoma in the thirties and again in the late forties. Every time the price of wheat went up more of the top cover went up in dust. The same thoughtlessness can be seen everywhere. It seems very difficult to drive the lesson home. Evidently we have to have a great many tremendous kicks in the pants before we learn anything.

We can only live in symbiosis with nature. If we treat the relationship intelligently we shall benefit. But thinking we can push nature around is absolutely wrong. It is absurd to attempt—to use that dreadful old-fashioned phrase—to conquer nature. We must take care before embarking on our grandiose technological schemes. The natural balance is easily upset, and we quickly get responses we have not anticipated.

Last summer in England I was saddened by changes that were unforeseen side-effects of technological progress. Walking in the countryside I was first struck with the extraordinary fact that there were virtually no butterflies and no cuckoos. I did hear one nightingale, but there were practically no chaffinches. The English hedgerows have been sprayed with weed killers. The weeds have gone and so have the caterpillars. Cuckoos, nightingales, and chaffinches live on caterpillars; caterpillars grow into butterflies. Perhaps this is not disastrous from an economic point of view, but to me it is very sad. These creatures have always played an important part in English literature. They belong to the English countryside. Are we not going to see the butterflies any more, not hear the nightingales? Even in Switzerland, in high Alpine meadows where there used to be the most magnificent butterflies there are very few—again because of weed killers.

Another disheartening change had occurred in a valley near where I used to live as a boy. It was a long valley down to the river Wey, with smooth grass sides and chestnut woods at the top on either side. I entered this valley by footpath and I didn't recognize it. The footpath now winds through brush about 20 feet high. I couldn't imagine what had happened, then it suddenly struck me. Later friends confirmed that this was a result of myxomatosis introduced to combat the rabbits. The rabbits had kept down the brush. Their extermination has changed the face of the countryside. The rabbits were mischievous in many ways, but again, what have we gained by their extermination, and what have we lost?

We have rushed into nature's domain as if we knew exactly what we were doing. But we did not. We never could predict what we were going to bring about. The ecological structure is so delicate and so complex that it is impossible to imagine all the effects of a given action.

We don't yet know the consequences for human health of the insecticides being sprayed on all our food plants. A friend of mine in The Conservation Foundation has been collecting information about this and none of it is very reassuring. Nobody knows what the long-range consequences are of artificially immunizing the entire population.

In the short run obviously it is a good thing. But if a population is created which genetically has no natural immunity to diseases, the slightest mutation in the cause of the disease means serious trouble.

DDT has spawned an unforeseen problem. Paeans of praise went up when DDT was first made available. Now there are large populations of insects that are not susceptible to the drug. In fact they seem to enjoy it as though it were a delicacy. The same thing has happened with antibiotics. When man tries to eradicate a species with a very rapid reproduction rate, he is up against natural selection and is almost bound to lose the fight. If one per cent of a rapidly reproducing species is genetically immune to a drug, it is clear that in a very short time the entire population will be immune.

One of the most serious unexpected consequences of advancing technology has been caused by the reduction of death rates without a balancing reduction of birth rates. Parts of the world are increasing their population at a rate of three per cent, even of four per cent per annum. The United Nations recently stepped up its estimate of the increase in India and Southeast Asia. Before the recent Indian census it was estimated to be at the rate of 1.7 per cent per annum. It is now known to be about 2.3 per cent per annum. On the basis of 450 million people this means nearly ten million more people every year.

Last autumn I talked with a number of Indian politicians and officials. They all said the same thing: "We have just started on our third five-year plan. It is an ambitious plan, and will be difficult for us to fulfill even with a good deal of foreign aid. If we do succeed we will create ten million new industrial jobs. When the plan is fulfilled there will be 15 million young people asking for the jobs. There are already between 50 and 100 million underemployed people with an annual income of less than $100 each who will hardly be touched by the plan." The best image one can make of this situation, it seems to me, is Lewis Carroll's parable in *Through the Looking Glass*. Alice and the Red Queen run at full speed for a very long time, until they are completely out of breath. When they stop Alice is amazed to see that they are at the same place. She says, "In my country if we ran like this we should have gone a very long way." The Red Queen replies, "Well, yours must be a very slow country. Here we have to run as fast as we can in order to stay in the same place. If we want to get somewhere else we have to run twice as fast as we can." This is a comic statement of the tragic situation in which much of the world now finds itself. A three per cent increase doubles the population in 24 years. 2.3 per cent doubles it in a little over 32 years. How on earth are these people going to keep up?

There is a tendency to discuss the population problem solely in terms of food, as though man lived by bread alone. Certainly he can't live without bread. The solution to the food situation alone is difficut to see. But how is a country without educated personnel, without capital, without technical devices going to produce not only the additional food supply but also the additional housing, roads, schools? Even a rich country like this has trouble keeping up with the school population. India and Southeast Asian countries are desperately poor. Capital is that which remains when needs have been satisfied. In a country where 70 per cent of the people never satisfy their needs there isn't much left over.

The headlong increase in population presses heavily upon our resources. Preventing a mining of the soil and general ruin of the surface of the planet is going to be more difficult as the population increases. Our mineral resources are going to last longer than we thought twenty years ago but they are not inexhaustible. In forty years America has consumed more than the rest of the world consumed since the Ice Age. Increasing amounts of energy and capital will have to be put into producing raw materials if anything like the present standard of industrial production is to be kept up. We will be forced to make use of poorer and poorer ores, finally getting down to sea water, the poorest ore of all. This won't happen for another one or two hundred years, but it will certainly happen. If there is a general industrialization, resources will be eaten up even faster. When the rest of the world is consuming as fast as America the acceleration in the destruction of raw materials will be enormous.

These tremendous problems have developed because technology accomplished something intrinsically good. They illustrate one of the greatest ethical questions of our time. Every one agrees that good ends do not justify bad means. The tragedy arises when good means result in catastrophic ends. This is a dilemma that requires a whole new type of ethical thinking.

The urgency of the need for answers has been stressed several times during this Conference. We don't have much time. In 15 years India will have added about another 150 million people, and China will have increased 255 million. The high expectations of a better life now prevalent in the underdeveloped countries will find themselves dreadfully frustrated. I think it will not take more than 15 years for the ensuing deep social unrest to break down into various kinds of dictatorship. In this country the 15 year period will probably coincide with a maximum consequence of wholesale automation. This will not be easy to adapt to, and will produce peculiar results. For example, if the proletarianized middle executives are going to be pushed down, they may form a potentially dangerous class like the unemployed intellectuals in Eastern countries.

In the 15 or 20 years before us a great many important decisions must be taken, decisions resulting in immediate action. I don't think disaster is inevitable. We can, if we choose to, use our intelligence and good will. As the Pope remarked the other day, if people would only use their heads and their hearts a little, a lot could be done. But if we don't choose to use our heads and our hearts a lot, we shall be in serious trouble in spite of technology, and in some sense because of it. We cannot retreat from technology. Gandhi's prescription is absurd. If we went back to the spinning wheel four-fifths of the human race would die in about two years. We must go on. But we have somehow to see that we don't destroy our planet. We must not eat ourselves out of house and home, into misery and ignorance by simply overbreeding. The problems are enormous, and we have just the next few years to meet them.

This leads me finally to the question, what should we demand of letters? What should the attitude of the man of letters be toward problems of science and technology? What should he do?

I feel strongly that the man of letters should be intensely aware of the problems which surround him, of which technological and scientific problems are among the most urgent. It is his business to communicate his awareness and concern. Literature sets up a vision of man which guides people to a better understanding of themselves and their world.

But we are up against a curious paradox. Something of immense importance to all of us does not find expression in the literary arts. The rational side of man, with its scientific and technological expressions, gets little literary space. It is curious that science and technology have always occupied so small a place in literature. What important literary figure, except Diderot, seriously occupied himself with the problems of technology? This is all the more extraordinary when one considers that literature is supposed to hold the mirror up to life. In life people spend a great deal of time involved in the technology of the period in which they live. They work, and their jobs are connected with technology and the organizations technology engenders. Yet one sees little evidence of this in literature.

The explanation is, I think, quite simple. Human beings are interested in a much livelier way in the passions than in reason. Great works of literature, drama, and narrative have always had as their theme the passional and violent aspects of human nature. We see, after all, the same thing in the modern newspaper. "The news" is by definition bad news, something disastrous, unpleasant, something sinful or violent. Ordinary rational behavior is never news. And "news" in this sense has been the subject matter of literature from Aeschylus to Dostoevsky. Human beings, although they reluctantly conform to social usages, do their duty, and earn their living, are considerably more excited by their passional side. Literature has, in consequence, held the mirror up to this side. For example, I recently saw three plays by the most gifted of American dramatists. In the first the hero was eaten by dogs. In the second the hero was eaten by children. In the third (it had a happy ending) the hero was only castrated. These plays aren't mirroring reality. If they reflected the state of a society, that society wouldn't last a week. But this exceptionally violent side of man has more attraction in the sphere of art.

Science and technology are the theoretical and physical embodiments of logic and reason; and reason comes into literature only as that which creates conflict. The battle is between passion and the dictates of reason and sense. Writers have not described at length the rational side of man. It is taken for granted; it is merely the obstacle to passion.

It is difficult to see how a concern with the scientific and technological in life can be introduced into literature. Wordsworth, in *Preface to Lyrical Ballads,* laid it down that the remotest discoveries of the botanist and geologist would become fit subject matter for poetry when and if they should be of direct emotional concern to people. But they have never been of direct emotional concern to most people. As a consequence, they have not got into poetry, except that of Erasmus Darwin, which is not very good poetry.

How can adequate expression be found for these things in terms which shall be moving to people? People are concerned with love and hatred, with the seven deadly sins, the four cardinal virtues and the conflicts in human nature. For the ordinary person a good deal of technology can certainly be described as humdrum. It is extraordinarily difficult, for example, to see how the subject matter of this Conference could be rendered in persuasive literary terms. I wonder how I could find an adequate fictional expression for the problems of the population explosion. These massive events, correlated with technological advance, are peculiarly difficult to put across in the penetrating way characteristic of good literature. Good literature has what may be called an " X-ray " quality that penetrates into the mind.

The man of letters has a real duty to seek powerful means of expressing the nature of technology and the crises it has generated. Perhaps something can be done in the more mundane forms of literature, such as the article or the popularization of science. Many men of letters are so occupied with the lyrical and passional sides of life that this would be out of the question. But for those whose talents are less focused there is an obligation to try to make our world's dangerous and confusing state clear.

Achieving a Perspective on
the Technological Order

COMMENTARY

ROBERT M. HUTCHINS*

Four questions occur to me that might be discussed in the time that remains. First, what is the significance of the world setting of the technological problem? Here at the Center for the Study of Democratic Institutions we are gradually coming to the conclusion that there is an emerging world legal order, political order, and economic order. It has been suggested that there is also a world technological order. Mr. Buchanan, reinforcing what Mr. Huxley has said, refers to it as a system of world exploitation. If it is a world system it would appear that the problems of guidance, control, and regulation with which we have been wrestling must be faced on a world scale. In that connection perhaps Mr. Theobald's proposals for world institutions received too cursory attention.

The second question is what is meant by planning? What the planners are actually going to be able to do has not been stated. What will they decide? What will their powers be? Professor Zvorikine indicated to us the Russian method of planning. This would be unacceptable to this country and several others because of the powers assumed by the central government to assign workers to jobs, to say nothing of the regulations on wages and prices. Are we agreed that the planning going on in the Western world is done largely by irresponsible private governments and that leaving planning to these governments will not work? Do we know to what extent planning and democracy are compatible or incompatible?

The third question is what are the possibilities of developing organized professional responsibility for the guidance of technology? Sir Robert Watson-Watt referred in our opening session to a Hippocratic oath for technologists, but who was going to take it and how he was going to get them to take it did not fully appear. Courses in legal ethics given in most law schools in my time dealt with keeping the

* Robert M. Hutchins is now Chairman of the Board of Editors of the *Encyclopaedia Britannica* and President of the Center for the Study of Democratic Institutions. His books include *No Friendly Voice* (Chicago, 1936) and *The Conflict in Education* (New York, 1953).

trust companies from getting legal business. Courses in technological ethics seem unlikely to be of a much higher order. Is there any way of creating effective professional responsibility for the control and regulation of technology?

My last question is what justification have we for placing our faith in education? I would like to begin with an introductory digression. I was charmed, as all of us were, by Rupert Hall's illustration in which all creation groaneth and travaileth together in pain until now to produce the plastic cup. Mr. Hall's intimation that the inevitable result of technology is quantity and the almost equally inevitable result is the disappearance of quality reminds me of Sir Richard Livingstone's remark that the Greeks could not broadcast the Aeschylean trilogy, but they could write it. Does the fact that we can broadcast it prevent us from writing it? Of course we can't even broadcast it in the United States because it couldn't get a sponsor. Every new means of communication could be a new means of education. But the investment required and the profit demanded makes it become a medium for promoting mass culture in accordance with Gresham's Law.

Are we justified in placing our hopes in education for the guidance, regulation, and control of technology? The question may perhaps be best introduced by the old Platonic line that what is honored in a country will be cultivated there. Education is a dependent subject. It depends on what is honored in the country. It perpetuates and accentuates accepted values. What ought to be honored as distinguished from what is honored is not learned within the country's educational system. Education reflects what the country wants. It is not a means by which the country can raise itself by its bootstraps into a different spiritual world—not where education is democratically or publicly controlled. There is no hope that education can lead to intelligent guidance of technology without a national resolution that that's what education should do.

The question then becomes how to get such a resolution. With it something can be done about education, and something can be done about technology through education. Without it, corrective efforts are foredoomed. Reference has been made to the beneficent influence we may expect from the liberal education of engineers. What this will probably mean is that engineers will take a few courses outside the field of engineering. What will these courses be? How can useful courses be created if the society does not value what they should at least nominally contain?

In the United States education is a word without content. It can be defined as what goes on in institutions that are called educational. The current definition of liberal education is that it occurs after four years in high school, and is 120 semester hours plus physical culture. The quantitative emphasis is remarkable and coincides with the efflorescence of technology and industrialization after the Civil War. Legislative appropriations for higher education in California depend on the number of students in the state universities. The merits of universities and university presidents are determined by attendance figures. Santayana tells the story of crossing the Harvard Yard when he was a young instructor at Harvard. He met Mr. Eliot. The President of Harvard said to him, " How are your classes going? " Santayana said that the young men seemed intelligent and keen; he thought that they were doing very well. " Mr. Eliot " Santayana said, " stopped me as though I were wasting his time and said ' What I meant, young man, was what is the number of students in your classes? ' "

Education has become a vast personnel system for the use of employers. The rate of technological change in the United States is such that almost any *ad hoc* content for an educational program is ridiculous. By the time the student graduates the job he is prepared for has been swept away. Yet job training courses proliferate. This is not confined to the United States. There is the story of the Dean of Christ Church a hundred years ago who was asked by a student what was the use of studying Greek. The Dean replied, " It is not only the immediate language of the Holy Ghost, but it leads to positions of great dignity and emolument." No doubt in that day Greek was a qualification for employment. At least the Dean did have the grace to mention the Holy Ghost.

Since the content of education has no importance, what is important is the degrees. Here again America is not unique. Bertrand de Jouvenel, referring to the educational system of France, said mournfully, " I would like my children to have an education, but they have got to have degrees."

Education as a personnel system is a technology assisting a technology. We have agreed that technology cannot guide itself. But can education be relied upon for this purpose? Whether universities can be centers of independent thought in the United States or in any other country committed to technology is a serious question. Specialization is inherent in the situation, and specialization means that an educational institution cannot be an intellectual center.

Universities in the United States are engaged in flattering the spirit of the age. In view of the difficulty of reforming these institutions, perhaps, as Mr. Theobald suggested, other types of institutions ought to be developed. The likelihood of educational reform is emphasized by Mr. Huxley's reflections on the number of kicks in the pants required to effect social change. I once thought very highly of the atomic bomb in this connection. I used to make a speech with a line I stole from Leon Bloy calling the atomic bomb " the good news of damnation." I thought it would scare us into a reformation of our academic system. It didn't. National humiliation is a traditional way of inducing educational reform, as we know from the history of Prussia after the battle of Jena and the history of Denmark after the humiliation of 1864. This is an unfortunate way to produce educational change. Moreover, there is no indication from our experience with Sputnik that a modest national humiliation can be long effective.

The hope that seems to characterize this Conference is the hope that the developed countries can go through technology and come out on the other side in a warless, wantless, workless world. But no developed country has an educational program appropriate to such a situation. Daily working time has been reduced by one-third in my lifetime, and the working life has been abbreviated at both ends. This time has been almost mathematically transferred to the television set. It is alleged that we watch television four hours a day. The mere fact that working time is reduced will not offer any reasonable hope in a culture like ours that the time will be used for the human development we all want.

In the developing countries the problem is at least *ab initio* quite different. These countries need scientists, technicians, and civil servants. *Ad hoc* training is therefore justified, though even here the rate of technical change is likely to render *ad hoc* training archaic during the training process itself. The danger is that the immediate needs will be so imperative that the ultimate aim of education will be forgotten. It seems important to separate those institutions aiming at moral and intellectual development and independent criticism of the society from those aiming at *ad hoc* training and the solution of practical problems.

Ninety per cent of all the scientists and research workers who have ever lived are alive today. We can have faith that every scientific and technical problem is going to be solved. The question is what kind of people are we going to be and what kind of a world are we going to have? Professor Zvorikine presented a kind of satire of the completely technicalized, dehumanized society which could conceivably result from an ill-managed technological culture. He said that his consolation was that people would not like this kind of a society. I'm afraid, on the basis of my slavish and repeated readings of Mr. Aldous Huxley's books, that they will like it. Our real problem is how to find new ways to mobilize character and intelligence on a world scale. If we can have understanding it may help.

Achieving a Perspective on
the Technological Order

A REPORT OF THE DISCUSSION

WARREN E. PREECE

Sir Robert Watson-Watt presided. Mr. White suggested that technology is poorly understood in our time and will only be understood after it has been subjected to the same kind of analysis and search for understanding which for 2,500 years has been directed at religion, literature, government, and similar matters. Technology, he said, has, after all, been "singularly ignored" in our history. Turning to Mr. Huxley's discussion of the difficulties involved in giving literary expression to technology, he said that the only lyrical expression of a technological subject of which he is aware is in a Greek poem to a labor-saving device. In thinking of the Greeks, he said, he is inclined to wonder if the separation of man from his nature discussed by Mr. Huxley might not be traced to the destruction of animism by Christianity. The Greeks, he pointed out, took nature seriously because they took the spirits of nature seriously, and they knew, therefore, that if a spirit lived on a mountain peak, man had to be careful about deciding to mine that peak. Christianity, he suggested, in replacing the nymphs of Greece with human saints gave humankind a monopoly over the spirit, thus laying nature open to exploitation by man. He said he was hopeful that the "relatively new notion of ecology" might turn out to be "a functional equivalent" of animism and might, thus, enable man to regain some of the psychic unity which he once had with the nature around him.

Mr. Huxley agreed with Mr. White, and suggested, further, that with the rise of modern biology man might somehow be getting back to totemism "on a higher level"; might once again be able to see himself as a part of nature.

Fr. Ong said he agreed with Mr. White's notion about the destruction of animism by Christianity, and that the problem now is to "re-situate man in nature." Further, he said, he agreed with Mr. White that the science of ecology "is a promising hope" by means of which man might yet develop some way in which his human psyche can come face to face with the facts of world evolution.

Pointing out that most of the Conference had been marked by controversy, Mr. Theobald summarized his argument as being, in general, that the present rate of technological change is not a natural phenomenon as much as it is something forged by nationalism and the desire for private profit. Recalling that the issue of the Conference had seemed to evolve in terms of whether the rate of technological development can be halted without disaster or recourse to further technology, he said that he was absolutely certain that unless it is halted the world will either have nuclear war or one of Huxley's technological worlds. Though 50 per cent of those at the Conference would "probably love" a technological world, he said, the fact is that we must arrest the rate of technological growth at least until we can see its consequences more clearly and until we have trained the brain and the heart to deal with the problem. He said he was still convinced that man can rule technology without being ruled by it, but that in order to do so man must find a way to abolish nationalism and the desire for private profit. Freedom and utopias, he warned, are "profoundly antithetical" and cannot exist together.

Mr. Kranzberg said that he would gather from what Mr. Huxley had said " that the ecological balance in nature is a good thing and should not be changed." Such a view, he argued, ignores the facts of evolutionary changes in the ecological balance and forgets that man and his technology, as parts of nature, are also elements in the ecology. Concerning Mr. Theobald's argument, he said he believes we can control or guide the development of technology, without destroying nationalism or the notion of private property " overnight."

Mr. Thai said he would want to reply to Mr. Theobald that one of the pressing necessities of our time " is to revive the whole notion of nationalism," though he would concede that some problems, such as that of the control of population, will require the development of the notion of " something above nationalism."

Fr. Ong said it seemed to him that " many important things about technology " had not been treated at the Conference, particularly those relating to the connection between technological communication systems and man's inner being. He suggested that decisions about the control of science and technology must be made in terms of " what is here and now and what is obtainable " and that we must make our personal decisions on the basis " of what we know and on our view of justice." It is reassuring in this connection, he said, that what looks like a large decision may frequently be only a concatenation of small ones best made one at a time.

Despite these considerations, Fr. Ong conceded that " there are difficulties." Many of our problems, he said, boil down to the fact that the human analogue no longer holds for larger groups and that nations, unlike human beings, seem to lose something of themselves in interacting with one another. This, he suggested, might mean that although a world order is now evolving, the notion is at this time, largely " an operating concept." The situation is made more complex, he continued, by the fact that the great depersonalization spurred by technology is taking place along side the possibility of the broadened personal contacts made possible by modern technological communications. This, he said, makes it important that we " attend to all persons as persons " and emphasize those factors which bear on the matter of personal integrity.

Fr. Ong said he agreed with those who had called for analysis of the concrete freedoms with which we should be concerned in a technological society. Two of these freedoms, he said, are the freedom of those men who wish to do so to follow non-technical pursuits, and the freedom of man's inner conscience. In connection with the latter, he urged that we must pay more attention to man's " spiritual problems " and be aware that technology affects both our exterior and internal lives, and, among other things, deprives man of a sense of a " real life in nature."

Continuing, Fr. Ong said he is certain that many of the external developments of the world are correlatives of changes in man's internal condition. If nothing else, he said, psychological evidence indicates that technological inventions have produced differences in the nature of the crises as we see them and our reactions to them.

Concluding, Fr. Ong said we must be aware that we are dealing " with real persons who have been affected by technology but remain personal despite it," and that " more and more in a technological society " we must say that the human being may never be violated, may " never be allowed to become means."

Mr. Calder said that while he agreed with Mr. Huxley and Mr. White that " ecology may hold the secret of our real need," we must remember, too, that man is also a part of the ecology, that the population explosion, for instance, is produced by both man and animals, and in both cases represents an ecological aberration.

Recalling Mr. Theobald's argument that, unless he acts now to correct the situation, man is faced with two disastrous alternatives—nuclear war or life in a totally technicized society—Mr. Ashmore said it would appear to him that the Conference had been unwilling to accept the necessity of "drastic action." He noted that the prevailing view was that we will not have either a nuclear war or the closed circle of technology. In this connection, he suggested that even such decisions as to resume atom bomb testing are not necessarily automatic responses dictated by the logic of technology any more than they are—whether right or wrong—rationally arrived at determinations to attempt to "buy time" pending a better accommodation of the world problem. Further, he said, he could not personally accept Mr. Piel's thesis that greed and fear are the dominant motivating forces in the present technological system, though, obviously, they are present. We are, he submitted, in the hands of politicians making political decisions. This is not to deny, he said, that the problems of technology are real nor that there is evidence to suggest that we may be moving toward "more and more technology."

Continuing, Mr. Ashmore suggested that discussion of the problems of the underdeveloped nations had raised two major questions: (1) whether it is desirable to impose an alien cultural pattern, whether one already in existence or one specifically developed for the purpose, on the people of these nations, and (2) whether, given internal resistances to change, it is even possible to do so.

Mr. Ashmore said in conclusion that he sees some hope for an ultimate resolution of the problems of technology in the fact that the matters raised during the Conference appear increasingly to be making themselves felt as items of general concern and are, indeed, imposing themselves in many ways on the politicians. "There is still a lot of work to be done," he conceded.

Professor Zvorikine pointed out that, although the participants had gathered in Santa Barbara "to look for some way out of a difficult contemporary situation," most of them seemed to be convinced that "we ourselves are slightly ill." To that extent, he suggested they were reflecting a point of view that seems to have "grasped all of humanity," namely, that man has lost his personality and therefore cannot "do anything in society," can neither coordinate nor influence the development of human nature or of society. Some, he continued, would resolve this problem "by a return to God" and others by limiting the power of science and technology over society in order that man might be "less a thing made by society" and more a human individual.

Since contemporary difficulties arise from the existence of social structures which do not sufficiently "reflect humanity," Dr. Zvorikine said, we need "new social relationships," and in this connection, he insisted that although many Western people believe that socialism denies the freedom of the human being, the belief is not true and is indeed based on a false notion of freedom. Those who argue in this way, he explained, assume that freedom is the ability to do whatever they wish to do, and forget "that fire may burn us" if we reach out for it merely because we wish to reach out for it. True freedom, he insisted, lies in "not going opposite to the laws of nature and society" but in acting in accordance with those laws and in utilizing them in finding answers to the problems that arise.

In order to have true freedom, Professor Zvorikine said, man must have an aim and must live in a social state that utilizes all of the accomplishments of society for the further development of the human being. Our problems, he concluded, cannot be solved " all at once "; it will take time and we must, there-fore, have co-existence of capitalist and socialist notions in order for man himself to be able to decide which road he wants to take. These discussions will have no value, he warned, if we do not eliminate the danger of war; a " singular solution " cannot now be found, and " man needs more time."

Mr. Hutchins pointed out that the basic question of the Conference had been whether it is possible to control, regulate, or guide technology and that the only solutions proposed had had to do with planning, education, professional respon-sibility, or further development of our understanding of ecology. He noted that no one had elaborated any of these proposals and he asked what " we propose to do about it."

Mr. Meier said that there are effective methods of attacking the problems noted by Mr. Hutchins. He suggested, for instance, that the technologist himself can be pressed into service; that the very nature of his work equips him to deal with the problem of control methods and systems. Pointing out that the technologist must always be aware of the necessity of controls to keep his own work from " getting out of hand," he said that the first requirement is to understand where the problems will develop. In the broader picture, he continued, these problem areas might be said to lie in those segments of the culture which are moving more rapidly than the growth of other segments would suggest was " natural," that is, in those areas in which technology is developing more rapidly than, for instance, the population, the Gross National Product, or similar other indices. The place where this kind of disproportionate growth might be found right now, he warned, is in the accumulation of technological and scientific knowledge itself.

Mr. Theobald replied to this that he is convinced that " we do not have any-thing remotely resembling control methods " available to us now and that, therefore, our only hope is to slow down the system by applying pressures against the artificial stimuli which are resulting in the unnatural growth of technology. Mr. Thai said he agreed that it is necessary to buy time, but that he also felt that it is not impossible that there are " built-in brakes " already existing in tech-nology which might be usefully developed. Mr. Tyler said that there are, of course, social controls already built into our system; that for example, our weapons systems, as an " outstanding example of technology," is not a simple broadside " exploitation of everything " so much as it is the result of a controlled evaluation of needs and capabilities. The important question, he said, may well be " which technology " we are going to control, whether the automation of jobs or the stimulation of cancer research. Technology as a whole, he insisted, " is not a bad thing," and in fact we might reasonably want to speed certain aspects of it.

Mr. Stover objected that it was wrong to include cancer research among the concerns he and Mr. Theobald had about technology. Mr. Tyler insisted that Mr. Stover was trying to make an artificial distinction; that, for example, there are many mental health problems which require a large and very complex tech-nological system for supporting a patient at the time of crisis. It is the exist-ence of this technology, he said, which enables society to provide five times as much mental health service as it was able to do five years ago. Mr. Stover said he did not want to retard man's " efforts to understand," and that what we need is a redirection of technology into those areas which are important but that to do so we must accept the fact that power does exist and that we have responsibility for its proper exercise. Knowledge is good, he said, but the attempt " to keep up with our system " has forced us to develop immediate applications of new knowledge—whether we want the end or not.

Where We Came Out

RALPH W. TYLER*

What I shall attempt is to mention some of the propositions which seemed to be generally accepted; to list some subjects about which I could detect no real consensus; and then talk more particularly about our discussion of what we can do to give more adequate control and better direction to technology.

Turning to matters in which I sensed we had almost complete agreement:

First, we were impressed with the helpfulness in giving perspective provided by Lynn White's and Rupert Hall's fine examples from the history of technology. They showed us that technology is not a recent, alien thing but something which has been part of the intelligence and the problem-solving nature of man for a long time. We *have* taken a more rapid leap forward as technology has been combined with the precise methods of science so that it is guided consciously by science.

Second, technology is developing at an accelerating rate throughout the world. It is obvious in the more advanced countries like the United States and much of Western Europe, but it is gaining speed in other countries as well. These other countries have aspirations and desires to make use of technology for the achievement of their purposes, which means that it is likely to move forward even more rapidly.

Third, technology is being used not only in material production and in national defense but also in commerce and the services, including the professional services. We are most conscious of it in the development of productive machinery. We are also aware of the tremendous uses of it in defense in this country and in the Soviet Union, but its use is not limited to production and defense. The obvious manifestations in commerce include vending machines and accounting machines; in services, washing machines and dishwashers in homes, and laundromats. In the health services we are less conscious of the adoption of technology, but it is largely responsible for the fact that in the last fifteen years we have increased our health services five-fold with an increase of only 50 per cent in the number of doctors, largely by the use of technology in organizing the services of the doctor. By the

* Ralph W. Tyler is Director, Center for Advanced Study in the Behavioral Sciences. Previously he was Dean, Division of Social Sciences, and Chairman of the Department of Education, University of Chicago.

use of laboratory technicians, nurses, practical nurses, nurses' aides, and orderlies we have developed the health services far beyond anything we had known before. In schools, colleges, and training programs, technology is being applied in the form of teaching machines. Encyclopaedia Britannica Films under the leadership of Maurice Mitchell, is rapidly developing machines and programed instruction to aid in the teaching of mathematics, foreign languages, and other school subjects. Of course, sound-motion pictures for the classroom represent another use of technology in education. Clearly, technology is much more than simply an instrument of production.

Fourth, technology affects not only the world external to man, but also his values, habits, and interests. Obviously, man today values various technical instruments such as television and motion pictures. These values were unheard of in years before the instruments existed. Perhaps the most important of the attitudes developed by technology, an attitude clearly evident in the emerging nations, is the expectation that man can solve his problems through the aid of science. There was a time when we viewed misery and starvation as the work of God and beyond our control. But now most people, even in the least developed nations, do not believe this.

Fifth, the results of technology are not only the more efficient achievement of desired ends and the attainment of ends not otherwise possible. Some outcomes are undesirable. Let me list a few of these that we seemed agreed upon in our discussion.

The first (and it was the one we noticed first because of our great concern about the hydrogen bomb) had to do with the use of technology in national defense. Technology has resulted in more expensive and more destructive weapons systems, the production of which makes it more difficult for the modern economy to reconvert to peace. If we pass this time of great tension without war and begin a program of extensive disarmament we shall discover that the amount of investment in the production of weapons systems is large enough to make it really difficult to reconvert to peace without great disruption of our economy.

A second undesirable consequence is the world-wide consumption of resources required by our kind of technology. In the expansion of printing, for example, we have drawn too heavily upon the pine and spruce forests of all parts of the world, especially of North America, to provide the paper we use.

Third, product choices are made technologically in a technological world. The decision of what shall be produced and the design of the product is based on estimates of the extent of the demand and efficiencies of production. This often limits the range of individual choice by removing from the market many objects formerly produced by craftsmen.

Fourth, some of us seem to believe that the availability of lower cost goods and services to those who had none before improperly tempts men to waste time and resources. Whether this is true in the large is a moot question. Even more uncertain is the responsibility of the society or individual men to remove this kind of temptation. It is a real temptation to buy cheap, easily available goods rather than to use time and resources for other things. What is not clear in our discussion, and I don't think this was developed far enough by our Catholic colleague who was concerned especially with moral issues, is whether we have a responsibility to protect other men from temptation or whether part of their own development as free men is to learn to resist temptation. These questions we did not get into, but the issue is apparent.

The fifth undesirable consequence is that some of the technological systems have been designed without carefully considering what they require of the workers who use them, and whether they are consistent with what workers can do without too great a strain intellectually, emotionally, or in other ways.

A sixth consequence is that continuing technological change shifts occupational patterns and opportunities among occupations and among geographic areas. Some of these shifts are disastrous to individuals and groups. Some have occurred without a complete disaster. What we have been doing over the years is perhaps most easily illustrated by looking at some of our census figures. When I was born at the turn of the century, 42 per cent of our people in the United States were engaged in farm labor and in work on farms. A total of about 60 per cent were engaged in farm labor, unskilled labor in factories and in services. Now we note in the 1960 census that only 11 per cent of our population is engaged in farm labor; that the total number engaged in what would be called semi-skilled and unskilled labor now represents only about 20 per cent of the population in comparison with about 60 per cent in 1900. Much of this change has been due to what we are calling technology. We have had to adjust and have largely been able to make the adjustment so that this change has not completely disrupted our economy. Our present concern is whether we can adjust soon enough as automation makes the changes more rapid. Now there are many fewer miners than there were 20 years ago. Miners generally stayed in the industry until they died, but their children went into other occupations. If occupational demands shift more rapidly it is probable that many people will have to anticipate carrying on more than one occupation in their lifetime. They may be mechanics for several years, and something else for the following years. Can we adjust to this kind of expectation, a fluidity of occupation which is required by technological change?

Seventh, much of the emerging technology, if it is to be utilized efficiently, requires large capital investments. To produce many things at an efficient rate it is necessary to have very large machinery, considerable capital, and a large market for the products. It takes a great deal of lead time to build the machinery, get the staff required, and plan the production schedule and the like. It takes time to determine what are the positive and negative effects of the use of a given technology. Such endeavors involve large organizations. They are not easily handled by an individual. Typically only big corporations or agencies of government can undertake them. Hence there are great problems of control, of direction, of modification in terms of experience. A large organization has difficulty in maintaining the kind of flexibility needed to change when particular technologies prove inappropriate or result in bad aftereffects.

Eight, we agreed that highly developed Western technology cannot be directly transferred to the underdeveloped countries. There was a good deal of testimony by those who have been working with the developing nations that American or Western technology could not be imposed on a nation that has different backgrounds, limited educational and training facilities, different traditions, and the like. If we are going to build a technology which is really useful, we must help each country build a technology which is appropriate.

I turn next to the subjects of discussion on which I could not sense general agreement. One of those had to do with conclusions drawn by the Frenchman Ellul, in his book, *La Technique*. There he says that man really no longer has any control over technology. In what senses, we asked ourselves, does man or society have no control or inadequate control over technology? Although we could not agree completely on these, we did identify several ways in which the problem of control was a real one.

In our Western society the use of market mechanisms as the basis for choices may not reflect long-range values. For example, if evergreen trees from Canada make the cheapest and most profitable newsprint, they are used. This choice does not consider whether the use of Canadian forests in the end will be good for the world, or whether we may have more erosion and lose the value of these forests. We fear that the present dependence on the private sector of our economy for such decisions may result in inadequate consideration of all the factors in large-scale technological operations.

A second area in which we have inadequate control at present is in defense expenditures. They are given top priority. Few questions are raised if the expense contributes to defense. We seldom question whether we are using resources wisely, whether we are getting all that we hope to get, and whether this really enhances our security.

Third, preoccupation with a particular end, a particular job to be done, may lead to inadequate control. One of the obvious cases in point has been the abuse of DDT. In trying to get rid of mosquitoes we have not considered sufficiently whether we are destroying other organisms which are important to the total ecology and eventually to some of the most productive parts of that ecology. We are now beginning to discover that DDT is not an unmixed blessing.

Fourth, the investments in a particular technology compel a continuing use of that technology. If you and I had built a factory in which we had made very large investments we would try to use its capacity and to seek outlets for it, even though other needs were more important. We might be torn between our desire to use our resources for human needs and our efforts to get complete utilization from our factory. This is also true with human resources. Having invested a great deal in engineers and other technologists we continue to want to use them, when perhaps we need artists and others quite differently trained.

Fifth, plans are drawn and decisions made with inadequate attention to non-technological matters. We think of the development problem of a particular technological instrument, perhaps a defense instrument, and don't ask ourselves what other things are being affected, such as the values of people, or how people are drained away from other fields. One illustration is what is happening now in career choices by young Americans. Before Sputnik, the most popular career choice for the top ten per cent of high school seniors was the field of medicine. At that time American and Canadian medical schools had seven times as many qualified applicants as they could admit. Then came Sputnik. Last year, the most popular choices for the top ten per cent of our high school graduates were physics and mathematics. Last year there were only 1.75 times as many qualified applicants for medical schools as they could admit, and a number of the less well-known medical schools did not have enough qualified applicants to fill their positions. I do not know what is the wisest distribution of our human resources. But this illustrates that if we do not consider non-technological aspects of technological decisions we may get a distortion we have not intended.

Sixth, the glamour of machines and new systems attracts interest and leads people to buy even when the product's usefulness may be limited . How many people have bought computing machines before they knew how they might be useful? I raised that question with several of my friends in the Palo Alto area. They have often bought the machines before they had any notion how they could use them because of their impressive appearance or because other people were using them so that it seemed to be the thing to do.

The seventh difficulty in the wise control of technology is the old problem of cultural lag. The technological system may continue to be used when it no longer serves the end. This was well said years ago by George Bernard Shaw who defined a fanatic as one who redoubled his efforts when he forgot his objectives. We often develop a system which seems to work very well and meets our present ends and continue to carry it on long after it has ceased to serve new needs effectively.

Another area in which I looked for points on which we were not perfectly agreed had to do with the question: What other inadequate responses to the development of technology have we touched upon in our Conference? Mr. Hutchins spoke eloquently this morning, as only he could do with his intimate experience of it, of the failures of education. Man, the citizen, needs to see and understand the whole problem. Father Clarke pointed out that the moral issue cannot be disposed of by asking the technologists to tell us what to do. Every man has a responsibility to make decisions and to use his power and influence in terms of his decisions. He cannot pass the buck to the technologist. A technologist has no special competence beyond the area in which he has had special training and experience. Looking at the whole picture rather than a particular technological phase is the responsibility of all citizens. But in this respect, as Mr. Hutchins pointed out, our education has been ineffective. We have not developed citizens who understand the whole picture so they can make wise decisions. We tend to let technologists make decisions for us, decisions which are really our own, which we cannot pass on to others. We have failed to educate our citizens to understand the essential nature of technology. As a result we have those who view science and technology as magic capable of solving all problems. Science only deals with scientific problems. Many of our important problems are not scientific at all. Then we have those who view science and technology as essentially bad, and who seek to return to the " good old days." Actually, of course, the " good old days " never were, and we couldn't return if we wanted to. But this is one way of dismissing responsibility; a way taken by people who do not seek to understand what science is about. We also have those who avoid coming to grips with problems created by technological change because they assume that technology's abundant production will solve all our problems. They assume that if man is provided with a wealth of goods and services he is thereby made free. These people have not learned that one does not achieve humanity by having someone provide goods for him. Each of us must become human by our own efforts.

Our inadequate education about technology can be remedied, but what is required is not simply teaching the so-called scientific facts, because this is really giving current answers to questions which will be answered differently tomorrow. To develop essential understanding the student himself must be involved in scientific inquiry, in technological invention, and the selection of technological means for required ends. It is possible for each of us as students to begin to partake in the scientific and technological enterprise just as we may partake partly in the artistic or the poetic or the musical enterprise. It is not enough to have some people who are artists and some people who are scientists and some people who are something else. Everyone needs some understanding of science, because only in this way can it be used intelligently for the good of society.

Another weakness we identified in education is the neglect of human-istic experiences, including religion. Modern man, like earlier man, must achieve happiness and meaning in his life. It isn't born to him, it isn't given to him. It is not attained by being fully fed, clothed, sheltered, and amused. A man may learn this the hard way after 60 years of futility. He can achieve humanity more economically by the use of the vicarious experiences of others, and reflecting upon his own earlier experiences and by sharpening the questions he asks about what he has experienced. He can learn the contributions made in seek-ing understanding by the whole range of the arts—the arts of music, the arts of literature, the arts of drama, the arts of painting, and the arts of worship and meditation.

We spent some time trying to talk about ways of giving better direction and more adequate control to the development and use of technology. We were stimulated in this discussion by the paper of Robert Theobald, the comments of Gerald Piel of the *Scientific American*, and the four pertinent questions raised by Mr. Hutchins. We recognized that technology is world-wide as a way of thinking and a mode of operation. It involves in it as consumers, producers, or owners of raw materials almost all sections of the world. Because it is world-wide and because we have no world organizations at present with power sufficient to deal with control of technology, we realized that any effort to talk about how to control it involved the question of how to get adequate means to deal with it as well as ideas about how it might be handled.

We considered kinds of strategy. We talked about the technocratic approach, the notion that the people with technological knowledge could solve the problem, and rejected it. Professor Zvorikine from the Soviet Union made an eloquent plea for the socialistic view, show-ing how they are able to handle technology in the Soviet Union through their control over all planning and all distribution of resources, education and the like. But we did not feel that this was appropriate for our country. We talked more about modifications that have been made in the free enterprise system, a balancing between individual choices and group needs. These kinds of modifications are found in large parts of the Western world. But we realized the difficulties of even designing a comprehensive control system at this time. Some of us were greatly concerned about the pressure of time, the danger of war, the feeling that there is an immediate step to be taken. But most of us believe that comprehensive control systems must be evolved by those entangled in the problem, not by us sitting as a kind of special brain trust. We here can only suggest directions of inquiry which seem promising. I think we did agree to certain points in this inquiry.

First, we felt that it is necessary and feasible to reduce the hegemony of nations. The problems of technology are world-wide and cannot be dealt with piecemeal by individual nations.

Second, we realized, and I think agreed, that we need and can establish institutions for the study of both the social and the technological world problems, though we did not spell out nor reach agreement on what these institutions would encompass, what their relations would be with international or national organizations and to universities.

Third, we noted the increasing establishment of technical assistance programs which seek to invent technologies appropriate for the nations or regions involved, and which deal with broader cultural problems as well as the technical ones. Mr. Goldschmidt, Mr. Calder, and Mr. Thai are all concerned with the development of appropriate aids to the improvement of the level of living in newly developing countries. They are convinced that we need to have development of technology appropriate to the level of these countries, not just a carry-over of American technology.

Fourth, I think we agreed also that it is necessary both for the technologists to accept and exercise professional responsibility for human decisions within their competence and authority, and for the citizen and his representative in government to become adequately informed and to be able to make wise decisions on issues which involve technology. We cannot blame technology for our ignorance or indifference. We felt that the technologist has as much influence on the life of people as the physician has on his patients, and that there is the same need for some kind of Hippocratic oath, some sense of responsibility for the humane values. We also felt that the technologist should not work alone, and that the other people—citizens, politicians, those who make use of his technology—have a responsibility for considering the consequences and moral rightness of acts which cannot be turned over to the technologists.

Although we could not agree on large, dramatic steps to deal with these international problems we do believe, as indicated by our participation in this Conference, that there is important value in study, discussion, and publication of thoughts and ideas on these complex problems. As Harry Ashmore reminded us, and we have had many other illustrations from the past, citizens and politicians do get ideas from sources like these. Though we may feel futile and helpless because of dramatic world decisions our hope is that we shall have time—time in terms of peace—to continue thought, study, discussion, and action on many small fronts. We hope that over the years it will take us in productive directions. We wish to leave both a fruitful world and difficult problems for posterity to deal with, and in so doing achieve more nearly for them their human potential. If we solve the problems for our children they will not grow.

Index

This book was designed by Richard Kinney. The text typeface used is Linotype Janson designed by Nicholas Kis about 1690, and cut by the Mergenthaler Linotype Company. For the display, Venus, cut by Bauer, 1907-1913, and Bulmer designed by William Bulmer about 1790.

The book is printed on Warren's Olde Style Antique and bound in Bancroft Linen Finished cloth. Manufactured in the United States of America.

Modern scientific-tec
ises to be both the 1
future and the instrument of his enslavement or his destruction. If we
are to avoid the disasters it lays open
to us and take advantage of the opportunities it presents, we must put it in
the control of reason. To do so, we
must understand what modern technology is, what it means, and what
must be done with it if it is to serve
man well. The purpose of the Encyclopaedia Britannica Conference on
the Technological Order was to help
achieve this understanding.

The 1962 Britannica Conference,
sponsored by the Encyclopaedia Brit-
annnica in cooperation with The
Center for the Study of Democratic
Institutions, undertook four separate
probes into the complex of problems
relating to technology, viz.,

1. *Ideas of Technology*—an examination of major contemporary
schools of thought about technology
and its use.

2. *The Technical Act*—a consideration of what can be learned about
technology from the history of its
development and use: How has it
served and been served by man?
Under what conditions does it serve
man well? What are the causes of
technical innovation? What are the
social implications of different kinds
and rates of technological development?

3. *Nature, Science, and Technology*—an exploration of the relationship between science and technology
and their joint relationship to nature.
Traditionally, science has been directed to understanding nature; technology to controlling and adapting it
to man's ends. Both are now linked
in an "attack" upon nature—an effort
to make it "give up its secrets" and
conform to human ends. What standards should guide and limit this
process?